THE HOUSING ENVIRONMENT AND FAMILY LIFE

THE HOUSING ENVIRONMENT AND FAMILY LIFE

A Longitudinal Study of the Effects of Housing on Morbidity and Mental Health

BY

DANIEL M. WILNER
ROSABELLE PRICE WALKLEY
THOMAS C. PINKERTON
MATTHEW TAYBACK

WITH THE ASSISTANCE OF

MARVIN N. GLASSER, JOHN M. SCHRAM,
CARL E. HOPKINS, CHARLES C. CURTIS,
ALAN S. MEYER, AND JOSEPH R. DALLAS

THE JOHNS HOPKINS PRESS

BALTIMORE, 1962

© 1962, The Johns Hopkins Press, Baltimore 18, Maryland
Distributed in Great Britain by Oxford University Press, London
Printed in the United States of America by The Horn-Shafer Co.
Library of Congress Catalog Card Number 62-10310

FOREWORD

Through all recorded history man has been concerned with adequate shelter against the elements and the development of a safe and comfortable physical environment. As civilization progressed, shelters became more and more adequate in terms of comfort and safety. With industrialization and associated urbanization, housing deteriorated and slums were created. This deterioration of housing apparently brought with it greatly increased hazards to health and well-being. Disease was prevalent in slum areas, accidents were frequent, psychological and social disturbances were often attributable, or thought to be attributable, to substandard housing. Improvement of these conditions through slum clearance and rehousing was quite generally thought to be justifiable on the grounds of physical, mental, and social amelioration.

The evaluation of the effects of improvement in housing have, however, been difficult because so many variables might conceivably be involved. There have been various efforts made over the years to determine the effect of good housing in terms of disease prevalence and psychological and social factors. Comparisons have been made of the incidence and prevalence of disease in well-housed populations and in poorly housed populations. Epidemiological techniques have been employed, but because of the numerous variables involved it has been difficult to evaluate accurately the effects of improved housing.

The study reported in this book was undertaken because of what appeared to be a unique opportunity to observe simultaneously a population moved from definitely substandard slum areas to new and much better housing and at the same time to observe a similar population, different only in that it continued to live in definitely substandard housing. The study was planned with an unusual degree of care and was carried out with meticulous uniformity in the observation of the two groups.

Several features of the research may have special interest for professional and lay groups. The study is an instance of a truly inter-

v

disciplinary effort. From the outset and continuing through the seven-year life of the project at Johns Hopkins, planning and execution were in the hands of professionals from a number of fields, in particular, epidemiology, behavioral science, mental hygiene, housing, and bio-statistics. The diversity of these interests led to the very comprehensive range of topics covered in this volume: morbidity, mortality, and childbearing experience; many facets of social adjustment and family life; and the school experience of children.

This is probably a more comprehensive study of the problem than has been undertaken up to this time. The findings range from solid confirmation of the hypotheses regarding morbidity among children, to more modestly suggestive findings of the social adjustment sections. The findings of this study may thus, on the whole, be less dramatic than previous cross-sectional studies might have led us to expect. These results point up the fact that over a given span of time, three years in this case, a social factor like housing may well have different levels of effect on different facets of existence.

There can, I believe, be no question of the basic value of the findings and of the general objectivity of the study. The plan of the research and the care with which it has been carried out can well be a model for future research of this type.

Ernest L. Stebbins

Dean, School of Hygiene and
Public Health

The Johns Hopkins University

AUTHORS' PREFACE

The study described in these pages represents the coming together of a number of professional objectives. The focus is a comparison of good and bad housing and their effect on aspects of physical health and social adjustment. This is a topic of wide general interest among lay and professional groups alike.

This report, then, may be considered as part of the continuing effort to understand the role of man's environment—in this case his provisions for shelter in relation to other factors in his life. The work may be considered as an evaluation of a conscious social intervention to alter this environment.

Housing and health administrators and planners of the physical plant of a community have a natural interest in the relationship between housing and human affairs. Many of the purported relationships between housing and health underlie the philosophies leading to programs of housing rehabilitation and demolition. It is also a fact that professional personnel eagerly await and utilize new data on the relationship between housing and pathology in buttressing appeals for, and execution of, housing and health programs.

The public health specialists responsible for carrying out the study very early attempted to divorce themselves from the dilemma engendered by the applied aspects of the problem. It was reasoned that if one of the American (or civilized society's) goals is housing of good quality for all, then general housing planning might well be independent of the findings of particular studies that show certain of the outcomes of that planning. As a perceptive public health colleague put it, "No one is waiting for the findings of the study before acting." The key was the implied question, "If the final results of the study showed that rehoused and slum groups did not differ in illness and other pathologies, are housing programs to stop?" Tying social action to the end products of single research efforts is dangerous. We are a long way from crucial experiments in many topical areas in which scientific energy is being expended. This is especially true

vii

of research in the broad socio-biological area, where many factors other than the one under examination (housing, in this case) are anticipated to have influence on almost every outcome-measure considered.

As a consequence of the foregoing considerations, a conscious effort was made to adopt points of view that bear similarities to the scientific public health attitude which is commonly held toward a causative, therapeutic or preventive agent under test.

First, an attempt was made to suspend for the duration of the study some natural inclinations, as citizens as well as investigators, to "side" with the data. Viewed from this aspect, bad housing became not the "enemy," but part of the venture to understand the role of physical and social environment in modern life.

Second, a framework was developed that placed the study in the same perspective as certain other substantive epidemiologic topics, for example, etiology of lung cancer and the role of dietary practice in cardiovascular disease. The natural history of investigations in a substantive area usually involves, for a certain period of time, the undertaking of cross-sectional studies in the effort to determine broad relationships. When sufficient clues are assembled from such research, the next steps are to attempt experimental or near-experimental approaches in prospective studies. The present study comes in at the later phase of this strategy in the development of researches in the field of housing.

Third, close analysis of the literature and systematic reflection on purported relationships led to formal statements in the form of "hypotheses" or expectations about the relationship between elements of housing experience and the outcome variables.

Fourth, an effort was made, that may be evident throughout this volume, to use reporting language that stays very close to the findings.

It may be relevant to remark on some changes in attitude of the investigators toward the study as a whole as time went on. Review of the literature (Chapter I) suggested that direct negative effects of housing improvement were unlikely and that possible ameliorative outcomes, if any, might extend over a broad spectrum of outcome variables. However, review of methodological issues at the outset revealed a number of complex and troublesome problems. These included the potential difficulties in assembling initially comparable test and control groups, in successfully interacting with housing authority procedures, and in avoiding excessive losses among the groups under study. Initially, therefore, it may be said that on the basis of prior studies, the investigators had some reason to forecast substantial relationships between housing and outcome variables, but at the same time to harbor grave reservations about the likelihood of study execution. After the study was under way for a time, these attitudes gradually began to reverse. Even before data analysis was undertaken, close working experience with the population under study began to throw doubt on the likely pervasiveness of the influence of the housing environment, but the feasibility of executing the study, even with all its imponderable elements, became clear.

For general methodology in the field of public health, the study may contribute to more than the substantive issues involved. There are numerous signs that, in the next decade, continued efforts will be made to understand the effects of environment and the etiology of physical and mental pathologies. Long before the etiology is completely known there will be many attempts to "try out" preventive and therapeutic social programs and to evaluate their effectiveness. These evaluative ventures have in common the features of definition and measurement of complex social intervention variables and the determination of outcomes in human populations in natural settings.

This study it is hoped, along with similar efforts on kindred topics now in progress (e.g., massive studies of community intervention in prevention of mental disease, studies in control of juvenile delinquency. etc.), will help to develop the methodological armamentarium of the future.

Acknowledgments

The conduct of the study involved the cooperation of many persons in several walks of life. The authors would like to single out a number for special mention, remembering that many others in addition have played a role in facilitating the carrying out of the study design to its conclusions.

First of all, the study staff owes a debt to members of the Study Advisory Committee, a group that sketched in the early versions of the study plan and later acted as a review board for various proposals for executing the design. The discussions before this committee and with individual members were helpful in shaping the study at various important points of development. The committee was composed of

Professor William G. Cochran, Drs. Paul V. Lemkau, Philip Sartwell, and Wilson Wing, Mr. Morton Hoffman, Mrs. Sara S. Hartman, and Dr. Thurber Fales (chairman, until his death in 1953). Dr. Matthew Tayback was chairman from 1953-1960.

A debt is also owed to other members of the staff of the School of Hygiene and Public Health at Johns Hopkins, who served as sources of advice and counsel. Persons to be singled out are Dr. John Gart and Professors Margaret Merrell and Jerome Cornfield of the Department of Biostatistics; also, members of the Departments of Epidemiology and Public Health Administration. Dr. Ernest L. Stebbins, Dean of the School, continuously encouraged prosecution of the study as a venture in evaluation in public health.

No public agency could have been more cooperative than the Baltimore Urban Renewal and Housing Agency. Without qualification, it may be said that the agency officials cooperated to the limit to provide the opportunity to undertake and complete the research. Appreciation for selfless cooperation is due, among others, to Messrs. Oliver C. Winston and Ellis Ash, formerly Director and Assistant Director, respectively; Mr. Harry Weiss and Miss Esther Siegel, Director and Assistant Director of Management, respectively; and Mr. Van Story Branch, Manager of Lafayette Courts, the project in which the test families resided.

The Baltimore City Health Department was helpful in many substantive ways. A special debt is due Dr. Huntington Williams, Commissioner of Health, long a pioneer in the movement to provide adequate housing facilities in the city. The study headquarters were, in fact, housed in the Eastern Health District Building; Dr. W. S. Harper, Health Officer of this well-known district, was a source of much information about the study environs. Miss Eleanor McKnight, Chief of the Division of Nutrition, performed an invaluable role as a consultant. Personnel of the Baltimore City Public Schools provided assistance in the collection of the school data.

The study had many consultants from various research specialties. Two may be singled out whose experience and advice were especially important to the study: Mr. Theodore Woolsey, at present an Assistant Director of the National Center for Health Statistics, Public Health Service, and Mr. Harold Nisselson, Director of Field Studies of the Bureau of the Census, and his staff of medical coders. Scaling of psychological materials was accomplished through consultation with Dr. Lee S. Christie, at present with the System Development Corporation, with assistance from Mrs. Elsie Gray of the Central Intelligence Agency.

The adjustment components of the study profited greatly at the earliest stages as well as later on from the advice and guidance of Professor Isidor Chein of New York University. Additional valuable consultation was obtained from Miss Eunice Cooper, now at McCann-Erickson, Inc., and Dr. Nehemiah Jordan, at present with the Rand Corporation.

The study staff is indebted to Mr. Lawrence Frankel of Punched Cards-Tabulating, Inc., for an interest that went beyond a commercial relationship, in punching and tabulating the voluminous data of the study. Mrs. Norma Lutins of the Department of Biostatistics was also helpful in this connection.

No study of this nature can proceed successfully without the co-operation of staff members charged with the responsibility of gathering the basic information which later become the "data." Recognition is due the field staff and office personnel who carried out this work in scientific spirit and manner appropriate to the nature of the study. Special recognition is due Mrs. Mary S. Tyler, Field Supervisor, for conscientious application in selecting and training of field staff, and in efforts to maintain a uniformly high quality of performance; and to Miss Ruth Hudson, who was helpful at many stages of the study, particularly in connection with data for initial matching and school performance.

To the study secretary, Miss Florence Nolan, general appreciation is due for an extraordinarily devoted and conscientious performance of duties for almost the entire period of the study activities.

Daniel M. Wilner, *School of Public Health, University of California, Los Angeles*

Rosabelle Price Walkley, *School of Public Health, University of California, Los Angeles*

Thomas C. Pinkerton, *Department of Biophysics, The Johns Hopkins University*

Matthew Tayback, *Baltimore City Health Department and School of Hygiene and Public Health, The Johns Hopkins University*

October, 1961

CONTENTS

PART 1. BACKGROUND OF THE STUDY

General review of forty selected studies. The independent variable. The dependent variable. Isolating the effects of housing, *per se.*

The specific impetus for the research. The study design and the independent variable. The hypotheses of the study and the dependent variables.

Source of test and control groups. Selection of test and control families. Attrition over time among families surveyed. Moves among test and control families. Problems arising from attrition and moves. Solutions to the problems of attrition and movement. Initial comparability of intact and reduced effective samples. Description of the test and control reduced effective samples. Instruments used.

PART 2. MORBIDITY

PART 3. SOCIAL PSYCHOLOGICAL ADJUSTMENT

PART 4. SCHOOL PERFORMANCE

PART 5. REVIEW OF FINDINGS

THE HOUSING ENVIRONMENT AND FAMILY LIFE

INTRODUCTION

The Johns Hopkins Longitudinal Study of the Effects of Housing on Health and Social Adjustment was undertaken in March, 1954.[1] The study compared the initial background and subsequent history of two matched groups of Negro families living in Baltimore, Maryland: a test group that moved from the slums into new housing, and a control group that for a period remained in generally poor housing. At the outset of the study, the samples consisted of approximately 400 test families (2000 persons) and 600 control families (3000 persons). Data collected from 1955 to 1958 constituted an investigation of the influence of housing quality during a period of approximately three years. The data were obtained through personal interviews with members of the test and control groups and from public agency records.

General planning for the study may be said to have begun in 1950. The principal agencies involved in the initial planning were the American Public Health Association (APHA), the National Association of Housing and Redevelopment Officials (NAHRO), the Baltimore Housing Authority, and the Baltimore City Health Department. Of the APHA and NAHRO organizations, the group most directly involved was the Joint Committee on Housing and Health. This Committee was instrumental in stimulating interest in undertaking the study among officials and faculty of the School of Hygiene and Public Health, The Johns Hopkins University.

Subsequent chapters provide an account of the following major study components: *the morbidity survey,* testing hypotheses regarding sickness and health; *the social survey,* testing hypotheses pertaining to behavior, attitude, and psychological state; and *the information from*

[1] The study staff members responsible for the research held appointments in the School of Hygiene and Public Health, The Johns Hopkins University, in the period 1954-1960. The investigation was supported by a research grant from the National Institutes of Health, Public Health Service, U. S. Department of Health, Education, and Welfare.

public agency records, testing hypotheses involving school performance of children.

The findings reported represent coverage of almost every aspect of the major components which were planned at the outset and measured during the course of the study. The analysis was conducted and the findings presented in each instance to test as succinctly as possible the hypotheses for the various matters discussed. For social adjustment data and school performance of children, this has meant, generally, comparison of total test and control groups except for contingencies which would make inclusion of total samples illogical; for example, only families with children were compared on items involving children. For morbidity data, proper assessment of the findings made necessary the comparison of test-control illness and disability rates by sex and various age groups.

The chapters are assembled into five parts: a section dealing with the background of the study (Chapters I-III), a section that describes the morbidity findings (Chapters IV-IX), a section dealing with social adjustment findings (Chapters X-XVI), a section that presents findings regarding school performance of children (Chapter XVII), and a final chapter that provides a summary and conclusions.

Background of the study (Chapters I-III)

Chapter I reviews the scope, methods, and findings of prior studies designed to investigate the relationship that housing bears to physical and social pathology. Chapter II describes the specific impetus for the research, its basic design, and hypotheses. Chapter III describes major procedures and two problems which arose (sample attrition, and the movement of control families to improved housing), and the solution which eventually was adopted. Data to evaluate the adequacy of the solution are also summarized, and include a review of the *initial comparability* of the test and control groups in regard to a number of characteristics. Finally, some details are given about the instruments used.

Morbidity (Chapters IV-IX)

In Chapter IV there is an elaboration of hypotheses concerning some specific housing elements that may be expected to influence the course of morbidity in dwellings of good quality. There follow some general, introductory data about illness experience, presented as percentages either by individual morbidity survey waves or by averages for groups of waves. In addition, information is given regarding hospitalizations and mortality in the test and control groups.

Chapter V presents detailed information about episodes of illness as a rate per 100 persons. Data are given for total episodes and for episodes of varying degrees of severity. The information is shown by "period," a cumulation of the data for three groups of morbidity survey waves, and rates are presented for various age-sex groupings. This mode of data presentation is also characteristic of Chapters VI through VIII.

Chapter VI contains findings pertaining to days of disability as a rate per 100 persons. In addition to total days, three kinds of disability also are distinguished: days hospitalized, days in bed, and days kept from usual activities.

Chapter VII and Chapter VIII describe for children and adults, respectively, the incidence of illness occurring in various disease categories. Episodes were classified according to type of illness, using definitions of the *Manual of the International Statistical Classification of Diseases, Injuries, and Causes of Death.*[2]

Chapter IX gives information regarding various outcomes of pregnancies and the prenatal morbidity experience of the mothers, as a per cent of all pregnancies terminating in an appropriate period during the study.

Social psychological adjustment (Chapters X-XVI)

The topics covered by the chapters pertaining to social adjustment may be summarized as follows: Chapter X, reactions to housing and space, including an appraisal of children's play places and possibilities for privacy; Chapter XI, activities and relations among family members; Chapter XII, interaction with neighbors and the role played by architecture in neighborly activities; Chapter XIII, social self-concept and aspirations for self and children in connection with such topics as education and jobs; Chapter XIV, group memberships of adults and children, and behavior and attitudes toward the immediate and the larger neighborhood; Chapter XV, indicators of psychological

[2] World Health Organization, Geneva, 1949.

matters pertaining to the self, such as tension, morale, self-esteem, and anxiety; Chapter XVI, ratings of appearance of home and person, various self-promotive and other activities, and possession of items of consumer goods.

School performance of children (Chapter XVII)

Chapter XVII presents the information obtained from records of the Baltimore public schools. It compares test and control children as to performance on intelligence, arithmetic and reading tests, number of promotions, and regularity of attendance.

PART **1**

BACKGROUND OF THE STUDY

CHAPTER I

REVIEW OF PREVIOUS STUDIES

For the past half century, programs of social action have been directed toward the achievement of improved housing for substantial segments of the population. These programs (such as health codes regulating housing infractions, and provisions for slum clearance) have stemmed, no doubt, from both humanitarian beliefs in social justice and the pragmatic belief that housing plays a central role in health and well-being. The belief that housing is a factor in physical and mental health has arisen from the clinical and common-sense observation of physicians, public health officials, criminologists, law enforcement agencies, sociologists, welfare workers, and others, that many health and social disabilities have greatest prevalence in slum neighborhoods.

Researches designed to investigate the relationship that housing bears to health and social adjustment have been undertaken at an accelerating rate in the last thirty years. Such researches, directly or indirectly, may serve to test and evaluate programs of social action, and at the same time serve more theoretical ends, testing the validity of commonly held beliefs and augmenting knowledge regarding the effects of different environments upon human populations. Whatever their individual missions, researches in this field have, together, probably buttressed the efforts of social planners to effect improvements in housing. This is suggested by a review of a number of these investigations, most of which, as will be described more fully in the first section of this chapter, have found a relationship between housing quality and physical or social pathology.

3

The researches reviewed constitute a sample of studies relating to housing quality, variously measured or defined, and various physical and social aberrations. The sample is not exhaustive. The main principle of selection was that the study should present first-hand analysis by the author (s) , whether of field data or of previously collected census and health data. General speculative and hortatory works based on previously obtained analytic results were excluded.

General Review of Forty Selected Studies

Sources and dates of the studies

Forty selected researches were reviewed, of which 24 are American in origin, while 16 are of European origin, including 15 British and 1 Danish study. Of the European studies, 5 were published between World Wars I and II (1919 to 1939) , 1 in 1945, and 10 in the 1950's. Of the 24 American studies, 4 were published prior to World War II, 11 during the 1940's, and 9 during the 1950's.

Major orientations

A marked divergence of emphasis or orientation is noticeable between the American and European investigations. Of the 16 European studies, 14 dealt specifically with the effects of housing on physical health, and only 2 dealt with psychological or social parameters, 1 with neurosis, and 1 with social adjustment. Of the 14 dealing with some aspect of physical health, 8 investigated solely the relationship between housing and tuberculosis, 5 analyzed general morbidity rates, death rates, birth rates, infant mortality, respiratory disease, accident rates, etc., and 1 studied the weight and height of pre-school children.[1]

Of the 24 American studies, on the other hand, 10 dealt with physical disease, these being equally divided among studies of single diseases or single disease types (e.g., respiratory infections) , and studies of general morbidity. The remaining 14 studies dealt with social and psychological matters, with a marked clustering about a single topic: 7 of

---

[1] References for European studies, which will be found in Appendix 1, are: tuberculosis (3, 6, 17, 23, 24, 32, 39, 40); other morbidity and mortality (11, 25, 28, 30, 38); height and weight (27); neurosis (22); social adjustment (26).

the 14 studies dealt solely with juvenile delinquency, and 2 others included it as a major component of the material under investigation.[2]

In summary, the British investigations screened seem to have been largely concerned with the effects of housing on physical health, with a high concentration on tuberculosis as the measured health variable. The American investigations reviewed have been more evenly divided between health and social adjustment, with a high concentration on juvenile delinquency.

General findings

In general, the findings of these studies showed a marked positive association between housing and health, poor housing correlating with poor health, better housing with better health. There were some mixed, ambiguous, or null findings, and a very small number of actual negative findings.

Of 24 studies (14 British and 10 American) involving physical morbidity, 15 showed positive findings, 7 seemed ambiguous or showed no relationship between housing and health, and 2 arrived at negative results (25, 23). Of the 16 studies dealing with some aspect of social adjustment, 11 found a positive relationship to housing, 4 gave ambiguous or null results, and 1 was negative (22).

Specific positive findings (morbidity)

Tuberculosis. Examples of clear-cut positive findings relating housing to tuberculosis are numerous. "A Study of Respiratory Tuberculosis in Relation to Housing Conditions in Edinburgh" by Stein (39) is characteristic. Using census tract data to establish measures of various person-density parameters for each electoral ward, and public health data on tuberculosis rates from 1930 to 1940, Stein found a consistent and highly significant correlation between both mortality and incidence of the disease, on the one hand, and over-crowding, on the other. For the years 1930-31 and 1931-32, for instance, the correlation coefficients for mortality rate and "persons per room" were .704 and .701, respectively. For mortality rate and "per

[2] References for American studies, which will be found in Appendix 1, are: single disease types (1, 4, 5, 12, 21); general morbidity (7, 8, 9, 31, 33); delinquency and crime (2, 13, 15, 16, 19, 29, 34, 36, 37); mental disorder (14, 35); social adjustment (10, 20); school progress (18).

cent (in electoral ward) living more than 2 in a room," the corresponding figures for the two years were .705 and .663.

Similar studies in Glasgow (40), London (3), and New York (21) have shown corresponding, although sometimes less marked, findings. Stein's Glasgow study (40) again showed high correlations of tuberculosis with "simple crowding" (persons per house), but much lower and in some cases not significant correlations with "overcrowding" (persons per room, or, per cent living more than 2 per room). B. Benjamin's statistically sophisticated treatment of London data (3) showed crowding to be one of the two most useful variables in predicting variation of tuberculosis mortality rates. Lowell, in New York (21), also found a high correlation ($r = +.71$) between poor housing and tuberculosis.

General morbidity.   Three papers by Britten, *et al.* (7, 8, 9), analyzing data collected in the U. S. National Health Survey of 1935-36 on the relationship between housing and a wide range of morbidity variables, indicated consistent positive correlations. Frequency of illness disabling for a week or longer was associated with degree of crowding (persons per room); rates of digestive diseases were higher for persons with no private inside flush toilet than for those having such facilities; frequency of home accidents decreased with rising rents; incidence of common communicable diseases of childhood occurred earlier as degree of crowding increased; secondary attack rates of tuberculosis were over 200 per cent higher for persons on relief living in crowded circumstances (more than 1.5 persons per room) than for *all* economic status groups living in less crowded quarters (1 person or less per room).

Taking diagnosed hospital admissions as the starting point, J. E. Benjamin, *et al.*, in Cincinnati (4), showed that 65 per cent of all pneumonia cases admitted came from 17 slum census tracts comprising only 25 per cent of the population. Christensen in Copenhagen (11), dealing with hospital admissions of children, observed rates for slum children to be at least twice as high as those for well-housed children in a wide range of diseases, including: acute upper respiratory infections, pneumonia, otitis media, meningitis, measles, infectious skin diseases, and acute dyspepsia, as well as anemia, rickets, prematurity, and congenital malformations. A study by Spence, *et al.*, in Newcastle-upon-Tyne (38), of 1000 infants (and their families) during their first year of life, showed a significant association between overcrowding and number of respiratory infections, and also between overcrowding and home accidents.[3]

Specific positive findings (social)

Research in urban sociology has shown social pathology to decrease consistently as distance from the center of cities increases, the authors generally mentioning housing as an important element in the slum complex. Representative of these are the studies of Shaw and McKay (36), who showed that delinquency follows this pattern, rates being highest at the center and lower with increasing distance from the center. Using the same zonal hypothesis, Schroeder (35), replicating the studies of Faris and Dunham, found that in 5 American cities, mental hospital admissions likewise decreased with increasing distance from the central zone, and moreover were highly correlated ($r = .62$ to .71) with such specific housing factors as "per cent of buildings needing major repair," "vacant dwelling units," "proportions of rental units," and "houses unfit for use."

Several other investigators, notably Dirksen (13) in Indiana, Harlan, et al. (16) in Alabama, and Schmitt (34) in Hawaii have found a definite positive relationship between some person-density factor and juvenile delinquency. In Hammond, East Chicago, and Gary, Indiana, Dirksen compared average housing in "delinquent blocks" with average housing for the entire city, "delinquent blocks" being those in which addresses of known delinquents had been located. In all three cities, he found higher percentages in the delinquent blocks of houses needing major repair, or having no private bath, or having more than 1.5 persons per room, than in the city as a whole.

Harlan, et al., using 15 separate indices of housing quality, compared delinquency rates per 1000 persons under 20 years of age for 52 census tracts in Birmingham, Alabama. He found the following correlations with delinquency: $+.632$ for "overcrowding" (2.01 or more persons per room), $-.436$ for economic value of house, $+.606$ for per cent built before 1890, $+.517$ for per cent needing major repairs, $+.749$ for per cent tenant occupied.

Schmitt's study of 29 census areas in Honolulu showed that in tracts where overcrowded dwelling units (1.51 persons or more per

---

[3] References for other positive morbidity findings than those given above are: 1, 28, 30, 31, 33, in Appendix 1.

room) constituted fewer than 10 per cent of all occupied units in the tract, the delinquency rate was 12.5 (per 1000 families); where overcrowded units constituted 10.0 - 19.09 per cent of the total, the delinquency rate was 20.2; and in tracts with 20 per cent or more overcrowded dwellings, the rate was 26.1. Corresponding crime rates were 0.56, 0.78, and 1.92 (per 1000 civilians 14 years of age and over).

Loring (20), comparing 83 "socially disorganized" families (identified from social agency and court records) and 83 matched "control" families, found a significant association between social disorganization and 7 out of 8 density factors measured.[4]

Specific negative findings

Actual negative findings are rare. Mackintosh (23) investigated housing quality for 400 cases of sputum positive pulmonary tuberculosis in Northamptonshire. Categorizing housing as: Group A, good in all essentials; Group B, reasonably good . . . but some overcrowding; and Group C, slums, he found the 400 cases distributed as follows: Group A, 58.25 per cent; Group B, 32.25 per cent; Group C, 9.5 per cent.

M'Gonigle (25) found higher death rates among 152 publicly rehoused families than among a group of similar slum-dwelling families. Infant mortality and birth rates, however, were lower in the rehoused group. In an attempt to account for the higher death rates among the well-housed, M'Gonigle investigated the diets of subsamples of each group, and concluded that "the variations in the composition of their diets constitute the only discovered adverse influences operative upon the Mt. Pleasant (rehoused) estate."

Martin, *et al.,* (22), comparing mental hospital admissions from a housing estate in Hertfordshire with those from all of England and Wales, found the housing estate rates to be from 23 to 74 per cent higher than "expected." Analysis by age and sex showed the most marked deviations to be among persons 55 years of age and over, and especially among women 45 and over. This latter subgroup accounted for only 13 per cent of the housing estate female sample, but contributed 55 per cent of female mental hospital admissions.

---

[4] References for other positive social adjustment findings than those given above are: 2, 15, 18, 26, 29, in Appendix 1.

Some ambiguous findings

Some ambiguous or null findings are of interest. Brett and Benjamin analyzed the results of a mass radiographic examination of 14,576 families in the Metropolitan Borough of Islington (6). The authors found that a rise in tuberculosis was not uniformly associated with increasing person density per room, the over-all rates per thousand for three density levels being: less than 1 person per room, 9.8 per 1000; 1 person per room, 16.9 per 1000; more than 1 person per room, 12.4 per 1000. The rates did vary inversely with "social class" but within each class there was no consistent increase of morbidity with increased crowding, *except* for the lowest class. In the latter, the rates were the highest for any class, and were, for the three density levels: 12.0, 16.1 and 17.1 per 1000, respectively.

On the other hand, a study of tuberculosis in Glasgow by McMillan (24) showed a high correlation (+.72) of rates with crowding in 21 wards where the rates were *lower* than the city-wide average, and very small correlation (+.13) with crowding in 16 wards where the rates were *higher* than the city-wide average. Stein's Glasgow results (40) were also somewhat anomalous in that tuberculosis was found to be distinctly less correlated with "persons per room" than with "persons per house."

The most thoroughly documented and analyzed findings showing a virtually null relationship are those of Lander (19) on the association of housing and juvenile delinquency. This study of delinquency in Baltimore found high correlations between delinquency and housing or housing-related variables, individually, such as "percentage of homes overcrowded," "percentage of homes substandard," "median rental," and "percentage of homes renter-occupied." Higher order analysis, however, elicited partial correlation coefficients of virtually zero between delinquency, and either overcrowding or substandard housing. Factor analysis indicated that delinquency was fundamentally related to an essentially non-housing factor rather than to the physical and economic aspects of housing itself.

The Independent Variable

Two general criteria of housing quality have been employed in the investigations reported in this review. The first consists of measures of one or more discrete elements of housing, usually obtainable from published characteristics of blocks or census tracts, and explicitly employing *some measure of crowding or person-density as one (and sometimes the exclusive) component.* The second housing criterion among the studies consists of more general indicators of housing quality, ordinarily not measured explicitly, but rather inferred from the general environs or employing relatively crude, subjective estimates of over-all quality. Typical studies in this category contrast public housing and slums, which represent "good" and "bad" housing, respectively.

Discrete measures utilizing crowding as principal or only feature

Twenty-eight of the 40 studies used discrete measures of housing quality, 15 relying solely on the criterion of crowding, the remaining 13 introducing one or more additional variables such as crowding and dilapidation; crowding, toilet facilities, and rental; crowding and state of repair. The general analytical procedure in these studies was to relate the dependent variable to each housing element considered.

The actual criteria for establishing degree of crowding vary. In general, the measures are of person-density within the dwelling unit or in the environs. Stein, in her studies of tuberculosis in Edinburgh and Glasgow (39, 40), used variously "average number of persons per house," "average number of persons per room," "percentage of ward population living at density of more than 2 persons per room," and "percentage of overcrowded houses in ward."

Schmitt, in investigating the connection between population density and delinquency and crime in Honolulu (34), used five density measures, "population per net acre," "average household size," "doubling-up," "per cent of dwelling units in structures with 5 or more dwelling units," and "overcrowding" defined as per cent of dwelling units with 1.51 or more persons per room.

Four "crowding ratings" used in studies of psychoneurosis (14) and of school progress (18) in the Eastern Health District of Baltimore were based largely on sleep-crowding, and ranged from *more than adequate* (more than one room for sleeping per person or per married couple, plus living room and kitchen) to *very unsatisfactory* (less than one room for sleeping for each 2 persons of suitable age and sex, plus kitchen). Loring (20) in his study of "social disorganization" of families in Boston included as "density-factors" the "number of heated rooms," "heated space," and an environmental index which included land use, street traffic, and distance from recreational and other facilities.

There were probably several reasons for the preponderant use of degree of crowding or some version of density as the principal or only measure of housing quality. First, this type of independent variable is a logical parameter to investigate in connection with a number of dependent variables such as tuberculosis and juvenile delinquency. Second, crowding is easily quantifiable and more precisely measurable than many other housing factors. Third, when the information to be analyzed is taken from previously collected census data, person-density figures are very probably more accurate and reliable than other kinds of items such as dilapidation, state of building repair, or rent.

However, restricting discrete housing measures largely to crowding limits the likelihood of establishing the role of other housing factors in relation to health and disease. In addition to crowding and space in various versions, there are a great many other elements, such as water supply, heat, ventilation, lighting, refrigeration, and infestation, that may be investigated as to their influence on health.

A general problem connected with the use of discrete elements like crowding as indicators of housing quality arises when the measures are obtained from published census descriptions of neighborhoods. Since these data consist of means, medians, or distributions, they do not, of course, identify particular dwelling units which may be appreciably different from an average. Thus, although an individual is classifiable as to his "precise" status on the dependent variable (health or adjustment), his classification on the independent variable (housing) reflects only the neighborhood average, which may or may not coincide with his own particular circumstances. The lack of precision in this kind of classification may, as a consequence, obscure the relationship between housing and health or adjustment.

More general measures of housing quality

The remaining 12 researches reviewed used broad rather than discrete measures of housing quality, and tapped sources of measurement other than census records. These studies investigated principally the effect of *generally* "good" or "poor" housing: 7 dealt with public housing as contrasted usually to slums, without the introduction of any specific measurements; 2 introduced an urban zone criterion; and 3 used a somewhat crude scale of housing quality based on some underlying measures of single components.

The studies which define "good" and "bad" housing quality in terms of public and slum housing will be examined in the final section of this chapter.[5] The use of *public housing* as the criterion of "good" housing quality is quite plausibly based on the common-sense supposition that it is thoroughly adequate in all or most respects. Moreover, the move of sizeable groups of hitherto slum-dwelling families into public housing provides for the first time a set of circumstances in which something approaching an experimental manipulation of the independent variable is possible. The significance of studies based on this criterion lies precisely in the fact that populations which are virtually identical in income, education, cultural and ethnic background, and previous life experience in general, may be subjected to a sharp differential change in housing environment alone, and then tested for subsequent change in one or more dependent variables.

On the other hand, the use of *slum housing* as the criterion of "bad" housing may be somewhat more problematical. Unquestionably, the slum is not as good as public housing, but it also may not be of uniformly poor quality. Failure to distinguish the varying degrees of quality of housing in the slum may interfere with the discovery of a relationship between housing and dependent variables, a shortcoming that might be overcome if the status of the individual dwelling units were assessed.

Efforts in this direction have been made by using measures of overall housing quality, based on the summation of specific components. McMillan (24), for instance, in addition to measuring crowding (as persons per room by electoral ward), also used a four-point scale as follows:

Standard:	Modern conveniences including separate toilet, bathroom, adequate food storage, and adequate cooking facilities.
Substandard A:	Falling short of Standard in some degree, but can be renovated.
Substandard B:	Deficient as in Substandard A and cannot be renovated.
Unfit:	Unfit for human habitation because of defective design or sanitary defects, or both.

[5] Reference for studies in which public housing was the criterion for "good" housing are: 1, 2, 10, 22, 25, 26, 31, in Appendix 1.

Such approaches go far toward overcoming the difficulties inherent in the more undifferentiated measures of housing quality. The problems that still await solution have to do with the range and kind of components to be measured, the precision of their measurement, and their utilization in some kind of an over-all rating of housing quality for the individual dwelling unit.

The Dependent Variable

In the studies reviewed, the dependent variables—topics whose association with housing is being sought—have generally been treated in one of two ways. In a majority of the cases, the attempt is made to investigate the relationship between housing and a small number, perhaps one or two, of morbidity or adjustment entities which generally have considerable medical or social importance. The remaining studies, considerably fewer in number, deal with somewhat broader and more numerous topics.

The summary of the studies in the first section of this chapter indicated the relative narrowness of the range of dependent variables in the morbidity field. This is typified by the concentration on tuberculosis as measured by rate of incidence or prevalence. Other studies with a single disease category as the focus involve, for example, pneumonia (4), respiratory infections (5), rheumatic fever and streptococcus infection (12). In the adjustment field, the emphasis on studies of delinquency has already been pointed out. Other studies with concentration on a single topic include research on crime (29), psychoneurosis (14), and children's progress in school (18).

Restricting a study to consideration of a single dependent variable probably arises from the primary concern with the particular medical or social pathology in question; many studies begin with interest in a particular dependent variable, and the relationship to housing is sought as possibly having etiologic significance. This *dependent variable* instigation to research is then sometimes buttressed by the fact that the data for the pathology in question, being of high professional significance, is available because of uniform municipal reporting schemes (as with communicable diseases in many cities).

Investigation of a small number of serious or traumatic dependent variables is of course a proper procedure when interest is primarily in the variables under consideration, although even in such instances, advantage can accrue from consideration of related variables. For the investigator who begins with an interest in *housing,* this type of study offers some handicaps to an understanding of the general range of influence of the housing environment on human affairs. Moreover, concentration on such matters as tuberculosis and infant mortality and on juvenile delinquency singles out only the "very serious" end of the range of possible physical and social variables. It is entirely possible that the major effects of housing—as indicated by influence on the largest numbers of persons—may well lie below the level of the seriously traumatic, and may not necessarily be measurable exclusively by the more traditional pathologies that reach the status of public statistics.

There is, furthermore, a question as to the adequacy of exclusively negative measures. Treating good or improved health as only the absence or lowered incidence of recognizable disease may possibly be sufficient. For psychological health and social adjustment, however, adequate measurement at the positive end of the scale seems unlikely to emerge from concentration on crime, delinquency, and suicide rates alone.

While the preponderance of the studies reviewed are of the variety investigating the relationship between housing and one or perhaps several "serious" entities, a few researches suggest a somewhat broader approach. Schmitt's "Housing and Health on Oahu" included infant mortality and other death rates, tuberculosis and venereal disease rates, suicides and mental hospital admissions. The major morbidity studies dealing with an extensive range of variables are the three by Britten, *et al.* (7, 8, 9), Christensen's Copenhagen study (11), a similar one by Riley of hospitalized children in Glasgow (30), and the Newcastle-upon-Tyne study by Spence, *et al.* (38)

Two major studies in the adjustment field that deal with a broader range of phenomena are Mogey's "Changes in Family Life Experienced by English Workers Moving from Slums to Housing Estates" (26), and Chapin's "An Experiment in the Social Effects of Good Housing" (10). Mogey examined such factors as intrafamilial relationships, interpersonal relationships with neighbors and friends, church and association memberships, attitudes and aspirations toward housing, and employment. Chapin measured "morale" (in terms of feelings of ability to cope with a given situation), "social participation" (largely in terms of membership in associations), "general adjustment" (feelings about other persons, social conditions, and institutions), and "social status."

The objective of tapping a broader range of health and adjustment issues in their relationship to housing quality suggests, in addition to more traditional sources of data (such as health department statistics, hospital admissions, and court records), the use of some form of mass observation. Typical examples of this method occur in the National Health Survey, the Baltimore studies of neurosis and school progress in the Eastern Health District (14, 18), the studies of Mogey (26), Chapin (10), Loring (20), and Spence, *et al.* (38). These studies all involved extensive efforts to obtain relevant information in the course of home visits conducted by professional or specially trained lay personnel.

Isolating the Effects of Housing, per se

In the researches reviewed, several study techniques have been employed in the attempt to demonstrate the strength of the association between housing itself and the various measures of health and adjustment. At the first level are the studies—a majority of those surveyed —which rely solely on simple or zero-order measures of association between the two sets of variables.

The possibilities of statistical control

Where the study design permits, and when sufficient demographic information has been collected regarding persons and families, it is possible to pursue further the relative influence of housing and various non-housing factors known or suspected to be correlative with housing. Even when pertinent data are present, higher order analysis may or may not be used, depending on the interests of the investigators. The Newcastle-upon-Tyne survey of 1000 infants and their families (38) was a detailed longitudinal observation of morbidity based on successive home visits, in which all relevant data were probably available. The authors present data on, for instance, "respiratory disease and social class (father's occupation)," "respiratory disease and overcrowding," and "respiratory disease and maternal capacity," but nowhere are such data combined or analyzed for partial correlation. A similar approach occurs in the three reports by Britten, *et al.*, based on the data of the National Health Survey (7, 8, 9), where rates are broken down by income, relief status, geographical area, type of dwelling, city size, and other variables, but measures of actual partial association are not computed, simultaneously holding constant some of these clearly relevant characteristics.

At least two studies, relying principally on census-type data, have exploited to a great extent the possibilities of further statistical control of a number of variables. Starting with nine socioeconomic prediction variables in which he was able to obtain measures from London census data, Benjamin (3) showed by multiple regression analysis that *income* and *crowding* were "as good a guide as any" to the variation of tuberculosis mortality among boroughs. Partial correlation coefficients between mortality rates and these two variables were: .45 for income (with crowding held constant); .35 for crowding (with income held constant).

Lander (19), who was investigating the underlying causes of juvenile delinquency, started from census-derived measures of several variables: education, rent, population density (crowding), substandard housing, racial composition, and owner-occupied homes. Initial analysis showed high zero-order correlation of juvenile delinquency with the housing-related variables such as: percentage of owner-occupied homes, —.80; percentage of overcrowding, +.73; percentage of substandard housing, +.69. Further analysis, however, produced partial correlation coefficients with delinquency such as .0052 for substandard housing and .0079 for crowding. Adjustment for curvilinearity of the data reduced the correlation in both cases to zero. Factor analysis of a number of variables established two underlying factors, one socioeconomic; the other, "anomic." While the physical and economic aspects of housing were part of the socioeconomic factor, it was with the anomic factor (essentially "normlessness," or the breakdown of traditional social controls) that juvenile delinquency seemed to be fundamentally related.

The possibilities of experimental control

The alternative to statistical control of demographic variables correlative with housing is the introduction of some measure of experimental or quasi-experimental control. Ideally, the non-housing variables would be held constant; housing quality alone would be permitted to change. In the researches reviewed, studies of the differential effects of public housing and some other type of housing are the principal instances of this type of design. Such studies may be classified as quasi-experimental in the sense that measurement is made of a population that has undergone change in the independent variable, housing quality (from "bad" to "good"); comparisons are then made on the dependent variable between this group and some other group residing elsewhere, usually in a slum area. The extent to which the non-housing factors have been held constant, however, varies considerably from study to study.

Martin, et al. (22) compared rates of hospital admissions from a Hertfordshire housing estate to rates for all of England and Wales. Barer's delinquency study (2) used a "before and after" design, employing one group of 317 families. Delinquency rates were "estimated" for the families during the period 1924-1940, before the move to public housing, and directly observed for the period 1940-1944, after the move.

Five studies directly contrasted public and slum housing. M'Gonigle (25) compared 152 families who moved into public housing from Housewife Lane, a slum area, to the *remaining* population of Housewife Lane, and also to the population of another slum area. No matching of the groups being contrasted was undertaken.

Mogey's Oxford study of English workers (26) used two samples of 30 families each, matched on an aggregate basis for demographic characteristics. One sample moved from the slum to public housing; the other remained in the slum.

Barer's tuberculosis study (1) involved 17 project-dwelling families having at least one tubercular member, and 17 slum-dwelling families who also had at least one tubercular member. The project and slum families were matched on certain demographic characteristics, and the tubercular persons were matched on variables such as sex, age, primary diagnosis, and status of disease at time of diagnosis. These persons were then observed for the subsequent course of their disease.

Rumney's study of the ". . . Social Effects of Public Housing in Newark, New Jersey" (31) compared morbidity and delinquency rates in three housing projects with those in the ward districts in which they were located. However, the racial composition differed markedly, being 69 per cent Negro in the project *vs.* 17 per cent in the ward in one case; 48 per cent *vs.* 63 per cent in another; and 55 per cent *vs.* 6 per cent in the third. In this case, statistical rather than experimental control of the non-housing variables was used, and the data were analyzed by race; but since the sources were exclusively census tract records or housing authority files, sufficient information for thoroughgoing statistical control may well have been lacking.

Perhaps the study most closely approximating an ideal experimental design is Chapin's Minneapolis study, "An Experiment on the Social Effects of Good Housing" (10), with rigorous matching of samples and sophisticated treatment of the data. Forty-four rehoused families were matched with 38 slum-dwelling families on 10 factors including race, employment, occupation, family size, income, age and education of wife. The two groups were tested after one year for changes in four social adjustment variables which had previously been measured for both samples prior to the rehousing of the test group.

These researches suggest that studies of public housing occupants would seem to offer an unusual opportunity for naturalistic experiments in this field. Here may be found population groups of generally large numbers introduced rapidly to a marked upward change in housing environment, probably without major antecedent changes in correlated variables like income and education. If studies can be undertaken in this setting, the basic problem of manipulating housing quality *alone* is essentially solved. The importance of the identification of a proper control group is also apparent, since measurement of test families alone, over time, will not reveal the true nature and extent of influence of housing change. Whatever the source of control persons and families, some procedures for matching test and control groups seem indicated, not for the purpose of improving the precision of the statistical assessment of dependent variable differences, if they occur, but simply to insure good initial comparability of the groups under observation.

CHAPTER II

IMPETUS FOR THE STUDY, ITS DESIGN, HYPOTHESES AND VARIABLES

The Specific Impetus for the Research

The review of the literature and history of the problem of housing and health suggests that several important problems remain unsolved. Consideration of the more important of these will help to describe the framework in which the present study was undertaken.

Dissatisfaction with cross-sectional studies as means of estimating the effects of housing quality

The studies surveyed in the preceding chapter are almost all of the cross-sectional variety; that is, in almost every instance an attempt was made:

(a)   To measure the quality of housing of a specified number of dwelling units,

(b)   To measure the medical, physical, or social pathology found among the occupants of the same dwelling units, and

(c)   To interrelate measures of housing quality and pathology.

The outcome has traditionally been the detection of an association between the two sets of variables. The question arises regarding the direction and magnitude of *causation* in this procedure. The

19

problem of direction and magnitude of causation in epidemiologic studies is a familiar one in the field of public health and welfare.

In medical epidemiology, the cross-sectional study leading to the discovery of association between two variables has for generations been a traditional and fruitful epidemiologic tool for the determination of the causes of infection and epidemics. Its basic methods are, first, the identification of a sub-population known to be suffering from some disease with characteristic complaints and symptoms; and, second, the accumulation of data about many *other characteristics* possessed by the victims of the disease and not by others in the larger population. If the year is 1900, the "other characteristics" may well be the microscopic observation that the blood stream of the victims is infested with microbial organisms. If the year is 1920, the "other characteristics" may be distance from a swamp in which mosquitoes concentrate, or it may be a particular water source. If the year is 1950, in which, for a given communicable infection, both micro-organisms and general means of transmission are both known, the "other characteristics" may be the more particular life experiences and general background characteristics of populations.

In general, the cross-sectional study has been highly productive in yielding understanding of the causes of many infectious diseases and in achieving their ultimate control.

In more recent times, this epidemiologic model has been adopted for use in the search for causes of pathologies, both medical and non-medical, that differ in important respects from the preceding. In preventive medicine today, the cross-sectional study is often addressed to problems in which the extent and nature of microbiological involvement is only poorly known, or even in which it is clear that the disease in question is non-inflammatory rather than inflammatory in origin. Examples of diseases and conditions of this kind are cancer in its various forms and sites, the cardiovascular diseases, and the common mental disorders. It is a characteristic of these diseases that clues regarding causation are not yet readily confirmable in the laboratory. What applies to such conditions also applies, even more forcefully, to the social pathologies like crime and delinquency; here also, correlations between the condition and background or environmental factors are difficult to confirm in the laboratory.

There are several difficulties besetting the field epidemiologist who seeks to derive clues regarding causation from the observed association (derived from cross-sectional studies) between pathology and background and environmental factors. One difficulty frequently arises in establishing the *direction* of causation. Thus, if a particular factor is shown to be associated with a disease (i.e., sufferers from the disease possess the factor and non-sufferers do not, or do to a lesser degree), the question arises whether or not the disease itself has given rise to the factor. Is it possible that the *disease* leads to the factor rather than the possibility that the factor causes the disease? A second possibility is that both the disease and the factor under examination may be caused by still a third set of determinants. Finally, another difficulty arises when an association is found between a disease and *many* factors. Even if the direction of causality is assumed to be one in which factor → disease, are the various factors all equally important or is there a hierarchy of importance?

To be sure, investigators often bring to bear corollary evidence in supporting theories of causation derived from cross-sectional studies. Often also, sophisticated analytic techniques involving sub-populations and partial correlation are applied in an effort to alleviate unclarities of interpretation arising from cross-sectional studies. These secondary analyses are sometimes helpful in strengthening an investigator's belief in the possibility that a given factor (or factors) plays a causative role in the onset and prolongation of pathology. But equally as often, despite repeated confirmation in successive cross-sectional studies of the existence of association between pathology and possible etiologic factors, and after brain-racking attempts to further understand the data, the careful student of a problem may still remain perplexed as to the direction and strength of possible causative factors.

The situation concerning housing quality and its presumed role as the causative agent in medical and social pathologies is a case in point. Some investigators, beginning with an interest in a particular disease (perhaps tuberculosis) or a particular social maladjustment (perhaps teenage use of narcotics), have sought to show the association between the condition and housing quality. Other investigators have employed a different approach. These are generally persons with a strong interest in housing itself, who then attempt to understand the effects of housing quality on not one, but a number of pathologies. Whichever the point of departure, most studies involving housing quality are of the cross-sectional variety. It is a fair statement that perusal of the literature leaves one perplexed as to the effects, if any, of housing *per se* on any pathology. The association is there—demonstrated many times—but beset (in summary) by the inconclusive direction of causality or by the possibility that housing is but one of a number of variables in a causal chain, and in itself perhaps not a very important element.

The general improvement in housing quality in the past fifty years

The other primary impetus for conducting the present study arises from the observations regarding improvements in housing quality in American cities generally over the past fifty years. Let us assume for the moment that housing quality has played a causative role in particular medical and social pathologies. One wonders how bad housing must be for its effects to be felt. The question is of some importance inasmuch as a number of forces have combined to improve the general quality of housing in many parts of the world. In the United States this improvement has come about in two general ways. First, since the early 1900's, and in particular since the 1930's, housing laws have been enacted on both state and local levels. In many cities there are health codes which pertain to such matters as: the extent of crowding to be tolerated in a given dwelling unit; the availability of heat, hot water, toilet and bath facilities; and the control of infestation in dwelling units. Regulations such as these have served to eradicate at least some of the worst housing conditions.

In addition to housing code enactments, improvement in over-all housing in the United States has come about through the joint processes of housing demolition and movement of populations in the city. Most American cities today are in the process of rebuilding their central core, sometimes replacing demolition with dwelling units for the population displaced; sometimes replacing with non-residential rebuilding. In any event, as a consequence of this demolition, the worst housing in the city tends to disappear. Another process which has resulted in the availability of better housing has come about through the movement to the suburbs of large segments of the population in American cities. This movement, occurring for the past forty years and especially since 1946, has made dwelling units of fairly good quality available for families who occupy housing of poorer quality but who, for economic and other reasons, cannot move to the suburbs. There is thus set up within the city the possibility of a succession of moves from lesser to better housing that, in time, affects even those families previously in the worst housing.

The result of these legal and social processes is that urban housing has improved especially markedly in the decade following World War II, and the very *worst* housing has, to a great extent, disappeared. This consideration generates a restatement of the second impetus for the present study as follows: Is the range of variation of the housing quality that prevails significantly related to medical and social pathology?

The Study Design and the Independent Variable

When planning for the study began in 1950, the principal consideration was the possibility of a study design that in a number of ways would circumvent the shortcomings of cross-sectional studies and would illuminate the effects, if they existed, of housing quality. The design envisioned was a longitudinal, controlled experiment, and involved the establishment of two study groups similar to one another at the start of the investigation. The test group would vary substantially over time in the independent variable, *quality of housing*; the control group would remain constant in this respect. Both groups would be measured at specified intervals to determine the effects of introducing the independent variable.

Preliminary explorations suggested the possibility of using as the test group, members of families moving into public housing developments. Such persons generally occupy "bad" housing prior to admission into a public housing development. Search for a housing development of suitable size and setting ended in the decision to concentrate on a new public housing project then under construction in Baltimore, Maryland. The housing project, Lafayette Courts, was located in the center of the deteriorated slum areas of Baltimore, and when completed in 1954 included 816 dwelling units of one to four bedrooms. Through action of the housing and health agencies participating in the initial planning, cooperation was obtained to use Lafayette Courts as the test site.

The study plan included provision of a control group consisting of families *not* scheduled to move to public housing. These families in general occupied deteriorated dwellings characteristic of the slums.

The detailed quantitative description of the slum dwelling units appears in the next chapter in the discussion of initial housing comparability of test and control groups. At that time it will be seen that both groups occupied a range of housing quality generally descriptive of the central areas of Baltimore largely inhabited by Negro families. For the present, it will be of interest to compare in more qualitative terms the physical characteristics of this slum with those of Lafayette Courts, the housing development to which test families moved.

The physical environments of the rehoused and slum families differed in many respects. Following is an account of some of these differences.

Characteristic	*Lafayette Courts*	*Slum*
Space in the apartment	Rooms numerous enough for family size.	Rooms generally not numerous enough for family size.
Facilities for necessary activities	Bathrooms (including toilet, bathtub) inside the apartment.	Some families with outdoor toilets or communal bathrooms and toilets.
	Equipped kitchen (including sink, hot water, good stove, mechanical refrigeration).	Kitchens less adequate, sometimes without running or hot water, badly functioning stove, ice refrigeration.
	Central heating. Automatic laundry facilities in building or in nearby building.	Often without central heating. Some own washing machines; many do not.
	Closet space ample—one closet to a room; but closets generally without doors.	Closet space generally less adequate.
	Concrete floors; resident may shellac, but must provide own carpets.	Wooden floors in various states of repair.
Special facilities	Playground and community center on project site; on each story of eleven-floor buildings, 16 x 30 foot exterior play area (well screened for safety) for children under 11 years of age.	In general no such facilities on the same block; sometimes access to back yards.
Condition of area, buildings and interiors	Walks and public areas and lawns outside buildings maintained by Housing Authority; buildings new; inside of buildings, halls, plumbing, etc., kept up by maintenance crew; apartments painted at regular intervals, tenants urged to paint apartments themselves; paint provided.	General state of repair of exterior not likely to come up to standard of Lafayette Courts; most buildings built before 1920; many not kept up, although some exteriors refinished; wide variation in maintenance of interior walls (largely papered); paint or wallpaper not customarily provided by landlord.

Characteristic	Lafayette Courts	Slum
Physical and functional proximity of neighbors	Four-fifths of residents lived in six 11-story buildings, with ten families to a floor (these buildings known as "high rise"); 1-, 2-, and 3-bedroom apartments on each story; long exterior corridor (well-screened for safety) connects all dwelling units on a floor; two centrally located elevators in each building; laundry facilities in each building; incinerator chute on each floor. One-fifth of residents lived in eighteen 3-story buildings with seven to ten 3- or 4-bedroom apartments in each building (these buildings known as "low rise"); individual entrances on street level, connected by walks; laundry facilities in some of these buildings; facilities for hanging clothing to dry in back of each apartment.	Mainly row buildings with entrance to street; where several families occupy the same building, frequently a common entrance; sometimes backyard for hanging laundry to dry; sometimes several families in same building sharing toilets, bathrooms, kitchen facilities.
Physical distinctiveness of neighborhood	High-rise buildings distinctly different in architecture from surrounding neighborhoods; also true to lesser extent of low-rise buildings; lawn space contributes to demarcation between Lafayette Courts and surrounding blocks.	Mainly 2-, 3-, or 4-story buildings in any block; average block not markedly different from other slum blocks.
Population homogeneity	Housing Authority policy results in fairly homogeneous population; preference given to veterans; families with children, families of certain income range (depending on size of family)[1].	Less homogeneous population in any block in the slum.

[1] In 1954, income limits per family size, in housing developments, as established by the Housing Authority of Baltimore, were as follows:

	2 persons	3 and 4 persons	5 or more persons
Admission	$2600	$2800	$3100
Continued occupancy	$3250	$3500	$3850
	Plus $100 for each minor		

Characteristic	Lafayette Courts	Slum
Rent	Scaled to income and size of family; e.g., average rental of 1-bedroom apartment $30.56, of 2-bedroom $36.43, of 3-bedroom $37.59, etc.	Average monthly rent of families in the slum likely to be about $7 a month higher than in Lafayette Courts[2].
Management personnel	Manager, assistant manager, management aides, recreation worker, clerical staff (including cashier for the collection of rent) and maintenance staff, all on premises with headquarters in administration building.	Landlord ordinarily not on premises.

[2] According to a study conducted in 1951 by the Housing Authority of Baltimore.

The Hypotheses of the Study and the Dependent Variables

For each component of the study, review of previous research and general reflection suggested particular dependent variables that had high probability of being related to housing quality change and the particular housing quality characteristic to which specific dependent variables might be related. The most detailed hypotheses were derived for the morbidity and adjustment components of the study; these are described in the following sections.

Morbidity suspected of being related to housing quality

What morbid conditions might be expected to be related to the inadequacies in housing quality which have been noted as likely to be characteristic of slum dwelling units? Following are some representative categories.

First are the less serious acute respiratory infections like colds, bronchitis, and grippe. These are likely to find the slum dwelling hospitable both to acquisition and spread of such infections. It is possible in this connection to consider as relevant such housing characteristics as sharing outside toilet and water facilities with other families, inadequate heating or ventilation arrangements, and inadequate and crowded sleeping arrangements.

Second are certain communicable diseases usually associated with childhood, such as measles, chicken pox, and whooping cough. The relevant housing characteristics are similar to those described for the respiratory infections.

The *third* category consists of the two communicable diseases tuberculosis and syphilis.

Fourth are the minor digestive diseases such as "upset stomach," food poisoning, diarrhea, and enteritis. The relevant housing characteristics may be poor facilities for the cold storage of food as well as inadequate washing and toilet facilities.

Fifth is the category of home accidents. For example, cuts and burns may originate during the preparation of food in crowded or inadequate kitchens, flash burns may occur from poor electrical connections, abrasions and falls may come from conditions in crowded rooms or on inadequately lighted stairways.

A *sixth* category has to do with infectious and non-infectious diseases of the skin. Relevant housing characteristics possibly are facilities for washing and bathing, as well as overcrowding.

Several other disease categories may also be considered that are perhaps more tenuously related to *particular* housing conditions, but are possibly associated with the whole constellation of health-related housing inadequacy in slum areas. Thus, poor housing quality may contribute to lowering of the general level of resistance to many diseases among the slum families. If this is so, higher incidence may be expected in the slum of such serious diseases as pneumonia. Moreover, it seems reasonable to believe that everyday living would be "harder" in the slum than in Lafayette Courts, and that such a circumstance could conceivably affect eruption (if not onset) of certain chronic conditions such as heart ailments.

Social psychological characteristics suspected of being related to housing quality

The observable qualitative differences between Lafayette Courts and the slum environment led to the general expectation that the change for the test families to good housing would be associated with measurable changes in certain aspects of their behavior, attitudes, and psychological state. It was felt that some of these changes would be a consequence of improvement in the sheer physical aspects of housing; for example, the unique architecture of the housing development and the greater space and attractiveness of both the individual dwelling unit and of the housing project as a whole. Other changes, it was suspected, would be the consequence of less direct, psychological factors; for example, it was presumed that the move from the slum to the housing project would minimize numerous depressive influences on aspirations for self and family, upon morale, and upon general outlook on life.

With these considerations in mind, a series of social psychological content areas were identified in which it was anticipated that differences between test and control families would ultimately emerge. Expectations were also formulated regarding the direction of these differences and the environmental factors that might reasonably account for them. The resulting content areas and hypotheses are summarized below and will be expanded as the findings for each area are presented in subsequent chapters.

Reactions to housing and space.   The most obvious and fundamental area in which test families might be expected to show positive attitude gains over control families was that involving recognition of the improvement in the quality of their living conditions. In fact, it was suspected that if test families did not perceive and express some satisfactions with the physical characteristics of the new environment, they would be unlikely to show gains in other, less obvious, areas. It was anticipated that test families would be more likely than controls to express satisfaction with their apartment (as a consequence of its greater attractiveness and better facilities), to indicate opportunity for privacy (due to more space and reduction of crowding), to express willingness to entertain in their homes, and to indicate improvements in work and play space for children.

Personal and family relations.   It was expected that differences in the physical environment of tests and controls would be related to the extent of interaction among family members and the quality of their relationships. Thus, it was hypothesized that there would be more intra-family activities among the rehoused tests than among the controls, that there would be more mutual assistance, greater feelings of warmth and compatability, and lessened friction between family members. It was felt that in the slum, due to the unattractiveness of the dwelling unit and its lack of facilities and space, individuals might very well be impelled to seek independent activities outside the home, whereas in Lafayette Courts the general amelioration of conditions might encourage group activity in the home. Finally, frictions that presumably might arise within the slum family due to competition for the use of limited space and facilities in the home were expected to be reduced within the test families.

Relations with neighbors.   The slum environment of the particular population with which the study was concerned was viewed as being characterized primarily by psychological coldness and physical isolation. The environment of the housing project, on the other hand, was considered to possess a potential for increased psychological warmth due, for example, to an expected greater commonality of interests and characteristics of the families living there. Furthermore, since approximately four-fifths of the test families would live in eleven-story, multiple-unit buildings in Lafayette Courts, it was expected that the physical isolation of the slum would be considerably reduced; it would be difficult to remain isolated when one encountered the same people day after day in the elevator, the corridor or the basement laundry room. These considerations led to hypotheses that test families, compared to controls, would be more likely to undertake both casual and intimate contacts with their neighbors, to engage in the exchange of services, to participate in mutual activities, and to evaluate their neighbors more favorably.

Social self-concept and aspirations.   It was recognized that for some groups in contemporary society a move to public housing might connote a loss of social status. For the population under study, however, it was felt that such a move would be construed as a step up the social ladder. It was conceded that attitude changes in this area, if they occurred, would be the consequence of more subtle factors in the new housing environment than those presumed to be connected with changes in the areas of reactions to space, personal-family relations and relations with neighbors. Nevertheless, it seemed reasonable to hypothesize that test families in perceiving their improved surroundings would view them as an indicator of material betterment and would conclude that as a consequence they had also enhanced their social standing. This in turn led to the supposition that having achieved as self-concepts the image of persons "on the way up," the test families might also have a broader concept of potentials for the future, if not for themselves (in connection with aspiration for home ownership or better jobs), then at least for their children (in connection with aspirations for schooling, future jobs and other benefits).

Attitudes and behavior toward neighborhood and community. In moving, the test families were to be provided not only with a new and improved dwelling unit but also with a new and improved neighborhood. Admittedly, the improved neighborhood would be limited largely to the confines of the housing development; outside there would be many features reminiscent of the slum. However, the project community in itself was expected to provide for the test families a kind of physical and psychological insulation from these undesirable outside characteristics, a circumstance which could not be expected to occur for the control families who would continue to live directly in slum areas. Moreover, the housing development would cover an area sufficiently large to permit its being conceived of as a "neighborhood"; architecturally it would differ from its surroundings. It was expected that test families would consider the new neighborhood as a distinct improvement over the old, and that consequently they would be more likely than control families to make favorable evaluations of both general and specific aspects of their surroundings, to take an interest in neighborhood upkeep, and to participate in the activities of neighborhood organizations. The foregoing, of course, pertains to expectations regarding test-control differences in their reactions mainly to the *immediate* community. It was anticipated that these differences might also carry over into attitudes and behavior regarding the *larger* community and be reflected in such factors as a greater liking, among tests than among controls, for Baltimore as a city in which to live, and in expressions of interest and concern in matters of public importance.

Psychological state. Coming as they did from a generally depressed and deprived environment, it was felt that the test families— or more specifically, the test respondents themselves—might eventually undergo some psychological alterations as the result of their experiences in good housing. Such changes, it was reasoned, would very likely not be relatable to the more obvious, specific elements of housing quality improvement. Rather, if changes occurred, they were seen as probably stemming from a number of secondary factors, perhaps eventually emerging in a sort of cumulative effect. Thus, greater ease of performing household duties and of caring for children, improved relations within the family, more interesting and satisfying daily experiences, increased feelings of security, and fewer day-to-day annoyances, might be among the many possible factors in the new housing environment accounting for a more satisfactory psychological state.

It was expected that, in comparison to the controls, the test group would manifest less moodiness, better control of temper, less nervousness, greater commitment to the efficacy of self-help, more optimism, and greater satisfaction with their personal state of affairs.

Style of Life. The several content areas just enumerated were those around which hypotheses related to housing quality were formulated. One remaining area, that of style of life was developed primarily for descriptive purposes and was not associated with any directional expectations of differences between the test and control groups. However, it did seem likely that a group of families whose environment underwent a marked alteration would also manifest some changes in their characteristic modes of life. It was felt that some information pertaining to such matters as the cleanliness and orderliness of the dwelling units, the personal appearance of the residents, the nature of leisure time activities, and the extent of acquisition of consumer goods would contribute to an understanding of the populations with which the study was concerned and would further describe the experiences associated with differential housing.

Summary. In general, it was expected that in matters of social-psychological adjustment, the slum environment would place inhibitions and restraints upon the development of wholesome personal and family relationships, sociality and neighborliness, and personal identification with the community. Slum housing was also considered from the point of view of personal psychological development, as producing inhibitions and restraints upon realistic aspirations for self and family, upon morale, and upon personal ability to cope with life's problems adequately. These deleterious influences of the slum were expected to be alleviated in the housing development.

However, there was recognition of the realistic possibility of negative effects of the changes from slum housing to the public housing project. In fact, it was realized that certain negative elements might even be found to be associated with anticipated benefits. For example, improved housing was expected to lead to more home-centered activities, but a consequence of these activities might be *more* intrafamily friction rather than less. Similarly, the housing project might foster greater interaction with neighbors but this might possibly result in infringements on privacy. Finally, it was felt that some kinds of attitudes might be sufficiently far removed from the influence of the physical environment or associated with such a complex of factors that mere change in housing *per se* might leave them relatively un-affected. For example, if roots in the old neighborhood were deep, then identification with the new community could be expected to be impeded regardless of how attractive the new community might be. Furthermore, in the area of psychological state, it was recognized that the new environment in itself might not have sufficient impact to alter long-standing patterns of emotional response and modes of coping with problems.

The formal statements of hypotheses do not include these negative possibilities although in each instance, items were included illuminating these issues that would make understandable the findings, whether they confirmed the expectations or not.

Elements of school performance suspected of being related to housing quality

Review of differences between the quality of slum and project housing led to the expectation of several direct and indirect relationships with school experience of children. Of greatest relevance were the factors of space and density. Granting equal motivation and desire to pursue homework on the part of slum and project children, it was clear that the rehoused children had opportunity for greater privacy to undertake school-connected activities in the home.

Several secondary matters were thought also to be relevant to the anticipated relationship between housing and school experience. These were morale, parents' aspiration and yearnings for their children's education, and the opportunity, if they wished, for parents to assist and guide children. The relationship of housing to these issues has already been touched on in the preceding sections, and any effects uncovered might be expected to affect school progress.

Finally, there was the matter of illness and its possible influence on general school activity and attendance. Since rehoused children were expected to suffer less frequently than slum children from common diseases, it was anticipated that they would be out of school less often, and by extension, do their work better.

Summary

The preceding comments on hypotheses and expectations were developed at the outset of the study after detailed considerations of the logic of housing. They have been stated in a formal, positive fashion customary in descriptions of scientific undertakings. However, the tone and manner of statement should not be taken to indicate any suppositions regarding the *extent* of the expected differences between slum and rehoused groups developing over time. From the very first, there was recognition of some of the harsh facts of life. The populations of the study were predominantly low income families, it was suspected that educational level was low, and it was known that all were Negro; the housing environment was, after all, only a single element in a complex social situation.

There have been several benefits derived from the positive statement of hypotheses pertaining to morbidity, social adjustment, and school performance as summarized above. One benefit comes from the fact that the very process of "hunching" about outcomes is an aid to thinking and planning. Another is that the investigators' own points of view regarding the issues being investigated are brought out into the open where all can see them. This is likely to be of some importance in a study like the present one which deals with effects of social policy about which investigators, as members of society, are likely to have partisan opinions. It is undoubtedly safe to say that many of the medical, public health, housing and research persons who are responsible for having conceived and carried out the plan of the study feel that "good" housing is more socially desirable than "bad" housing. Open recognition of such a point of view known both to the investigators themselves and to other interested persons is an important aid to intelligent and rigorous planning of a study. It leads to the use of check points at various stages of a study, thereby providing safeguards against self-deception in the planning of the study, the collection and analysis of data and their final interpretation.

CHAPTER III

METHOD OF THE STUDY

The experimental, longitudinal study, if some basic premises are maintained, permits a much clearer account of the causative effects of a single variable than is ordinarily possible in cross-sectional studies. If the critical basic premises are not maintained either through neglect or inadvertence, then inroads are made in the possibility of attributing observed relationships to the independent variable. In the present study, the critical basic premises may be described as follows:

(a)   That the attrition, or loss, in sample size be kept to a minimum; or if sizeable, that it exhibit little bias.

(b)   That the test and control families remain detectably different in the independent variable—housing quality—in the "after" period of the study.

(c)   That the test and control families be well matched at the outset.

This chapter, following a discussion of the source and selection of the test and control groups, describes the problems that arose during the study in connection with the maintenance of these critical basic premises, and outlines the methods devised for coping with them. An account is presented of:

(a)   The rate and nature of the losses in the test and control samples in the three years of the study, and the final sizes of the two groups.

(b)   The extraordinary, regular rate of movement of the control families, both to public housing and to improved private housing; a movement that had the effect of gradually diminishing the difference in housing quality between the test and control groups.

(c)   A plan for grouping test and control samples in order to alleviate the consequences of attrition and moves.

(d)   The initial comparability of test and control groups, both at the outset, and under the new grouping plan.

The chapter's concluding discussion of the method of the study concerns the instruments used: those for the collection of survey data and those for the collection of data from public agency records. Examples of the survey instruments are given in Appendix 2, and an account of data collection and processing procedures is given in Appendix 3. In the latter, the discussion of the collection of the survey data includes an explanation of the survey cycle, interview assignment procedures, recruitment and training of interviewers, various aspects of quality control, and devices for keeping the samples intact. An account of the methods of collecting data from public agency records is also included in Appendix 3, as well as a statement of the processing procedures for both kinds of data.

Source of Test and Control Groups

The test and control groups were both obtained from the files of the Baltimore Housing Authority. For the test families, this source was established when the decision was made to use Lafayette Courts, the new, predominantly Negro public housing project, as the site of the uniformly "good" housing component of the independent variable.

For sources of a suitable control group, two possibilities suggested themselves initially. The first to be considered was that of sampling the general population in Baltimore. This possibility was discarded on the basis of being beyond the scope of funds, personnel, and time available before Lafayette Courts was scheduled to open. A better source from which to choose the control group appeared to be the Housing Authority file of Negro applicants who were *not* scheduled to move to Lafayette Courts. This alternative had three advantages: the first was that both groups, test and control alike, would have displayed the same sort of "social know-how" and initiative that led to applying for public housing; the second was that certain basic data regarding demographic characteristics of families were available in the application records, thus providing a ready source of information on which preliminary matching and selection could be made;

the third was that the potential control families would be living in dwelling units predominantly of the kind which would constitute the "bad" housing component of the independent variable. These considerations, together with the results of a thorough analysis of all Housing Authority files, led to the conclusion that the latter were a suitable source for controls who could be matched to the test families.[1]

Selection of Test and Control Families

The size of the test and control groups

Various considerations suggested that an optimal total combined test-control sample size would be about *1000 families* (approximately *5000 persons*). This number was considered administratively manageable from the standpoint of the repeated and frequent data collection procedures being planned, and sufficient in size to allow for some expected attrition and still be large enough for analytic purposes. In determining the relative size of the test and control groups within the approximate total of 1000 families, two principles were applied. The first principle was that the control sample should exceed the test sample in size. This seemed desirable because some control families, still applicants for public housing, might at any time be awarded an apartment in any project in the city even after Lafayette Courts had been completely occupied. The second principle was that there should be at least 100 test families from each of the major dwelling unit sizes in Lafayette Courts. Dwelling unit size is clearly related to family size, and this was one way to insure that the various family sizes would be represented in the study. In addition, a sufficient number of families of each dwelling unit size would thereby be provided for sub-group analysis if necessary.

Table 1 shows the sampling scheme for test and control families that resulted from the application of the principles just described. The first two columns of the table show the dwelling units of various sizes in Lafayette Courts and the test samples aimed for in each size category. The last two columns of the table show the matching ratio of controls to test families of the various unit sizes. The 3½-

---

[1] A description of the Housing Authority files and an account of the analysis of the applications are given in Appendix 4.

TABLE 1.   Sampling scheme for test and control families by size of dwelling unit.

Size of dwelling unit	Total in Lafayette Courts	Test group	Control group	Matching ratio, control to test
3½ rooms	110	100	200	2:1
4½	412	110	220	2:1
5½	252	150	150	1:1
6½	42	42	84	2:1
Total	816	402	654	1½:1

and 4½-room families were matched in the ratio of 2:1, because previous analysis of Housing Authority data had suggested that control families most eligible to move into other projects in the city would be those appropriate to that dwelling unit size. The 5½-room families were matched 1:1 because the smallest control turnover would be expected in this size dwelling. The largest families (6½ rooms) were matched 2:1 on the principle that the number to begin with was small, and any attrition that occurred would be damaging. Finally, it will be seen from Table 1 that this sampling scheme and its various attendant principles resulted in a total of 402 test families and 654 control families; the final size of each group was slightly different from these predesignated totals, as will be explained in the section in this chapter on rematching.

Criteria for choosing test families

Two major considerations were emphasized in selecting particular test families within a given dwelling unit size. First, a test family was chosen only if a satisfactory control match could be found. This reinforced the restriction of the entire sample to Negroes only, and excluded white families from consideration as possible members of the test group. The reason for this restriction was that the number of white applicants in the Housing Authority files was relatively small, and thus the chances of finding a good control match would be greatly limited. The second major consideration in the selection of test families had to do with the degree of expectation that once matched, there would be a good likelihood that a test family would retain its control "mate" at least for a year. This stipulation resulted in the fact that the selection of veteran families as members of the test group was kept to a minimum because they would have to be matched to veteran controls, and the latter, by city ordinance, had the highest priority for entrance into a project.

Procedures for choosing test families

Actual occupancy of Lafayette Courts began in April, 1955, when the first buildings were completed; new buildings were readied at irregular times over most of the ensuing year, the last building being readied for occupancy in February, 1956. Beginning in March, 1955, and for almost a year thereafter, the Housing Authority forwarded to the study office a series of complete lists of applicants to whom apartment awards in Lafayette Courts were to be made. In the handling of each list, a mutually agreed-upon procedure was followed uniformly. First, the Housing Authority refrained from notifying the applicants of the apartment award prior to forwarding the list; second, the study staff immediately instituted the test sampling scheme and selection principles described earlier; third, the initial interview was conducted with the designated test family; fourth, as soon as the initial interview was obtained, the study staff so informed the Housing Authority; fifth, the Housing Authority notified the applicant of the apartment award.

The arrangement whereby the Housing Authority withheld notification of applicants of the availability of an apartment was deemed desirable from the study's standpoint in order to avoid a possible euphoric effect that such knowledge might create and which might in turn be reflected in initial measurements. Agreement to this plan on the part of the Housing Authority was viewed as a significant gesture of cooperation in the interests of good research practice.

In connection with the sampling of test families from the list of applicants, the practice was to attempt interviews with half a given list, since the test sample was to total about half of the entire project population. In addition, a safety factor of 15 to 25 per cent was included in anticipation of the fact that not every family named on a list would actually accept an apartment at the time offered.

Once possible test families were selected, control matching began shortly thereafter. Interviewing of controls was thus initiated almost simultaneously with interviewing of test families, although a time gap

developed as a function partly of the erratic activity initiated by unexpected building openings. Inasmuch as there was over-interviewing among possible test families, there was also comparable over-interviewing among the controls for these possible tests.

The matching procedure

The principal reason for matching was to avoid gross inequality or uncomparability between test and control groups which, had it occurred, would then have necessitated adjustment or correction. Matching was not intended to accomplish presumed increased precision in the statistical assessment of differences between groups. Despite the fact that group comparisons rather than pair-by-pair analysis of data were contemplated, the actual matching was undertaken on a pair-by-pair basis. In those instances in which two control families were designated for a single test family, the identical procedures were followed for each pairing.

Twenty-six items of information, as shown in Appendix 5, were originally extracted from the Housing Authority files for each potential test and control family. Throughout matching, the thirteen most relevant items were used in a particular sequence. The matching variables and their sequence are shown in Appendix 6. Those items which were considered as most likely to bear a relationship to initial measures on morbidity and adjustment were the ones chosen for matching. Most of the items were demographic in nature: size of dwelling unit, rent, presence of husband, age of female head of household, age of oldest child, number of children, and so forth. In addition, some initial matching was also sought on housing quality, although matching on these variables was not always possible since for certain categories of applicants—veteran families, for example—a housing assessment was not required by law and thus often did not appear in the application.

Matching on most of the items required identical matches within the category ranges specified, although even at the outset, adjacent category matches were permitted on a few items. However, especially as matching proceeded and certain groups in the general pool became depleted, some additional adjacent category matching was tolerated, recognizing that systematic and cumulative errors might make for ultimate inequality between the groups. Early tabulations, however, revealed no cumulative biases.

Rematching

Of the 816 families living in Lafayette Courts at the time full occupancy was achieved, approximately half were found to be tests, each test family having been interviewed in the slum dwelling unit occupied prior to the move. However, at that time a number of the tests were either without a control altogether or lacked one control when two were needed. The main reason for this deficit was that during the year that elapsed since test selection and matching procedures were started, a number of control families had moved into a public housing project. A lesser reason for the deficit was that about 5 per cent of the original families designated as controls were not available for the initial interview.

Moreover, a comparison between the original data used for initial matching and similar data obtained in the initial household interviews showed that certain of the original information was somewhat out of date.

These various considerations led to a decision to undertake a complete reassessment of all the matched pairs. Case by case, the still intact test-control matches were reviewed for quality of matching: thirteen matching variables, brought up to date from study interviews, were used in the review, and some additional items of information obtained in the initial interviews were included. Those that passed as still satisfactory matches based on the currently correct information were retained. Where substantial mismatching had occurred, a new, better match was attempted. This process was facilitated by the over-interviewing that had occurred earlier among both the tests and controls. A number of new pairings emerged in this way, although a majority of the original pairings remained intact. For the test families who lacked entirely one or two controls, matching began afresh, the controls also being drawn from the excess initial interviews.

The final count revealed 396 test families, a sample size which seemed close enough to the original target of 402 to be satisfactory. The final count of controls showed 633 families, all of whom at the beginning of the second data collection period were still living in the city. This figure also came satisfactorily close to the originally designated total of 654 controls.

Retrospective consideration of the matching procedures suggests some of the complexities involved in the matching of families in field situations. The steps followed were not the procedures of random sampling. The guiding principle was always that of near-identical matching, not only on demographic variables, but also on the dependent variables of the study on which later measurement was to be made. A later section in this chapter will summarize the degree of comparability of the test and control samples obtained in this way.

Attrition Over Time Among Families Surveyed

Most studies involving repeated surveys of the same families suffer sample attrition over time. Losses may be permanent: for example, families move out of the city or respondents refuse to continue in the study; or losses may be only temporary: for example, a family may be away from the city on one survey wave but back the next. Whether temporary or permanent, the best account of sample attrition is given by the number of families with whom contact has been made and who have been successfully surveyed over a specified period of time.

The status of attrition in the present study is shown in Table 2 for each of the eleven surveys, or waves, undertaken. Wave 1 was

TABLE 2. Number of families surveyed, by wave.

Wave No.	Date wave began	Items surveyed	Test	Control	Total
1	April 9, 1955	M A HQ[a]	396	633	1029
2	April 9, 1956	M	394	632	1026
3	June 18, 1956	M	391	624	1015
4	August 27, 1956	M	389	608	997
5	November 5, 1956	M A	381	594	975
6	January 14, 1957	M	380	589	969
7	April 1, 1957	M A	377	583	960
8	August 12, 1957	M	370	563	933
9	October 21, 1957	M	356	544	900
10	January 13, 1958	M A	344	531	875
11	April 7, 1958	M A HQ	352	539	891

[a] "M" designates the standard morbidity inquiry.
"A" designates the adjustment and mental health inquiry.
"HQ" designates the housing quality assessment made for all families on Waves 1 and 11. In addition, and not shown above, a housing quality assessment was made of the dwelling unit of every family who had moved since the preceding survey-wave.

the "before" survey which, for both tests and controls, took place prior
to the time the test families moved to Lafayette Courts; Waves 2-11
constituted the ten "after" surveys of the study. From Table 2 it may
be seen that the Wave 1 effective sample sizes of 396 test families and
633 controls underwent a small but steady reduction with the passage
of time. The table indicates that for the test and control groups
combined:

(a)   Losses were steady: on every wave but the last, the number of
        families surveyed was somewhat smaller than on the preceding
        wave; on the last wave, there was an increment over the preceding
        wave rather than a loss.

(b)   The number of families surveyed on Wave 11 constituted 87 per
        cent of the Wave 1 effective total sample; thus, the losses totaled
        13 per cent or approximately 1.3 per cent per wave.

(c)   The number of families surveyed on Wave 7 constituted 93 per
        cent of the sample with approximately 1.2 per cent loss per wave.
        The rate of loss per wave was somewhat higher after Wave 7 than
        before.

Comparison of the test and control groups in Table 2 shows that
control losses were, on the average, somewhat higher than test losses.
By Wave 7, completed surveys with test and control families were
95 per cent and 92 per cent of the Wave 1 figures, respectively. By
Wave 11, the corresponding percentages were 89 per cent and 85
per cent.

In general, the rate of attrition shown in Table 2 compares favorably
with previous studies in the epidemiologic field. That the loss figures
were not larger is in great measure due to the assiduous and expensive
field work procedures described in Appendix 3.

Attention has already been called to the distinction between temporary and permanent losses. On any given wave, many families not
contacted were considered only temporary losses. For some families,
however, permanent loss was clear from the field records as time went
on. Table 3 gives a tabulation of reasons for withdrawal due to
eventual permanent loss of 102 families[2] of which 33 were test families

---

[2] It will be noted that 102 families are shown as permanent losses in Table 3,
whereas a total attrition of 138 families may be seen in Table 2 (the difference
between the Wave 1 and Wave 11 totals). The smaller figure in Table 3 is accounted for by the fact that not all uncontacted families at the end of Wave 11
were considered as "permanent" losses.

TABLE 3. Reasons for permanent withdrawal from the study sample, Waves 3–11.

	Test	Control
N:	(33)	(69)
	Per cent	
Moved out of city	3	1
Moved out of state	21	14
Refusal to continue participation in the study	61	67
Untraced, persistently not at home	6	10
Death of respondent	6	7
Miscellaneous reasons	3	1

and 69 were controls. Approximately two-thirds of the permanent losses in both groups were respondents who refused to continue participation in the study. Moves out of state accounted for 21 per cent and 14 per cent of additional test and control losses, respectively; the few remaining losses came under such categories as "moves out of city," "untraced," and "death of respondent."

Moves Among Test and Control Families

All the test families moved into Lafayette Courts between Wave 1 and Wave 2. Approximately 20 per cent moved again after that; of these, a few moved from one project apartment to another, as family size increased and for other reasons as well. The remainder, 59 families, moved back into non-project dwelling units. There were varied reasons for the moves out of the project and these are shown in Table 4, tabulated from Housing Authority records. More than half appeared to be "hardship" moves; that is, rent delinquencies, moves without notice, "rent too high," deaths, and institutionalizations. Seventeen per cent of the reasons for moving suggested that occupants had bought or rented a house, or that their income exceeded the maximum indicated by Housing Authority rules.

Of much greater consequence were the movement patterns of control families. Field experience from Wave 2 forward revealed that approximately 70 to 90 control families moved during each ten-week survey wave. Table 5 shows the frequency of moves for the 539 control

TABLE 4.   Reasons for moving from project of test families who moved prior to Wave 10 (from Housing Authority records).

	N: (59) Per cent
Rent delinquency, moved without notice, "rent too high," etc.	44
Moving in with relatives	10
Buying a house, renting a house	12
Change in family composition due to death, institutionalization, etc.	12
Over income	5
Other: environment, neighborhood difficulties, "don't like it up high," etc.	17

families surveyed on Wave 11, the final wave of the study. There were 722 recorded moves among these families since first contact on Wave 1, an average of 1.3 moves per family. One hundred and forty-one families (26 per cent) did not move in the three-year period; 211 moved once; 101 moved twice; 56 moved three times; a total of 30 families moved from four to seven times.

Since this is a study of the effects of the *quality* of housing, it is of concern to investigate what change took place in housing quality characteristics as a consequence of these movements. Table 6 shows the housing quality distribution of test and control families at Wave 1 and the distribution for controls at Wave 7 and again at Wave 11.

TABLE 5.   Frequency of moves of control families between Wave 1 and Wave 11.

No. of moves	Frequency	Total moves
0	141	—
1	211	211
2	101	202
3	56	168
4	16	64
5	8	40
6	5	30
7	1	7
Total	539	722

TABLE 6. Housing quality of test and control families in the "before" period and of control families 18 months later (Wave 7) and 3 years later (Wave 11).

Housing quality description	H.Q. deficiency summary score	N:	"Before" period (Wave 1) Test (396)	"Before" period (Wave 1) Control (633)	18 months "after" (Wave 7) Control (583)	3 years "after" (Wave 11) Control (539)
			Per cent			
"Good"	0		3 ⎫	6 ⎫	23 ⎫	35 ⎫
	1		6 ⎬ 9	8 ⎬ 14	11 ⎬ 34	11 ⎬ 46
"Moderately bad"	2		11 ⎫	11 ⎫	14 ⎫	17 ⎫
	3		20 ⎬ 31	24 ⎬ 35	23 ⎬ 37	20 ⎬ 37
	4		18 ⎫	20 ⎫	14 ⎫	11 ⎫
	5		22	20	10	5
"Bad"	6		10 ⎬ 60	7 ⎬ 51	3 ⎬ 29	1 ⎬ 17
	7		6	2	1	a
	8		4 ⎭	2 ⎭	1 ⎭	a ⎭

a Less than one-half of one per cent.

The table presents the deficiency summary scores derived from the APHA Appraisal Method; the instruments used in the collection of these data are discussed in a later section in this chapter, and the details of the scoring scheme appear in Appendix 7. Scores of 0 and 1 may be considered "good" housing—that is, without notable deficiency; scores 2 and 3 represent "moderately bad" housing; and scores 4 to 8 represent "bad" housing. The Wave 7 housing quality scores for control families were derived as follows: for families who had not moved by Wave 7, the housing quality score is that of Wave 1; for families who had moved by that time, the score is that of the dwelling unit of occupancy at Wave 7. The Wave 11 housing quality scores were derived from the complete reassessment of housing quality undertaken at Wave 11.

As shown by Table 6, three-fifths of the test families occupied "bad" housing at Wave 1; this proportion exceeded that of controls who lived in housing of similar quality at the time. It will be recalled that by Wave 2, all test families were in "good" quarters where the majority of them remained for the duration of the study. The differences between test-control groups in regard to housing quality at Wave 1 will be discussed later in this chapter when the general initial comparability of the two groups is assessed.

The most notable aspect of Table 6 is the shift it reveals in the quality of housing that occurred among the controls as the study progressed:

(a) At Wave 1, half the control families occupied the "bad" stratum of housing circumstances, about a third were in "moderately bad" housing circumstances, and 14 per cent were in "good" quarters.

(b) By Wave 7, control families in "bad" housing had dwindled to 29 per cent and the proportion in "good" housing had risen to 34 per cent.

(c) By Wave 11, control families in "bad" housing had further been reduced to 17 per cent, and in "good" housing, the proportion had increased to 46 per cent.

The control families who moved into "good" housing are of special interest. By Wave 7, a substantial proportion of those in "good" housing had moved through routine Housing Authority procedures into *public housing*, thus paralleling the circumstances of the test families. This movement into good, public housing continued through Wave 11, by which time 110 control families (about two-fifths of those in "good" housing) were living in public projects.

Problems Arising from Attrition and Moves

As indicated in Chapter II, the study design provided for two groups of families, matched at the outset on a number of characteristics but appreciably different in the quality of their housing in the "after" period. The general analysis plan involved the comparison of these two groups over the three-year period of the data collection. The more specific aspects of the plan of analysis were:

(a) Comparisons were to be made of sets of families for whom both morbidity and social adjustment data had been obtained uniformly.

(b) In the adjustment data, comparisons of "before" and "after" measures were to be made on the same families.

(c) In the morbidity data, comparisons of the test-control groups were to be made by cumulated annual periods after Wave 1 in order to provide a more solid basis for estimating differences.

Problems due to test and control group attrition

There were two major by-products of the steady loss rate occurring as the study proceeded, which in turn affected implementation of the analysis plan just described. The first by-product was that the basic matching principle was jeopardized because a number of test-control matched pairs were broken up. Losses took place in all possible combinations with respect to the matching scheme; for example, some single-matched tests lost their only control; some double-matched tests lost one control or even both.

The second major result of attrition was that varying and diminishing numbers of test and control families occurred from one wave to another, as shown earlier in Table 2. One consequence to the plan of analysis was that in the adjustment data, comparisons of "before" and "after" measures could not be made on the same families. Another consequence was that in the morbidity data, the pattern of losses for both test and control groups made complex the proposed annual cumulation of illness experience, especially since test and control losses were not identical in proportion.

Problems due to test and control moves

The movement patterns of both tests and controls impeded that aspect of the analysis plan which stipulated comparison of one group of families in good housing to another group of families in poor housing. As indicated previously, a relatively small proportion of the tests, but a large proportion of the controls, underwent a change in experimental status during the course of the study. Test families changed their status when they moved back to private housing; most of these moves were to housing of lesser quality than that provided in Lafayette Courts. Control families who altered their experimental status did so in two ways: first, by moving to public housing; second, by moving to private housing which was of better quality than that of their previous dwelling units.

Solutions to the Problems of Attrition and Movement

The considerations of the preceding sections led to the development of a plan for grouping or subdividing the test and control samples in order that the desired plan of data analysis could be carried out. The objectives of subdividing were: to recreate some of the housing quality disparity between the groups, to reduce variation in numbers from wave to wave, and to re-establish two well-matched groups of

TABLE 7. "Reduced effective samples" (families) and other sub-samples resulting from principles of exclusion, partial elimination of test-control similarity in housing quality, and rematching.

	Test			Control			
	Excluded due to attrition [1]	Test moves out of the project [2]	Reduced effective test sample [3]	Reduced effective control sample [4]	Control moves into a project [5]	Residual after rematching controls to tests one-to-one [6]	Excluded due to attrition [7]
Wave			Number of families				
1	61	35	300	300	95	100	138
2	59	35	300	300	95	100	137
3	56	35	300	300	95	100	129
4	55	35	299	298	95	100	115
5	46	35	300	300	95	100	99
6	45	35	300	299	95	100	95
7	42	35	300	300	95	100	88
8	35	35	300	296	95	98	74
9	25	35	296	296	95	97	56
10	9	35	300	300	95	100	36
11	17	35	300	300	95	100	44

families. The new subdivisions gave rise to the concept of the "reduced effective samples" and to a number of sub-samples to be set aside for the present. Reference in what follows will be made to Table 7, in which the total original test and control groups of *families* are shown subdivided. Table 8 gives the same information for *persons* in the families.

The principles of exclusion

To achieve stable populations and reduce wave-to-wave numerical variations, several principles of exclusion were adopted. Families were excluded from the basic analysis who missed any two waves or who missed any of Waves 5, 7, 10, or 11 when the social adjustment measurements were made. Columns [1] and [7] of Table 7 show that of the total families surveyed on Wave 1, 61 tests and 138 controls were eventually excluded because of missing crucial, or too many, waves of data collection. This left 335 and 495 families, respectively,

TABLE 8. "Reduced effective samples" (persons) and other sub-samples[a] resulting from principles of exclusion, partial elimination of test-control similarity in housing quality, and rematching.

	Test			Control				
	Excluded due to attrition [1]	Test moves out of the project [2]	Reduced effective test sample [3]	Reduced effective control sample [4]	Control moves into a project [5]	Residual after rematching controls one-to-one to tests [6]	Excluded due to attrition [7]	Others excluded, test and control combined [8]
Wave				Number of persons				
1	291	151	1341	1349	407	462	606	155
2	278	151	1341	1347	407	462	595	126
3	264	150	1337	1347	407	462	557	117
4	263	151	1339	1339	406	462	487	95
5	222	151	1341	1347	407	462	419	88
6	215	151	1339	1347	403	461	389	76
7	193	151	1338	1349	407	462	359	76
8	162	151	1332	1329	406	454	295	45
9	115	151	1329	1338	407	450	239	31
10	36	151	1340	1347	407	461	169	26
11	79	151	1334	1342	402	459	180	31

[a] Columns [1]–[7] show the number of persons involved in the various sub-samples of families presented in Table 7. Column [8] shows an additional number of persons who, although belonging to one or another of the sub-samples shown in columns [2]–[6], did not themselves meet the principles of inclusion in one of these sub-samples.

among whom attrition was absent or negligible. As can be seen, each wave yielded a number of test and control families who were surveyed insufficiently and thus were excluded, but the number decreased steadily as the waves progressed.

Since the morbidity data were on a person basis, person-exclusion principles also had to be applied. All members of an excluded family were automatically in this category; the number of persons thereby excluded is shown in Table 8, columns [1] and [7]. In addition, there were "itinerant" persons in non-excluded families. Persons for whom morbidity data were lacking for any three waves or for two successive waves were also excluded. The number of such persons in otherwise non-excluded families is shown in Table 8, column [8], for tests and controls combined.

Setting aside certain movers

After the principles of exclusion were applied, two further groups were identified from the remaining families, who in the course of the study had changed their independent variable classification. The first group consisted of the test families who had moved from the housing development back to the city; these numbered 35 families, and are shown in Table 7, column [2]. The second group was composed of the control families who had moved into a public project (good housing); this group numbered 95 families and appears in column [5] of Table 7. The numbers of persons involved in these families are shown in Table 8, columns [2] and [5].

The reduced effective test sample and the matched controls

Application of the subdivision scheme just described resulted in a total of 300 test families (on all but two waves) who then constituted the "reduced effective test sample," a group that showed no attrition and that remained in "good" housing for the duration of the "after" period. The next objective was to establish for each of these 300 test families a one-to-one match from among the controls who remained after exclusions for attrition and movement to public housing. Each test was reviewed for the status of its control match: any still intact single matches were retained; in the case of original matches in the ratio of one to two, if both controls were still intact the "better" of the two matches was retained; any completely missing original match was rematched from among the residual, excess controls, using standard procedures.

This procedure gave rise to the "reduced effective control sample," matched one-to-one with the analogous test sample. There remained a group of about 100 residual control families who were no longer needed as matches for any test family. The two reduced effective samples and the control residuals are shown in columns [3], [4], and [6] in Table 7. The numbers of persons in these three groups are shown in the same columns in Table 8.

Advantages accruing from the reduced effective samples

Imposition of the subdivision plan on both the originally constituted test and control groups resulted in several advantages of consequence in pursuing the desired plan of analysis of the data. The reduced effective test and control samples, resulting from the subdivision, made completely uniform the numbers of families involved in "before"–"after" analyses of the adjustment data, and greatly increased the uniformity of the numbers involved in the "after" morbidity waves. Of even greater benefit to the morbidity data was the fact that the reduced effective samples of *persons* provided similar bases for the calculation of morbidity and mortality rates for any wave or any combination of waves.

Another benefit arose from the fact that in deriving the reduced effective samples, two well-matched groups were re-established, thus fulfilling one of the basic aspects of the study design.

Finally, the removal of a number of the families who had changed their experimental status during the study fulfilled to some extent the other basic aspect of the study design: that the test and control groups should be distinguishably different in the quality of their housing in the "after" period. This was true even though only those control families who had moved to one type of good housing, public projects, had been removed; there remained among the reduced effective control sample a number of families who had improved their circumstances in private housing.

The possibilities of bias

It was realized that, although numerous advantages accrued from the sample subdivision plan, certain undesirable consequences might also be associated with it. The possibilities of bias and the resulting likelihood that the data would thereby be difficult to interpret could not be overlooked. Possible bias resulting from subdivision of the samples might conceivably manifest itself in one of two ways. First, it might *depress* the likelihood of finding differences. This would occur, for example, if the control losses who were set aside in the subdivision scheme were made up of families with very high sickness rates and very low morale. Removing them from the control sample would leave a population with lower sickness rates and higher morale than initially. Those remaining might even be families who could profit over time from their own exertions irrespective of the influence of housing. Thus, there might develop control gains of a magnitude to match the hypothesized gains of the test families due to improved housing.

On the other hand, possible bias might *enhance* the likelihood of finding differences between test and control groups. If, for example, control losses were all well-off, socially mobile families, removing them from the initial control group might leave for comparison with test families those with less potential for improvement. The likelihood then might be of enhancing the discovery of test-control differences in favor of the test group.

In order to investigate the possible bias that might have arisen as a consequence of subdividing the two groups, comparisons on a number of initial or "before" characteristics were made between the *intact samples* (before any subdivisions were made) and the *reduced effective samples* (remaining after various categories of families were set aside). It was felt that if substantial differences were found in these comparisons, then the reduced effective samples could not be used to determine the effects of housing quality on the dependent variables. However, if no biasing effects were found to exist or if they were small, then the reduced scheme could be utilized, with the consequent substantial advantages that were enumerated earlier.

Initial Comparability of Intact and Reduced Effective Samples

The initial characteristics measured in the Wave 1, "before" survey, which were used in the comparisons between the intact and reduced effective samples, pertained to family composition and background, to housing quality, to items of medical background and history, and to selected items of social behavior and attitudes. The tabular material was analyzed in two ways. First, the possibility of bias arising from the reduction scheme was investigated through a comparison of intact and reduced tests and a comparison of intact and reduced controls. Second, the similarity of the reduced groups was investigated by comparing the test and control samples after reduction. The tabular material on which this analysis was based and a discussion of the tables will be found in Appendix 8. For present purposes, the findings and conclusions will be summarized.

Comparability of intact and reduced tests, intact and reduced controls

The data showed that intact and reduced tests compared closely on initial characteristics as did intact and reduced controls. The largest differences tended to be of approximately 5 per cent, and these occurred in a negligible number of the comparisons. In the vast majority of the items, differences were virtually nonexistent. It was concluded that no marked bias would be introduced through the use of the reduced effective test and control samples since they were not noticeably different in initial characteristics from the intact test-control samples.

Comparability of test and control reduced effective samples

Use of the reduced effective samples was considered to rest upon the degree of initial comparability between the families remaining in the test and control groups after reduction. With relatively few and fairly minor exceptions, review of the data showed that the test and control families were closely matched on personal and demographic characteristics, on individual items of initial housing quality, and on initial measures of the dependent variables of the study: morbidity and social adjustment. The most notable inequalities between the reduced test and control groups were in connection with length of residence in Baltimore (fewer tests than controls specified ten or more years of residence), and in the total index of initial housing quality when the individual items were summed (more tests than controls lived in "bad" housing). Other differences between the reduced test and control samples tended to be of lesser consequence.

It is interesting to note that the items which revealed inequalities between the *reduced* tests and controls were the same ones which showed inequalities between the *intact* tests and controls. For example, initially fewer intact tests than controls had lived in Baltimore for ten or more years (by a difference of 9 per cent), and more intact tests than controls had lived in "bad" housing (by a difference of 11 per cent on the total index of housing quality). Reduction, therefore, did not markedly enlarge the differences that had arisen in initial matching, but neither did it minimize them.

As a consequence of the similarity between the intact and reduced comparisons, it was felt that proceeding with a test of the hypotheses using the reduced groups was justified. This was not intended to imply that the families set aside in the reduction process were considered to be the same in all respects as those remaining in the reduced effective samples. On the contrary, the groups of families who for a variety of reasons underwent attrition in the course of the study or who changed their independent variable status through moving might conceivably possess some unique characteristics and thus in themselves be worthwhile subjects for study.

Description of the Test and Control
Reduced Effective Samples

Since all remaining chapters will present data on the test and control *reduced effective samples,* a brief account of the nature of these groups will provide relevant background for understanding the findings to be reported subsequently. What elements characterized the test and control samples as persons and families at the beginning of the study? The data on which this description is based will be found in Appendix 8.

It will be recalled that all the families were Negro and that they lived in Baltimore, Maryland, a border city which largely adhered to various patterns of segregation. Data in Appendix 8 show that almost three-quarters of them originated in Maryland and that an even larger proportion had lived in Baltimore for ten years or more. Although the study families did not appear to be a geographically mobile population, an inkling of their mobility within the city was shown by the fact that almost three-fifths had lived at their initial, Wave 1 address, for less than three years. About a third were veteran families.

Primarily, the samples constituted a young adult population with young children: nine-tenths of the families initially had one or more children, and about one-fifth had five or more. The oldest child was less than ten years of age in about half the families. Although there was a female head of the household in each family, in two-fifths of the families there was no husband present.

Economically, the families were predominantly low income, three-fifths earning less than $2500 a year (in 1955); about a quarter were receiving public welfare assistance. Approximately three-tenths of the female heads of household worked full or part time, the majority of them in service-type occupations. Two-fifths of the husbands, where present, worked in unskilled occupations. Three-fifths of the families paid less than $50 a month rent, and almost the same proportion was living in "bad" housing at the start of the study.

Educational level tended to be low: approximately three-fifths of both female and male heads of household had completed less than tenth grade.

In summary, demographic and personal characteristics indicate that the groups under study were relatively deprived with respect to a number of social and economic factors. The chapters that follow will reveal whether the change to good housing for one segment of this population—the test group—had detectable effects.

Instruments Used

The instruments for the measurements made in the various components of the study were specially devised for the purpose and underwent systematic pretesting[3] and revising before being used. In all waves of interviewing and in the collection of data from public agency records, identical instruments were utilized for test and control groups.

The morbidity survey forms

Several methods of measuring morbidity were considered at the outset. One possibility involved regular medical examinations of all

[3] For an example of morbidity, adjustment, and housing quality survey forms, and for some comments on pretesting the survey instruments, see Appendix 2. Data collection and processing procedures are described in Appendix 3.

persons in the study families or at least representative members. Such a plan would have had the advantage of making available, as basic data of the study, considered medical opinion supported by laboratory workups. Among the anticipated disadvantages were: low yield of information per cycle of such examinations, especially about non-chronic conditions; prohibitive cost on a repeated basis; anticipated large non-response rate.

The second possibility was the diary method, in which a responsible family member would make daily records of complaints of all family members. To provide meaningful data, this method requires a fairly high level of literacy in the person who keeps the record, as well as consistent record-keeping for several years. Difficulties anticipated on both counts raised serious questions about the advisability of this method.

The method finally chosen was the classical morbidity survey conducted in the home by a trained lay interviewer. This method of measuring illness also has its drawbacks, and attention has recently been focused on some of them in the public health literature. The principal issues have to do with the reliability and completeness of enumeration of conditions, using such a procedure. While the several studies on this topic are not in complete agreement, it is apparently reasonably established that there is a tendency to under-reporting of chronic conditions in the home interview when compared with the results of clinical examinations. On the other hand, home interview reports of length of stay in a hospital and the reasons for hospitalization apparently are well corroborated by comparison with actual hospital data. While the morbidity phase of the study is of course interested in the possible role of housing quality in the exacerbation of *chronic* illness, the basic expectations regarding housing and *acute* conditions should be kept in view. It is possible that some desired data, like the occurrence of the relatively minor acute conditions and *upsurges* of chronic conditions, cannot best be obtained with sensitivity in clinical examination.

The morbidity survey form used was an adaptation of a fold-out format developed in recent years by the Bureau of the Census. The form, when folded, measured 8½ by 12 inches, the front quarter containing identifying information. When unfolded, the form was four times as large and permitted enumeration of episodes of illness for families with six members. For larger families, two forms were used. In general, illnesses recorded for each person in a family were followed up for extent and nature of medical attention and for disability incurred, if any.

The initial morbidity survey (Wave 1) had some features not shared by the ten succeeding surveys. On Wave 1 there was concentration on items of medical history including an enumeration of chronic complaints. The chronic condition survey was made from a detailed list of chronic ailments, an inquiry being made about each family member for each condition. The existence of the chronic conditions still actively present was confirmed on Wave 2, and there resulted a core of chronic conditions present in all persons in the study in the two years preceding Wave 2.

Aside from confirmation of chronic conditions on Wave 2, the surveys of Waves 2-11 were very similar in format. The adult female head of the household reported the morbidity experience of the preceding two months for each member of the household. The general questioning proceeded as follows:

(a)   Inquiry about "any sickness whether serious or not."

(b)   Inquiry from a small check-list of six acute conditions: colds, skin rash or breaking out, digestive disturbances, headaches, accidents, and frequent aches or pains.

(c)   Inquiry about upsurges of chronic conditions that had been established as existing in the two years prior to Wave 2. For this purpose, the questionnaire used with a given family on a given wave had been pre-recorded for each person with his or her chronic conditions.

(d)   Inquiry about stay in a general hospital or in a tuberculosis hospital.

For each condition thus enumerated as bothering any family member, there was a follow-up inquiry:

(a)   Whether a doctor had been seen for the condition, his diagnosis, and whether the contact had been as a private or clinic patient.

(b)   The number of days hospitalized, spent in bed, kept from usual activities, or not feeling well.

Aside from the "standard" items of inquiry, different waves also included other items of interest; for example, work status of family members and use of preventive medical facilities.

The adjustment interview schedules

Through interviews with the female head of the household, there was intensive exploration of the several social psychological content areas described in Chapter II in the section dealing with the hypotheses. The interview schedules for the adjustment surveys were in self-contained booklets 8½ by 11 inches in size. A majority of questions were precoded, a number had free-answer components, and some were entirely free answer, the respondent's comments being entered verbatim after appropriate questioning. A special category of precoded questions were items pertaining to the measurement of psychological state. These items were designed to form a series of *scales:* morale, nervousness, moodiness, etc. The answers of the respondents in the pretests were used to perform the operations involved in unidimensional (Guttman) scaling.

The adjustment survey data were gathered in the course of five interviews as follows:

Wave 1.   The "before" adjustment survey conducted for the purpose of establishing initial comparability of samples and certain base-line measures.

Wave 5 and Wave 7.   The first "after" adjustment survey, conducted when the test families had been living in Lafayette Courts for approximately eighteen months. Topics covered, with a few exceptions, were identical to those covered in the "before" survey. Because the "before" interview was lengthy, it was split up into two sections for the "18-month" measurement, part administered Wave 5, and part Wave 7.

Wave 10 and Wave 11.   The second adjustment survey, conducted approximately three years after the test families were rehoused. Some topics covered were identical with those covered on the "before" survey. A number of new topics were introduced as well. As before, and for reasons of length, the three-year survey was split up into two sections.

The housing survey

Housing quality of the entire sample was measured in the course of the initial (Wave 1) interview. Furthermore, a housing quality assessment was also obtained whenever a family—test *or* control—moved into a private housing dwelling unit. Finally, there was a recapitulation of housing quality measurement on the final "after" wave of interviewing (Wave 11) for all families in the study at that time living outside public housing.

The measurement scheme used was adapted from the "Dwelling Unit Schedule" of the American Public Health Association "Appraisal Method for Measuring the Quality of Housing." The housing survey form consisted of a booklet 8½ by 11 inches in size in which entries were made from questions asked of the respondent regarding certain features of housing and from direct observations of the enumerator. The housing quality assessment was arranged in four subdivisions; the individual items in each subdivision were scored for deficiencies and compiled into an index. These four indices were then summed, thus resulting in a single combined index reflecting total housing quality. Following are the four indices and a brief description of their components:

Index I:	*Structure:* consisting of items covering main access to the apartment, location of apartment, and dual egress.
Index II:	*Unit facilities:* kitchen, toilet, and bathing facilities; extent of sharing of the foregoing; water supply and other washing facilities; heating, lighting, etc.
Index III:	*Maintenance:* structure deterioration, maintenance of unit facilities and infestation.
Index IV:	*Occupancy:* persons per room and persons per sleeping room.
Combined Index:	*Total housing quality:* the sum of the deficiency scores of Indices I-IV, incl.

Since the housing survey instrument itself was a modification of the APHA Appraisal Method, the deficiency scoring scheme for the various items also was modified. A consequence was that the maximum total deficiency score possible was considerably less in the study's housing survey than in the APHA Appraisal Method. However, the proportional contribution of individual items to the grand total score in the housing survey was the same as in the APHA Appraisal Method. A list of the items used in the housing survey, the deficiency weights (penalty score) for each item, and the maximum score for each index are shown in Appendix 7.

Public agency record forms: school performance of children

In addition to data on morbidity, social adjustment, and housing quality collected by means of the household survey, information was also obtained from the records of the Baltimore public school system regarding the school performance of children.

On Waves 3 and 11, a single-fold 8½ by 11 inch interview schedule was administered in the household to ascertain the whereabouts of all school-age children in the test and control families. In each case, inquiry was made as to the name or number of the school, the address, and the child's current grade.

Following Wave 3, a single page "School Record Form" was devised which provided space for entering identifying information for the child, and a section for recording three initial comparability measures for a period of approximately a year and a half before the start of the study: I.Q. test scores, number of promotions, and number of days of school attendance. A "School Record Form" was prepared for each child enumerated as attending school in the Wave 3 questionnaire, the necessary identifying information being transcribed from the questionnaire to the form. The forms were then taken to the appropriate school, the child's record was located, and the required information was transcribed to the form.

After Wave 11, each child's "School Record Form" was brought up-to-date for current whereabouts and grade, and the appropriate schools again were visited, this time to obtain information on the child's performance during the period of the study. The kind of information obtained was similar to that used as measures of initial comparability; in addition, achievement test scores were also recorded on the forms.

PART **2**

MORBIDITY

Introduction

Basic modes of data presentation in the morbidity chapters

Several basic modes of data presentation characterize the morbidity chapters, particularly Chapters IV through VIII. Chapter IX, as will be explained subsequently, departs from the pattern because of the particular nature of its data.

Dependent variables, i.e., illness and disability data, are presented on a person basis as "per cent of persons" or "rates per 100 persons."

Uniformly in Chapters V through VIII and to some extent in Chapter IV, morbidity data are cumulated into *three time periods* or groups of survey waves in the "after" period. In Chapters IV through VIII, age-specific morbidity rates are presented in terms of standard "median age" groupings.

The three "after" time periods. In order to obtain a more concise view of morbidity experience, the data were cumulated for three time elements in the "after" period of the study as follows: the "interim" period, referring to data collected during Waves 2 and 3, and "early after"[1] period, referring to data collected during Waves 4-7, and the "late after"[1] period, referring to data collected during Waves 8-11. A summary of the "periods," together with the interviewing dates of the component waves, is given in the following chart.

Period	Waves	Interviewing begun	Interviewing of 95% of sample completed
Interim	2	April 9, 1956	June 2, 1956
	3	June 18, 1956	August 11, 1956
Early after	4	August 27, 1956	October 20, 1956
	5	November 5, 1956	December 29, 1956
	6	January 14, 1957	March 9, 1957
	7	April 1, 1957	May 25, 1957
Late after	8	August 12, 1957	October 5, 1957
	9	October 21, 1957	December 14, 1957
	10	January 13, 1958	March 8, 1958
	11	April 7, 1958	May 31, 1958

[1] These terms correspond to designation of the "after" points in time when the social psychological adjustment data were collected. "Early after" adjustment measures were made at Waves 5 and 7; "late after," at Waves 10 and 11.

The three "after" periods had some interesting calendrical aspects. Since each survey inquired about illness in the preceding two months, the dates which the actual morbidity experience covered were always two months prior to the interviewing beginning and ending dates shown in the chart above. The "interim" period, nearest the Wave 1 survey, covered something short of six months of morbidity experience. The "early after" and "late after" periods each covered just less than a year's morbidity experience, and were directly comparable on a seasonal basis.

Pooling of data into periods required combining and summarizing the illness experience of each person in the study. Thus, for each individual, episode information and other data such as that pertaining to disability, medical attention, and type of illness, were summarized for Waves 2-3, for Waves 4-7, and for Waves 8-11. Period episode rates, which in the "early after" and "late after" periods corresponded roughly to annual rates, were calculated by summing episodes for particular sub-samples, and dividing by the appropriate number of persons.

Median age. Most of the morbidity data are presented by age and sex. Except for a few instances in Chapter IV, wherever age appears in the text or in the tables, it is in terms of the "median" ages of persons in the study samples. By "median age" is meant the age of all persons on April 1, 1957, the approximate midpoint of the "after" period of the study.

Application of the median-age concept involved some error in age classification for all waves except Wave 7, when, in most instances, median and exact age coincided. The error was greatest at Waves 2 and 11; in these waves, all persons were a year younger and a year older, respectively, than their median age. However, identical classification criteria were applied to persons in both test and control groups, so that the error was uniform for the samples being compared.

The standard median age groups. In several of the morbidity tables, data are presented for "children" (persons whose median age was under 20) and for "adults" (those of median age 20-59). In the bulk of the tables, five standard median age groups are shown: under 5, 5-9, 10-19, 20-34, and 35-59 years of age. The category "under 5" includes only children who were born before Wave 1. The number of persons in the standard age-sex groups of the reduced effective samples of 300 test and 300 control families is shown in Appendix 9.

It will be noted that, in most of the tables, the age bracket including the oldest persons terminates at age 59. Persons of age 60 and older were excluded because of the differential test-control mortality occurring in this group during the course of the study. It will be shown in Chapter IV that there were 20 tests and 20 controls of ages 60 and older at Wave 1, and that 5 controls in this group died subsequently. In the "after" period, the morbidity of these 40 persons, including the deceased controls until their death, consisted of a high prevalence of complaints and chronic degenerative conditions characteristic of old age. Among the complaints reported in the "after" period were various aches and pains, nervousness, incontinence, constipation, colds and other respiratory infections. Chronic conditions included arthritis and rheumatism, cardiovascular involvements, diabetes, and neuritis. Episodes of illness, whether acute or chronic, were in general accompanied by a large number of days of disability, resulting, for both test and control components, in the highest disability rates of any age groups in all of the samples. Thus, the five control deaths left a disproportionate number of test and control persons in an age category with highest episode and disability rates. Because of the difficulties of properly estimating the morbidity of the deceased controls, age 60 and older, it was deemed advisable to remove from the ensuing presentations the illness experience of all persons, both test and control, in that age category.

Statistical significance

Statistical tests were applied to test-control differences in basic incidence and disability data of Chapters V and VI. The test used was Student's "t" test, corrected for family clustering. The details of the rationale, formula, and procedures used in computing corrected "t" are given in Appendix 10.

CHAPTER IV

GENERAL ILLNESS EXPERIENCE AND MORTALITY

At the beginning of the "after" period of the study (Wave 2), many elements of housing quality differentiated the test from the control families. All of the test group had moved from the slum to Lafayette Courts, whereas almost all the controls still lived in the slum. In the test housing circumstances, there was lessened density in the apartments, as measured by the number of persons per room; there was adequate heating for all rooms, made possible by modern central heating; abundant hot and cold running water and efficient new toilet and bath facilities were available; new screening was provided on all windows and doors; rodent infestation was eliminated by virtue of the new building construction and subsequent maintenance; every dwelling unit had mechanical refrigeration and modern equipment for the storage and preparation of food; and adequate garbage disposal facilities were provided and maintained. These and many other factors suggested substantial advantage of test over control housing.

Were these improvements in housing quality of the test families likely to be conducive to improvements in health and reduction in illness? The basic morbidity hypotheses of the study, enumerated in Chapter II, suggested an affirmative answer. Beginning with two groups essentially similar in relevant background characteristics, prior morbidity, and history of illness, it seemed reasonable, from the epidemiologic viewpoint, to expect that differential morbidity experience in the "after" period of the study would be related to differential housing quality. This expectation was based on the health-related aspects of several features of the housing environment:

65

(a) *Density.* Reduction in density of persons in the apartment might be expected to affect the spread of a number of airborne bacterial and viral infections within the dwelling unit. It is probably true that the presence of infecting organisms in a dwelling unit is determined to a great extent by personal habits of hygiene and household habits concerning ventilation. Despite this, environmental factors may play an important role. With fewer persons per room in the dwelling unit, the concentration of infecting organisms in the atmosphere is reduced and contamination is therefore less likely.

(b) *Hot water and facilities for cleanliness.* Hygiene is a matter of long-standing habits of cleanliness. However, availability of an adequate supply of hot water and facilities for hand washing, bathing, and cleaning food utensils may be expected to affect contact transmission and sources of infections.

(c) *Toilet.* The availability of properly functioning toilet facilities may be expected to reduce spread of a number of conditions transmitted through excreta. A water closet in good repair will in itself reduce the likelihood of physical contact with infective materials.

(d) *Exclusive, not shared use of facilities.* Toilet, bathing, and hand-washing facilities that are not shared with other families are less conducive to the spread of infective agents from outside the family.

(e) *Screening.* The presence of tightly fitting screens may be expected to reduce entry into the apartment of flies and other insects that are potential agents for the dissemination of intestinal and other bacterial organisms.

(f) *Rodent infestation.* Elimination of rodents removes a safety hazard and carriers of disease and disease vectors.

(g) *Food storage and refrigeration.* Adequate provision for the storage of food (safe from flies and infestation) and for the refrigeration of perishable items may be expected to reduce the risk of food contamination.

(h) *Space, maintenance, and repair.* Sufficient space which overcomes crowding of furnishings, adequate lighting in rooms, hallways, and stairways, elimination of makeshift heating facilities and electrical wiring are among the factors that may be expected to reduce home accidents from falls, cuts, abrasions, and burns.

The preceding suggests ways in which amelioration in aspects of the housing environment may affect both the initial introduction of infective organisms into the dwelling unit, and the primary and secondary attack rates of any organisms introduced. It is possible that personal habits may, in some instances, work to counter the benefits of physical improvements in housing, but on some issues (those related, for example, to elimination of sharing of facilities with other persons or families), personal habits are likely to be of lesser consequence.

The remainder of this chapter, and Chapters V through IX, will provide information on various aspects of the morbidity experience of the reduced effective test and control samples. Test and control group comparisons will be made in order to illuminate the kinds of influences that differential housing environments had upon the physical health of the two groups.

This chapter presents data intended to give a general, introductory overview of illness experience. There will be an account of the persons who were free of illness, persons who had episodes of illness of varying severity, and those who experienced hospitalization. The chapter also will present findings regarding mortality in the test and control groups. Some of the data will be shown in terms of the time period in which they were ascertained; i.e., wave by wave. This will provide a detailed view of the results of selected morbidity measurements made at ten different points in time during the "after" period. However, wave-by-wave presentation does not permit the concise view of morbidity experience that is made possible if the data are cumulated for larger periods of time (annually, for example); for this purpose, the concept of the "period" as the unit of time will be introduced in connection with some of the data in this chapter, and will be more fully developed in subsequent chapters.

Illness Experience

"Illness experience" involves a distinction between persons who had no illness whatsoever and those who experienced any; among the latter, an additional distinction is made between illnesses of varying severity but without regard to number or diagnosis of episodes. The general expectation for this section was that persons in the test sample would be more likely than those in the control sample to be without illness altogether, for each wave, and would be less likely to have experienced illness, whether severe or not.

Persons with and without illness

Table 1 gives data relevant to expectations regarding any illness at all for persons in the reduced effective test and control samples. The table shows, wave by wave, the proportions of individuals with and without illness in the test and control groups in the "after" period of the study. From first to last, the differences between the groups were small, for the most part being of the order of 2 per cent. However, a modest directional trend was discernible: tests were more likely than controls to be free of illness in nine out of ten waves, the most marked difference occurring in Wave 7.

TABLE 1. Persons with and without illness, by wave.

Wave	Group	Persons without illness	Persons with illness
		Per cent of persons[a]	
2	Test	28	72
	Control	26	74
3	Test	39	61
	Control	43	57
4	Test	48	52
	Control	46	54
5	Test	41	59
	Control	39	61
6	Test	43	57
	Control	41	59
7	Test	51	49
	Control	44	56
8	Test	57	43
	Control	54	46
9	Test	28	72
	Control	26	74
10	Test	47	53
	Control	45	55
11	Test	54	46
	Control	52	48

[a] For N's on which per cents are based, see Chapter III, Table 8, reduced effective samples.

Severity of illness

"Serious episodes" of illness were defined as those which were either medically attended, or disabling, or both. Medical attention involved professional consultation during the episode of illness, either at a hospital, a clinic, a physician's office, or in the patient's home. A disabling episode was one involving "days in the hospital," "days in bed," or "days kept from usual activities"; many serious episodes entailed more than one kind of disability.

The persons shown in Table 1 as having any illness were subdivided, each wave, into those with one or more episodes that were medically attended or disabling (serious), and those that were neither medically attended nor disabling. The results are shown in Table 2. As with the preceding table, there was general close similarity between test and control groups for illness, whether serious or not, on all waves; and similarly modest trends were detectable over time. For both kinds of conditions, on a majority of waves, control persons were a little more likely than test persons to have been ill. For the category of serious episodes, this was the case for all waves after Wave 6.

Some general characteristics of the illness experience of both groups also are evident from Tables 1 and 2. Table 1 indicates that, with exceptions at two points (Waves 2 and 9), persons without illness averaged from two-fifths to one-half of both study groups; at Waves 2 and 9, only about one-quarter of the population was free of illness. In addition, Table 2 reveals that for both test and control groups alike, episodes on any given wave were distributed almost equally between the more serious and the less serious illnesses. The one exception was Wave 9, when more than twice as many persons suffered serious illness as suffered the less serious variety; a relevant fact in this connection is that the morbidity survey of Wave 9 occurred during the period of the Asian influenza epidemic of late fall, 1957.

Males and females without illness, by age

Since subsequent chapters will deal exclusively with various, more detailed aspects of illness, *per se,* the topic of *persons without illness,* originally referred to in Table 1, will not be touched upon again.

TABLE 2.   Persons with episodes of illness of varying severity, by wave.

		Persons with episodes	
		Medically attended or disabling	Not medically attended nor disabling
Wave	Group	Per cent of persons[a]	
2	Test	37	35
	Control	37	37
3	Test	32	29
	Control	27	30
4	Test	26	26
	Control	27	27
5	Test	31	28
	Control	29	32
6	Test	28	29
	Control	27	32
7	Test	24	25
	Control	31	25
8	Test	22	21
	Control	24	22
9	Test	50	22
	Control	53	21
10	Test	24	29
	Control	25	30
11	Test	23	23
	Control	25	23

[a] For N's on which per cents are based, see Chapter III, Table 8, reduced effective samples.

Therefore, it is desirable at this time to investigate further the extent of freedom from illness among the test and control samples, by comparing the experience of several age groups for each sex. Tables 3a and 4a give, for males and females, respectively, the per cent of each age group without illness.[1] The tables show average per cents of persons without illness during each wave of a given

---

[1] Unless otherwise indicated, ages shown in the tables of this chapter are "median" ages, that is, the age of all persons at April 1, 1957, the approximate midpoint of the "after" period of the study. Discussion of the concept of "median" age appears in the Introduction to Part 2.

TABLE 3. Males without illness, by age.

a. Per cent of males, averaged per wave, for each of three groups of waves
Per cent of persons[a]

Age	Waves 2-3		Waves 4-7		Waves 8-11	
	Test	Control	Test	Control	Test	Control
Under 5	24	30	39	35	42	43
5-9	34	34	53	44	52	46
10-19	56	48	63	52	60	50
20-34	56	51	64	62	64	65
35 and over	40	44	49	46	53	44

b. Test-control differences from data above
Difference in per cent[b]

Age	Waves 2-3	Waves 4-7	Waves 8-11
Under 5	−6	+ 4	− 1
5-9	0	+ 9	+ 6
10-19	+8	+11	+10
20-34	+5	+ 2	− 1
35 and over	−4	+ 3	+ 9

[a] For N's on which per cents are based, see Appendix 9.
[b] Plus indicates that test per cents were higher; minus, that test per cents were lower.

"period." The "periods" consist of three groups of waves: Waves 2-3 (the "interim" period), Waves 4-7 (the "early after" period), and Waves 8-11 (the "late after" period).[2] Tables 3b and 4b summarize the test-control differences from the data in the preceding section of each table.

The Waves 2-3 data showed mixed test-control differences by age for both sexes, with no consistent trend apparent. Thereafter, however, the direction of the differences tended to stabilize, revealing a somewhat larger proportion of tests than controls to be without illness. This occurred for the males of all age groups during the Waves 4-7 period and, with two exceptions, was maintained through the Waves 8-11 period. For the females, a similar trend did not emerge until the Waves 8-11 period, and even then, test females,

[2] Details of the grouping of waves into "periods" are given in the Introduction to Part 2.

TABLE 4.   Females without illness, by age.

a. Per cent of females, averaged per wave, for each of three groups of waves
Per cent of persons[a]

Age	Waves 2–3		Waves 4–7		Waves 8–11	
---	Test	Control	Test	Control	Test	Control
Under 5	26	20	41	38	42	39
5–9	35	44	51	45	50	49
10–19	46	42	53	55	51	50
20–34	21	23	34	29	34	33
35 and over	20	18	21	26	26	25

b. Test-control differences from data above
Difference in per cent[b]

Age	Waves 2–3	Waves 4–7	Waves 8–11
Under 5	+6	+3	+3
5–9	−9	+6	+1
10–19	+4	−2	+1
20–34	−2	+5	+1
35 and over	+2	−5	+1

[a] For N's on which per cents are based, see Appendix 9.
[b] Plus indicates that test per cents were higher; minus, that test per cents were lower.

in contrast to controls, were only very slightly more apt to be free of illness, although the differences were consistent throughout all age groups.

A general characteristic of the study population also is apparent from Tables 3 and 4; namely, the familiar U-curve relationship between age and illness. In general, *fewer* persons without illness were found among the very young and among persons 35 years and older; *more* persons without illness occurred in the age groups between these two extremes.

Hospitalizations

Information concerning the hospitalization of persons in the test and control groups was obtained regularly during each morbidity survey. An average of about 25 persons per wave in each of the test and control samples had hospital experience of relatively short

TABLE 5.   Persons hospitalized, by age and sex.

a. **Males:** All hospitalizations summed for each of three groups of waves
   Number of hospitalizations per period

Age	Waves 2–3		Waves 4–7		Waves 8–11	
	Test	Control	Test	Control	Test	Control
Under 5	2	1	3	5	1	2
5–9	6	2	6	10	5	1
10–19	2	—	4	1	2	3
20–34	1	2	7	2	2	4
35 and over	3	3	2	4	6	5
All ages	14	8	22	22	16	15

b. **Females:** All hospitalizations summed for each of three groups of waves
   Number of hospitalizations per period

Age	Waves 2–3		Waves 4–7		Waves 8–11	
	Test	Control	Test	Control	Test	Control
Under 5	1	2	3	1	3	4
5–9	7	3	5	2	1	1
10–19	3	1	3	3	5	8
20–34	27	37	50	61	62	45
35 and over	4	4	17	9	12	13
All ages	42	47	78	76	83	71

term. This number represented approximately 2 per cent of the total test and control persons.

Table 5 (a and b) shows the number of hospitalizations by age for males and females, respectively, for the three groups of waves in the "after" period. The heaviest concentration of hospitalizations occurred among females 20-34 years of age, mainly in connection with childbirth. No systematic trends in test-control differences appeared for any age group in any period of the study.

Mortality

The final data of this chapter refer to deaths occurring in the samples among persons living at the time of Wave 1, when the study

TABLE 6.   Mortality, by wave.

	Deaths	
	Test	Control
Wave		Number
2	1	2
3	—	1
4	—	—
5	—	3
6	—	1
7	—	—
8	1	2
9	—	—
10	—	—
11	—	1
Total	**2**	**10**[a]

a Test-control difference significant at level of .02 to .05 (see Appendix 11).

began.[3] Deaths were noted at the time of the Wave when death occurred, and cause of death was confirmed from official mortality records.[4] Table 6 gives the basic mortality data for the reduced effective test and control samples; Table 7 shows the age and cause of death. In the "after" period of the study, as Table 6 indicates, there were two deaths in the test group, one each occurring at Waves 2 and 8. In contrast, ten people died in the control group, at various waves throughout the study. The statistical assessment of this difference appears in Appendix 11.

Seven of the deaths occurred among children under 6 years of age (Table 7). Two of them were in the test group; the remaining five were in the control group. Cause of death among the children included two automobile accidents (one test and one control death), and one each from bronchitis, hypokalemia, dehydration and malnutrition, tuberculous meningitis, and acute otitis media.

The remaining five deaths, out of the total of twelve, were among persons 60 years of age and older (Table 7). All of these deaths occurred among the controls; none among the tests. The control deaths were caused by cerebral hemorrhage (two cases), pneumonia (two cases, one of them with prior cardiac involvement), and one

[3] Deaths among infants born after the study began will be treated in Chapter IX.
[4] Bureau of Vital Statistics, Baltimore City Health Department.

TABLE 7. Cause of death[a] by age and sex.

a. Test deaths	Age at time of death	Sex	Primary cause
	1	F	Bilateral purulent bronchitis
	5	M	Crushing injury of head and chest (struck by truck)
b. Control deaths			
	7 mos.	F	Hypokalemia; **antecedent causes:** diarrhea and dehydration
	1	M	Dehydration and malnutrition
	2	F	Tuberculous meningitis due to pulmonary tuberculosis
	3	F	Acute otitis media
	5	F	Fracture dislocation of 1st cervical vertebra. Head injury and bilateral comminuted fractures of femurs (struck by auto)
	60	M	Bronchopneumonia due to virus pneumonia
	62	M	Cerebral hemorrhage; **antecedent cause:** hypertensive cardiovascular disease; **other contributory conditions:** diabetes mellitus
	67	M	Cancer of the stomach[a]
	70	F	Valvular heart disease; **antecedent cause:** chronic myocarditis; **other contributory cause:** pneumonia
	81	F	Cerebral vascular accident; **antecedent cause:** arteriosclerotic heart disease; **other contributory cause:** diabetes mellitus

[a] From records of the Bureau of Vital Statistics, Baltimore City Health Department, except for one case, "cancer of the stomach," in which death occurred in Army hospital in Baltimore County.

case of cancer of the stomach. In view of the differential number of deaths in the test and control groups among persons 60 years of age and older, inquiry into the number of persons originally in these subgroups at Wave 1 seems relevant. Table 8 reveals that there were 20 test and 20 control persons in this age group at Wave 1, and that there was similar test-control representation in the more refined age classifications. The subsequent control deaths resulted in a deficit

TABLE 8.   Persons 60 years of age and older, living at Wave 1.

	Living at Wave 1	
	Test	Control
Age	Number	
60–64	7	8
65–69	6	5
70–74	5	5
75 and over	2	2
Total	20	20

of five persons in the age group of 60 years and older. It will be recalled from Table 7 that these deaths were fairly well distributed throughout this age group: the youngest person was 60 years old at time of death; the oldest was 81.

Summary

The general, introductory data presented in this chapter only suggestively affirm the hypothesis that persons in the test group would have indications of lower morbidity than persons in the control group. In the "after" period, the test group was a little more likely than the control group to be free of illness altogether (Table 1), and to be without episodes of either major or minor severity (Table 2). Test persons of all ages tended to be freer of illness than control persons, more so for males (Table 3) than for females (Table 4). There were no appreciable test-control differences in the number of hospitalizations that occurred during the "after" period (Table 5).

With respect to mortality (Table 6), there were significantly more deaths in the control group than in the test group in the "after" period of the study (10 controls and 2 tests). Mortality data by age showed that five of the control deaths occurred among persons 60 years and older, whereas no deaths occurred in the test group among persons in this age category (Table 7).

CHAPTER V

EPISODES OF ILLNESS

The "illness experience" section of the preceding chapter presented on a *person* basis some general, introductory findings pertaining to the extent of morbidity in the test and control groups. More revealing of the nature and intensity of morbidity experience are the traditional *rates* of episodes of illness. This chapter will deal, first, with total episodes of illness. Second, it will make a distinction between rates of illness for episodes of major severity and those of lesser severity.

General expectations were that rates of episodes would, because of a variety of housing-connected reasons, be lower among the test than the control group. The supposition was not only that fewer test than control persons would be ill in the "after" period of the study, but also that they would be ill less often. In addition, it was expected that the effects of housing would be apparent in the rates of episodes of both greater and lesser severity.

Total Episodes of Illness

The data of this section pertain to episodes of illness of all kinds, regardless of severity. As a consequence of the move to good housing, it was anticipated that total illnesses would be fewer in the test than in the control group. Tables 1 through 3 compare the test and control samples as to the rates of all episodes during the three "after" periods. The data are given for the two sexes, and, in addition, by various age groupings. Thus, Table 1 shows, for males and females, the rates of all episodes for children and adults; Table 2 distinguishes among the five "standard" age groups for males; Table 3 shows the same age

TABLE 1.   Total episodes of illness by sex: children vs. adults.

A. Rates

Episodes per 100 persons, per period[a]

	Interim period Waves 2–3		"Early after" period Waves 4–7		"Late after" period Waves 8–11	
	Test	Control	Test	Control	Test	Control
(1) Males: **Age**						
All, under 60	192	185	262	305	252	292
Under 20	208	191	276	329	266	309
20–59	153	170	226	239	216	245
2) Females: **Age**						
All, under 60	294	288	431	455	423	439
Under 20	207	192	275	300	275	296
20–59	418	424	656	674	636	641

B. Test-control differences from data above

Difference in rate per 100 persons[b]

	Interim period	"Early after" period	"Late after" period
(1) Males: **Age**			
All, under 60	− 7	+43	+40[c] (t =2.00)
Under 20[d]	−17	+53[c] (t =2.16)	+43
20–59	+17	+13	+29
(2) Females: **Age**			
All, under 60	− 6	+24	+16
Under 20[d]	−15	+25	+21
20–59	+ 6	+18	+ 5

[a] For N's on which rates are based, see Appendix 9.

[b] Plus indicates that test rates were lower; minus, that test rates were higher.

[c] Test-control difference significant at P < 0.05 level, corrected for within-family correlation (see Appendix 10).

[d] Test-control difference, corrected for within-family correlation, significant at P < 0.05 for all persons under 20 (both sexes combined) for the combined "after" waves, 4–11 (see Appendix 10).

groupings for females. Part "a" of each table provides the episode data as rates per 100 persons, the rates being rounded to whole numbers. Test-control differences based on the rates are shown in part "b" of each table.

TABLE 2. Total episodes of illness for males, by age.

A. Rates

Episodes per 100 persons, per period[a]

Age	Interim period Waves 2-3		"Early after" period Waves 4-7		"Late after" period Waves 8-11	
	Test	Control	Test	Control	Test	Control
Under 5	264	217	355	379	319	332
5–9	214	193	263	337	265	317
10–19	130	164	212	270	205	275
20–34	133	156	176	195	179	186
35–59	186	192	312	313	279	343

B. Test-control differences from data above

Difference in rate per 100 persons[b]

Age	Interim period	"Early after" period	"Late after" period
Under 5	−47	+24	+13
5–9	−21	+74[c] $(t=2.47)$	+52
10–19	+34	+58	+70[c] $(t=2.11)$
20–34	+23	+19	+ 7
35–59	+ 6	+ 1	+64

[a] For N's on which rates are based, see Appendix 9.
[b] Plus indicates that test rates were lower; minus, that test rates were higher.
[c] Test-control difference significant at $P < 0.05$ level, corrected for within-family correlation (see Appendix 10).

Males and females, children and adults

Males. Table 1 indicates that for *all males* under 60 years of age, rates of total episodes of illness were somewhat higher for the test than for the control group in the "interim" period. Thereafter, test rates were uniformly lower than control rates: by 43 and 40 episodes per 100 persons in the "early after" and "late after" periods, respectively.

The over-all higher test rate in the "interim" period was accounted for by the male *children* (under 20 years of age), the test-control difference being 17 episodes per 100 persons. Thereafter, rates among the test male children were lower than those for the controls of the same age-sex category (by 53 and 43 episodes per 100 persons in the "early after" and "late after" periods, respectively).

TABLE 3. Total episodes of illness for females, by age.

A. Rates

Episodes per 100 persons, per period[a]

	Interim period Waves 2–3		"Early after" period Waves 4–7		"Late after" period Waves 8–11	
Age	Test	Control	Test	Control	Test	Control
Under 5	236	234	301	339	291	326
5–9	196	172	264	287	261	282
10–19	191	173	262	273	279	280
20–34	377	390	563	614	522	575
35–59	529	507	902	817	938	799

B. Test-control differences from data above

Difference in rate per 100 persons[b]

Age	Interim period	"Early after" period	"Late after" period
Under 5	− 2	+38	+ 35
5–9	−24	+23	+ 21
10–19	−18	+11	+ 1
20–34	+13	+51	+ 53
35–59	−22	−85	−139

[a] For N's on which rates are based, see Appendix 9.
[b] Plus indicates that test rates were lower; minus, that test rates were higher.

Among male *adults* (ages 20-59), test rates were lower than control rates even in the "interim" period, and the test-control differential was maintained in this direction in both later periods.

Females. The pattern of test-control differences among the females was similar to that of males. Rates of total episodes were somewhat higher for tests than for controls in the "interim" period for *all females* under 60 years of age; again, the higher test rate was accounted for by the *children*. However, episode rates were lower for tests than for controls in all other instances: in "early after" and "late after" periods, for *all females* of the specified ages, and for the female *children*; in all three periods, for the female *adults*.

Table 1 also indicates that the episode rates for females differed from those for males in two respects. First, the magnitude of the test-control differences in rates (Table 1b) was in general smaller among

TABLE 4.   Per cent of serious episodes of illness medically attended for males: children vs. adults.

A. Per cents
Per cent of serious episodes[a]

Age		Interim period Waves 2–3		"Early after" period Waves 4–7		"Late after" period Waves 8–11	
		Test	Control	Test	Control	Test	Control
All, under 60	Medically attended	60	59	62	59	57	54
	Disability only	40	41	38	41	43	46
Under 20	Medically attended	55	55	61	57	53	52
	Disability only	45	45	39	43	47	48
20–59	Medically attended	77	72	64	66	67	63
	Disability only	23	28	36	34	33	37

B. Test-control differences from data above:
medically attended
Difference in per cent

Age	Interim period	"Early after" period	"Late after" period
All, under 60	1	3	3
Under 20	0	4	1
20–59	5	2	4

a For N's on which per cents are based, see Appendix 12.

the females than among the males, for both children and adults. Second, male-female total-episode rates, whether test or control, were similar for *children*; but among the *adults, female* rates were considerably higher than *male* rates (Table 1a).

Males and females, five age groups

Tables 2 and 3 show the data of Table 1 for more refined age groupings: in these tables, each of the sexes is subdivided into five age groups, three for children and two for adults.

Males.   It will be recalled from Table 1 that, among the males, a higher test than control episode rate occurred only in the "interim" period and only for the group under 20 years of age. Table 2 shows that this "excess" test rate was, in fact, concentrated in the males under 10 years of age. In the periods following, however, these age groups underwent a change: total episode rates were lower among the tests than among the controls.

The three remaining age groups among the males (10-19, 20-34, and 35-59) all showed consistently lower test than control episode rates throughout the "interim," "early after," and "late after" periods, although the size of the test-control difference varied among age groups and by periods.

Females. Among female *children,* the higher test than control episode rate in the "interim" period, as observed in Table 1, is shown in Table 3 to be distributed throughout the three age groups: under 5, 5-9, and 10-19. However, as with males, each of these three age categories showed lower test than control episode rates during both later periods.

For the female *adults,* Table 3 reveals a finding not apparent earlier. Although Table 1 showed a somewhat lower test than control episode rate for females, ages 20-59, for all three periods, Table 3 indicates that this difference was actually restricted to the females in the age category 20-34. The 35-59 year-olds showed a consistently different pattern. For this. group, test episode rates were higher than control rates for all three periods: by 22, 85, and 139 episodes per 100 persons in the "interim," "early after," and "late after" periods, respectively.

Episodes of Illness of Varying Severity

In the remainder of this chapter, a distinction by degree of severity is made among the total episodes of illness that were presented in the preceding section. The less severe episodes were those that neither had received medical attention nor had involved any days of disability. The more severe, or "serious," episodes were those requiring medical attention or involving days of disability, or both.[1] The majority of these serious episodes were medically attended.

---

[1] It will be recalled from Chapter IV that medical attention included examination or treatment by a physician or a nurse in a hospital or clinic, in a physician's private office, or in the patient's home. Disability involved at least a day or part of a day hospitalized, bed-ridden, or being kept from usual activities. In many of these episodes of "serious" illness, both medical attention and disability were involved; in many, more than one kind of disability existed.

TABLE 5. Per cent of serious episodes of illness medically attended for females: children vs. adults.

A. Per cents
Per cent of serious episodes[a]

Age		Interim period Waves 2-3		"Early after" period Waves 4-7		"Late after" period Waves 8-11	
		Test	Control	Test	Control	Test	Control
All, under 60	Medically attended	53	54	64	59	60	61
	Disability only	47	46	36	41	40	39
Under 20	Medically attended	52	51	59	52	49	48
	Disability only	48	49	41	48	51	52
20-59	Medically attended	54	56	66	64	66	70
	Disability only	46	44	34	36	34	30

B. Test-control differences from data above: medically attended
Difference in per cent

Age	Interim period	"Early after" period	"Late after" period
All, under 60	1	5	1
Under 20	1	7	1
20-59	2	2	4

[a] For N's on which per cents are based, see Appendix 12.

This is shown by Tables 4 and 5, which give the proportions of serious illnesses that received medical attention (with or without associated disability) and those involving disability only. The data are given for each of the three "after" periods and for children and adults of each sex. It will be seen from the tables that between one-half and three-quarters of the serious episodes of illness were medically attended in any period for any age-sex group, test-control differences being relatively small throughout.

Tables 1 through 3 have shown that the hypothesis concerning total episodes was borne out, particularly in the "early after" and "late after" periods, for adults and children, both males and females, and, by and large, was further substantiated by the findings for the more refined age groupings. This section tests the expectation that, in addition to fewer over-all episodes, there would also be fewer episodes of varying degrees of severity in the rehoused than in the

TABLE 6. Serious episodes of illness by sex: children vs. adults.

A. Rates
Episodes per 100 persons, per period[a]

	Interim period Waves 2–3		"Early after" period Waves 4–7		"Late after" period Waves 8–11	
	Test	Control	Test	Control	Test	Control
(1) Males: Age						
All, under 60	79	67	103	115	114	139
Under 20	85	71	104	127	116	153
20–59	63	55	101	83	111	99
(2) Females: Age						
All, under 60	119	111	182	191	198	201
Under 20	84	74	104	112	131	137
20–59	169	165	294	301	295	292

B. Test-control differences from data above
Difference in rate per 100 persons[b]

	Interim period	"Early after" period	"Late after" period
(1) Males: Age			
All, under 60	−12	+12	+25
Under 20[c]	−14	+23	+37[d] ($t = 2.72$)
20–59	− 8	−18	−12
(2) Females: Age			
All, under 60	− 8	+ 9	+ 3
Under 20[c]	−10	+ 8	+ 6
20–59	− 4	+ 7	− 3

[a] For N's on which rates are based, see Appendix 9.

[b] Plus indicates that test rates were lower; minus, that test rates were higher.

[c] Test-control difference, corrected for within-family correlation, significant at $P < 0.05$ for all persons under 20 (both sexes combined) for the combined "after" waves, 4–11 (see Appendix 10).

[d] Test-control difference signifiant at $P < 0.01$ level, corrected for within-family correlation (see Appendix 10).

control group. The data concerning test-control comparisons of serious illness and of illness without medical attention or disability are shown in Tables 6 through 11, for both sexes by various age groups, paralleling the earlier presentation of total episodes of all kinds.

TABLE 7.   Serious episodes of illness for males, by age.

A. Rates
Episodes per 100 persons, per period[a]

Age	Interim period Waves 2–3		"Early after" period Waves 4–7		"Late after" period Waves 8–11	
	Test	Control	Test	Control	Test	Control
Under 5	104	97	130	130	132	146
5–9	93	74	93	138	113	167
10–19	48	44	95	105	101	138
20–34	45	45	66	72	88	79
35–59	93	73	162	102	152	133

B. Test-control differences from data above
Difference in rate per 100 persons[b]

Age	Interim period	"Early after" period	"Late after" period
Under 5	− 7	0	+14
5–9	−19	+45[c]$(t = 2.60)$	+54[c]$(t = 3.12)$
10–19	− 4	+10	+37
20–34	0	+ 6	− 9
35–59	−20	−60	−19

[a] For N's on which rates are based, see Appendix 9.

[b] Plus indicates that test rates were lower; minus, that test rates were higher.

[c] Test-control difference significant at $P < 0.01$ level, corrected for within-family correlation (see Appendix 10).

Children under 20 years of age, males and females

"Early after" and "late after" periods.   The hypothesis pertaining to severity of illness was confirmed in the two later periods for total children under 20 years of age: for males and females alike, test rates were lower than control rates both for the serious and the less severe episodes (Tables 6 and 9). This pattern was in general maintained throughout the more refined age groups (under 5, 5-9, and 10-19), where again both serious and less severe episode rates were lower among tests than among controls (Tables 7, 8, 10, and 11).

"Interim period."   As with total episodes, for male and female children alike, rates of serious and less severe episodes, separately, in the "interim" period were higher for tests than for controls.

TABLE 8. Serious episodes of illness for females, by age.

A. Rates

Episodes per 100 persons, per period[a]

Age	Interim period Waves 2–3		"Early after" period Waves 4–7		"Late after" period Waves 8–11	
	Test	Control	Test	Control	Test	Control
Under 5	91	82	98	104	128	132
5–9	84	67	104	108	129	140
10–19	74	73	110	130	136	137
20–34	152	161	261	287	257	281
35–59	215	173	385	334	399	320

**B. Test-control differences
from data above**

Difference in rate per 100 persons[b]

Age	Interim period	"Early after" period	"Late after" period
Under 5	− 9	+ 6	+ 4
5–9	−17	+ 4	+11
10–19	− 1	+20	+ 1
20–34	+ 9	+26	+24
35–59	−42	−51	−79

[a] For N's on which rates are based, see Appendix 9.
[b] Plus indicates that test rates were lower; minus, that test rates were higher.

Adults 20 to 59 years of age, males and females

The pattern of severity of illness among the adults in the "interim," "early after," and "late after" periods differed from that of children. There was only partial confirmation of the hypothesis regarding severity of episodes. For both sexes in the age group 20-34, both serious and less severe illnesses followed the pattern of total episodes; in general, test rates were lower than control rates in all three periods. For the age group 35-59, there was differentiation dependent upon sex. Among males, test rates were lower than control rates for the _less severe_ episodes, but higher for the _serious_ episodes. Among females, on the other hand, both serious and less severe episodes contributed equally to the higher test than control rates already observed for total episodes.

TABLE 9. Episodes of illness without medical attention or disability, by sex: children vs. adults.

A. Rates

Episodes per 100 persons, per period[a]

	Interim period Waves 2–3		"Early after" period Waves 4–7		"Late after" period Waves 8–11	
	Test	Control	Test	Control	Test	Control
(1) Males: Age						
All, under 60	113	118	159	190	137	153
Under 20	122	120	172	202	150	156
20-59	90	114	125	156	104	145
(2) Females: Age						
All, under 60	175	177	249	264	225	237
Under 20	124	119	172	187	144	159
20–59	249	259	361	373	341	348

B. Test-control differences from data above

Difference in rate per 100 persons[b]

	Interim period	"Early after" period	"Late after" period
(1) Males: Age			
All, under 60	+ 5	+31[c] (t=2.22)	+16
Under 20	− 2	+30	+ 6
20–59	+24	+31	+41[c] (t=2.05)
(2) Females: Age			
All, under 60	+ 2	+15	+12
Under 20	− 5	+15	+15
20–59	+10	+12	+ 7

[a] For N's on which rates are based, see Appendix 9.
[b] Plus indicates that test rates were lower; minus, that test rates were higher.
[c] Test-control difference significant at P < 0.05 level, corrected for within-family correlation (see Appendix 10.)

Summary

This chapter has presented findings regarding rates of total episodes of illness, and, in addition, has distinguished rates of serious episodes from those of lesser severity. The data were given for each of three

TABLE 10.   Episodes of illness without medical attention or disability for males, by age.

A. Rates

Episodes per 100 persons, per period[a]

Age	Interim period Waves 2-3		"Early after" period Waves 4-7		"Late after" period Waves 8-11	
	Test	Control	Test	Control	Test	Control
Under 5	160	119	225	249	187	186
5–9	121	119	170	199	152	151
10–19	82	120	117	165	104	137
20–34	88	112	110	123	91	107
35–59	93	118	150	212	128	210

B. Test-control differences from data above

Difference in rate per 100 persons[b]

Age	Interim period	"Early after" period	"Late after" period
Under 5	−41	+24	− 1
5–9	− 2	+29	− 1
10–19	+38	+48	+33
20–34	+24	+ 13	+ 16
35–59	+25	+62	+82

[a] For N's on which rates are based, see Appendix 9.
[b] Plus indicates that test rates were lower; minus, that test rates were higher.

periods of time: the "interim," "early after," and "late after" periods which corresponded to illness incidence in Waves 2-3, 4-7, and 8-11, respectively. Rates for each period were computed by summing the illnesses that occurred in the waves of the particular period and dividing by the number of persons in the appropriate age-sex group.

The basic hypothesis tested in this chapter was that, as a consequence of the influences of housing, there would be lower rates in the test than in the control group, of total episodes of illness of all kinds. This hypothesis was expanded subsequently when data were presented which tested the expectation that fewer serious and less severe episodes, alike, would occur in the rehoused than in the control group.

For the data as a whole, the conclusion seems justified that the chapter's hypothesis was, in general, confirmed for episodes of illness of all kinds, *totalled* (Tables 1 through 3) as well as *subdivided by*

TABLE 11. Episodes of illness without medical attention or disability for females, by age.

A. Rates
Episodes per 100 persons, per period[a]

Age	Interim period Waves 2–3		"Early after" period Waves 4–7		"Late after" period Waves 8–11	
	Test	Control	Test	Control	Test	Control
Under 5	145	152	204	234	163	194
5–9	112	105	160	179	132	143
10–19	117	100	152	143	142	143
20–34	225	228	303	327	266	294
35–59	313	334	518	483	539	478

B. Test-control differences from data above
Difference in rate per 100 persons[b]

Age	Interim period	"Early after" period	"Late after" period
Under 5	+ 7	+30	+31
5–9	− 7	+19	+11
10–19	−17	− 9	+ 1
20–34	+ 3	+24	+28
35–59	+21	−35	−61

a For N's on which rates are based, see Appendix 9.
b Plus indicates that test rates were lower; minus, that test rates were higher.

degree of severity (Tables 6 through 11), for most age-sex groups in the "after" period of the study. Lack of confirmation occurred in two notable instances (for episodes both totalled and subdivided by severity): among *children in the "interim" period* and among *adult females, ages 35-59 in all three "after" periods.* Lack of confirmation also occurred among males, ages 35-59, but only in connection with serious episodes of illness. Subsequent chapters will provide additional morbidity information on these goups, and ultimately will endeavor to account for their illness status.

CHAPTER VI

DAYS OF DISABILITY

In Chapters IV and V, it will be recalled, a serious episode of illness was defined as one involving either medical attention *or* one or more days of disability. This chapter will deal with the concept of disability *per se* as another measure of the morbidity of the study's test and control samples. The hypothesis regarding disability paralleled that for episodes of illness, and was predicated upon the same test-control differential in housing quality in the "after" period. As a consequence of the move to good housing, it was expected that test persons, in contrast to controls, not only would experience fewer episodes of illness, but when illness occurred, it would be associated with fewer days of disability.

Information about days of disability was gathered in the course of the morbidity surveys of the "after" period of the study. For each episode of illness enumerated, the nature and extent of disability were established through inquiry about the number of days, if any, spent in a hospital, days spent in bed at home, or days kept from usual activities. Sometimes all three types of disability were experienced for a single episode of illness.

In some instances, an individual experienced more than one illness either simultaneously or at least overlapping in time. This led to a distinction being made between "person" and "episode" days of disability; for each wave, each individual's disability days were summed in these two ways. "Episode" disability consisted of the sum of days for each illness regardless of simultaneity or overlap. " Person" disability consisted of the sum of days with overlap eliminated; on this basis the number of days of disability for an individual on a given wave could not exceed 58 to 62 days. The subject matter of this chapter pertains exclusively to "person" days of disability.

Total days of disability for various age-sex groupings are shown in Tables 1 through 3 for each of the three "after" periods of the study; Tables 4 through 9 show the same information subdivided as to type of disability. All data are expressed as a rate of days of disability per

TABLE 1.   Total days of disability by sex: children vs. adults.

A. **Rates**
Days per 100 persons, per period[a]

	Interim period Waves 2-3		"Early after" period Waves 4-7		"Late after" period Waves 8-11	
	Test	Control	Test	Control	Test	Control
(1) Males: **Age**						
All, under 60	389	254	388	354	424	573
Under 20	306	210	288	343	381	571
20-59	605	374	650	386	538	580
(2) Females: **Age**						
All, under 60	507	475	813	824	886	964
Under 20	273	244	284	319	481	528
20-59	844	803	1579	1538	1472	1579

B. **Test-control differences from data above**
Difference in rate per 100 persons[b]

	Interim period	"Early after" period	"Late after" period
(1) Males: **Age**			
All, under 60	− 135	− 34	+ 149[c]$(t=2.01)$
Under 20[d]	− 96[c]$(t=1.96)$	+ 55	+ 190[e]$(t=2.95)$
20-59	−231	−264	+ 42
(2) Females: **Age**			
All, under 60	− 32	+ 11	+ 78
Under 20[d]	− 29	+ 35	+ 47
20-59	− 41	− 41	+107

[a] For N's on which rates are based, see Appendix 9.

[b] Plus indicates that test rates were lower; minus, that test rates were higher.

[c] Test-control difference significant at P < 0.05 level, corrected for within-family correlation (see Appendix 10).

[d] Test-control difference, corrected for within-family correlation, significant at P < 0.05 for all persons under 20 (both sexes combined) for the combined "after" waves, 4-11 (see Appendix 10).

[e] Test-control difference significant at P < 0.01 level, corrected for within-family correlation.

100 persons; part "b" of each table gives a test-control difference summary.

Total Days of Disability

Table 1, which gives over-all data for males and females, shows that the general trends were similar for both sexes. For children of both sexes, test rates were lower than control rates in both the "early after" and "late after" periods. For adults of both sexes, test rates were lower than control rates only in the "late after" periods. In the "interim" period, test rates were higher than control rates for both children and adults.

Tables 2 and 3 show data for more refined age groups among both sexes. For *children,* in five of the six age-sex groups under 20 years

TABLE 2. Total days of disability for males, by age.

A. Rates
Days per 100 persons, per period[a]

Age	Interim period Waves 2–3		"Early after" period Waves 4–7		"Late after" period Waves 8–11	
	Test	Control	Test	Control	Test	Control
Under 5	373	218	238	342	286	510
5–9	338	210	284	345	427	584
10–19	161	205	352	340	395	603
20–34	129	180	218	195	270	372
35–59	1426	700	1395	708	1000	930

B. Test-control differences from data above
Difference in rate per 100 persons[b]

Age	Interim period	"Early after" period	"Late after" period
Under 5	−155	+104	+224[c](t = 2.08)
5–9	−128[c](t = 2.05)	+ 61	+ 157[c](t = 1.99)
10–19	+ 44	− 12	+208
20–34	+ 51	− 23	+102
35–59	−726	−687	− 70

[a] For N's on which rates are based, see Appendix 9.
[b] Plus indicates that test rates were lower; minus, that test rates were higher.
[c] Test-control difference significant at P < 0.05 level, corrected for within-family correlation (see Appendix 10.)

of age, test rates tended to be lower than control rates in the later periods of the study. The notable exception was girls under 5; for this group, test rates were higher than control rates in both the "early" and "late after" periods. In the "interim" period, four of the six age-sex groups contributed to the higher test than control rate observed among children in Table 1; the two exceptions in which lower test than control rates occurred were among older boys (10-19) and girls under 5.

Data for the more refined *adult* age groups showed sharp differences depending on age. For both sexes of ages 20-34, test disability rates tended to be lower than control rates in all periods of the study, the difference being especially marked in the "late after" period. On the other hand, for both sexes of ages 35-59, test rates were higher than control rates in all periods.

One general characteristic of disability levels is apparent in the

TABLE 3. Total days of disability for females, by age.

A. **Rates**

Days per 100 persons, per period[a]

Age	Interim period Waves 2-3		"Early after" period Waves 4-7		"Late after" period Waves 8-11	
	Test	Control	Test	Control	Test	Control
Under 5	219	246	210	199	461	402
5-9	270	258	305	330	430	585
10-19	344	217	337	450	595	589
20-34	729	787	1432	1485	1272	1543
35-59	1150	841	1971	1664	2001	1666

B. **Test-control differences**
   from data above

Difference in rate per 100 persons[b]

Age	Interim period	"Early after" period	"Late after" period
Under 5	+ 27	− 11	− 59
5-9	− 12	+ 25	+155
10-19	−127	+113	− 6
20-34	+ 58	+ 53	+271
35-59	−309	−307	−335

a For N's on which rates are based, see Appendix 9.
b Plus indicates that test rates were lower; minus, that test rates were higher.

data of Tables 1 through 3, and parallels an observation made earlier regarding episodes. In general, disability rates of boys seemed to be of the same order of magnitude as rates for girls, age for age. But, as with rates of episodes, disability rates were far higher for adult females than for adult males.

Days in Hospital, Days in Bed, and Days Kept from Usual Activities

An account of each of the kinds of disability incurred by the study samples is provided in Tables 4 through 9. The material is presented by sex and age, the age divisions being children (persons under 20) as a group, young adults (20-34), and older adults (35-59). It will

TABLE 4.   Males under 20 years of age: days in hospital, days in bed, days kept from usual activities.

A. Rates

Days per 100 persons, per period

Type of disability-days	N:	Interim period Waves 2–3 Test (412)	Control (449)	"Early after" period Waves 4–7 Test (412)	Control (449)	"Late after" period Waves 8–11 Test (412)	Control (449)
Total days of disability[a]		306	210	288	343	381	571
Days in hospital		11	5	17	31	11	23
Days in bed		153	104	191	179	227	309
Days kept from usual activities		141	102	80	134	142	239

B. Test-control differences from data above

Difference in rate per 100 persons[b]

Type of disability-days	Interim period	"Early after" period	"Late after" period
Total days of disability	−96	+55	+190
Days in hospital	− 6	+14	+ 12
Days in bed	−49	−12	+ 82
Days kept from usual activities	−39	+54	+ 97

[a] Total may differ from sum of components because of rounding errors.
[b] Plus indicates that test rates were lower; minus, that test rates were higher.

be noted from the tables as a whole, that for any age-sex group in any period, whether test or control, "days in hospital" accounted for fewest of the total days of disability. In general, "days in bed" accounted for more of the total disability than did "days kept from usual activities."

Tables 4 and 5 summarize the data for males and females less than 20 years of age. In the "interim" period, higher test than control rates occurred for each of the three types of disability among males, and for two of the three types among females. In the later periods, for both sexes there was a tendency for lower test rates to predominate in all types of disability, consistently so in both later periods for "days in hospital" and "days kept from usual activities."

Tables 6 and 7 give the data for young adults of each sex, ages 20-34. For both sexes, test rates were lower than control rates for each type of disability in the "interim" period. A similar finding occurred con-

TABLE 5.   Females under 20 years of age: days in hospital, days in bed, days kept from usual activities.

A. **Rates**

   Days per 100 persons, per period

Type of disability-days	N:	Interim period Waves 2–3		"Early after" period Waves 4–7		"Late after" period Waves 8–11	
		Test (444)	Control (424)	Test (444)	Control (424)	Test (444)	Control (424)
Total days of disability[a]		273	244	284	319	481	528
Days in hospital		32	12	11	12	9	21
Days in bed		128	114	166	151	270	283
Days kept from usual activities		113	117	107	156	203	224

B. **Test-control differences**
   from data above

   Difference in rate per 100 persons[b]

Type of disability-days	Interim period	"Early after" period	"Late after" period
Total days of disability	−29	+35	+47
Days in hospital	−20	+ 1	+12
Days in bed	−14	−15	+13
Days kept from usual activities	+ 4	+49	+21

[a] Total may differ from sum of components because of rounding errors.
[b] Plus indicates that test rates were lower; minus, that test rates were higher.

sistently in the two later periods for "days kept from usual activities" among males, and "days in bed" among females.

Tables 8 and 9 show findings for persons of ages 35-59. Test rates of days of disability were lower than control rates only among the males and only for hospitalization experience in the "early" and "late after" periods, and for "days kept from usual activities" in the "late after" period. The remaining data for males and all the data for females showed higher test than control rates.

Summary

The data just presented have described the pattern of disability and type of incapacity resulting from illness in the test and control groups. The hypothesis tested in this chapter was that, as a consequence of the move to improved housing, test persons in contrast to controls would experience fewer days of disability associated with illness.

TABLE 6.   Males 20–34 years of age: days in hospital, days in bed, days kept from usual activities.

A. Rates
Days per 100 persons, per period

Type of disability-days	N:	Interim period Waves 2–3 Test (100)	Control (101)	"Early after" period Waves 4–7 Test (100)	Control (101)	"Late after" period Waves 8–11 Test (100)	Control (101)
Total days of disability[a]		129	180	218	195	270	372
Days in hospital		7	20	45	3	7	70
Days in bed		92	96	90	103	7	108
Days kept from usual activities		30	64	83	89	179	194

B. Test-control differences
from data above

Difference in rate per 100 persons[b]

Type of disability-days	Interim period	"Early after" period	"Late after" period
Total days of disability	+51	−23	+102
Days in hospital	+13	−42	+ 63
Days in bed	+ 4	+13	− 71
Days kept from usual activities	+34	+ 6	+110

[a] Total may differ from sum of components because of rounding errors.
[b] Plus indicates that test rates were lower; minus, that test rates were higher

In general, it may be said that the findings regarding total days of disability have shown only partial confirmation of the hypothesis in the sense that there were some, but not many, consistent trends by age-sex groups throughout the "after" period of the study (Tables 1, 2, and 3). The data for total days of disability may be summarized as follows:

Males. Among the total group of males, there was general confirmation of the hypothesis in the "late after" period only, the various groups under 35 years of age all contributing. Instances counter to the hypothesis, i.e., test disability rates being higher than control rates, were: in the "interim" period among the children, and in all three "after" periods among the adults 35-59 years of age.

Females. Among the total group of females, there was a general tendency to confirm the hypothesis in both the "early" and "late after" periods.

TABLE 7. Females 20–34 years of age: days in hospital, days in bed, days kept from usual activities.

A. Rates
Days per 100 persons, per period

Type of disability-days	N:	Interim period Waves 2–3 Test (223)	Control (212)	"Early after" period Waves 4–7 Test (223)	Control (212)	"Late after" period Waves 8–11 Test (223)	Control (212)
Total days of disability[a]		729	787	1432	1485	1272	1543
Days in hospital		73	74	97	145	118	98
Days in bed		337	392	875	926	748	904
Days kept from usual activities		319	321	459	414	406	541

B. Test-control differences
from data above
Difference in rate per 100 persons[b]

Type of disability-days	Interim period	"Early after" period	"Late after" period
Total days of disability	+58	+53	+271
Days in hospital	+ 1	+48	− 20
Days in bed	+55	+51	+156
Days kept from usual activities	+ 2	−45	+135

[a] Total may differ from sum of components because of rounding errors.
[b] Plus indicates that test rates were lower; minus, that test rates were higher.

This was contributed to mainly by the females 5-34 years of age, particularly the 20-34 year-olds. Exceptions to the general trend were the same as those for males: children in the "interim" period, and adults 35-59 years of age in all three "after" periods.

The direction of the test-control difference in each of the three types of days of disability was in general congruent with that of total days, for children under 20 both males and females (Tables 4 and 5), and for females 35-59 years of age (Table 9). Among the remaining age-sex groups (Tables 6, 7, and 8), there was less correspondence in the direction of differences between the total and the component types of days of disability.

TABLE 8. Males 35–59 years of age: days in hospital, days in bed, days kept from usual activities.

A. Rates
Days per 100 persons, per period

Type of disability-days	N:	Interim period Waves 2–3		"Early after" period Waves 4–7		"Late after" period Waves 8–11	
		Test (58)	Control (60)	Test (58)	Control (60)	Test (58)	Control (60)
Total days of disability[a]		1426	700	1395	708	1000	930
Days in hospital		45	25	26	108	14	112
Days in bed		648	260	1007	418	881	270
Days kept from usual activities		733	415	362	182	105	548

B. Test-control differences
from data above

Difference in rate per 100 persons[b]

Type of disability-days	Interim period	"Early after" period	"Late after" period
Total days of disability	−726	−687	− 70
Days in hospital	− 20	+ 82	+ 98
Days in bed	−388	−589	−611
Days kept from usual activities	−318	−180	+443

[a] Total may differ from sum of components because of rounding errors.
[b] Plus indicates that test rates were lower; minus, that test rates were higher.

TABLE 9. Females 35–59 years of age: days in hospital, days in bed, days kept from usual activities.

A. Rates
Days per 100 persons, per period

Type of disability-days	N:	Interim period Waves 2–3		"Early after" period Waves 4–7		"Late after" period Waves 8–11	
		Test (84)	Control (88)	Test (84)	Control (88)	Test (84)	Control (88)
Total days of disability[a]		1150	841	1971	1664	2001	1666
Days in hospital		13	9	186	37	107	102
Days in bed		706	643	1342	1257	1358	1222
Days kept from usual activities		431	189	444	369	536	342

B. Test-control differences from data above
Differences in rate per 100 persons[b]

Type of disability-days	Interim period	"Early after" period	"Late after" period
Total days of disability	−309	−307	−335
Days in hospital	− 4	−149	− 5
Days in bed	− 63	− 85	−136
Days kept from usual activities	−242	− 75	−194

[a] Total may differ from sum of components because of rounding errors.
[b] Plus indicates that test rates were lower; minus, that test rates were higher.

CHAPTER VII

TYPES OF ILLNESS AMONG CHILDREN

Chapters V and VI revealed findings among children and certain adult groups which confirmed the study's general hypothesis that test persons would have lower rates of illness and attendant disability than would control persons. Further examination of the morbidity data by type of illness will provide the opportunity to test the speculations advanced earlier about the possible role of housing in the spread of communicable disease, in accidents, and in upsurges of chronic illness.

It will be recalled that in formulating the hypotheses of the study, it had been reasoned that six categories of morbidity conditions might be related to inadequacies of housing quality. These categories as enumerated in Chapter II were as follows: (1) acute respiratory conditions, (2) communicable diseases of childhood, (3) tuberculosis and syphilis, (4) digestive complaints, (5) home accidents, (6) diseases of the skin. With the exception of home accidents, communicability is a characteristic common to many, if not all, of the specific diseases which constitute these major categories. The introduction to Chapter IV, moreover, mentioned some specific ways in which characteristics of housing might be related to the introduction and propagation of disease organisms and viruses in the dwelling unit and thus, to contamination of individuals in the study samples.

Classification of Types of Illness

This chapter and Chapter VIII, for children and adults, respectively, will contrast test and control groups as to incidence of illness occurring

TABLE 1. Total episodes of illness by selected types: all persons under 20 years of age.

A. **Rates**

Episodes per 100 persons, per period

	N:	Interim period Waves 2–3		"Early after" period Waves 4–7		"Late after" period Waves 8–11	
		Test (856)	Control (873)	Test (856)	Control (873)	Test (856)	Control (873)
(1) Infective and parasitic		32	28	14	23	16	29
(2) Allergic, endocrine, etc.		12	13	17	16	14	17
(3) Respiratory system		98	94	153	172	169	167
(4) Digestive system		21	16	32	35	21	24
(5) Accidents, poisoning, etc.		16	16	20	27	14	25

B. **Test-control differences from data above**

Difference in rate per 100 persons[a]

	Interim period	"Early after" period	"Late after" period
(1) Infective and parasitic	−4	+ 9	+13
(2) Allergic, endocrine, etc.	+1	− 1	+ 3
(3) Respiratory system	−4	+19	− 2
(4) Digestive system	−5	+ 3	+ 3
(5) Accidents, poisoning, etc.	0	+ 7	+11

[a] Plus indicates that test rates were lower; minus, that test rates were higher.

in various disease categories. Disease groupings used were those of the *Manual of the International Statistical Classification of Diseases, Injuries, and Causes of Death.*[1]

Based on Volume 1 of the *Manual,* a briefer, working code book was assembled containing the model categories of illness found among the study samples. The actual coding was done with the assistance of a group of expert medical coders from the Bureau of the Census who served as consultants to the study. Each episode of illness was given a four-digit *International Statistical Classification* code. For accidents, of the two alternative categorization schemes provided in the *Manual* ("Nature of Injury" and "External Cause of Injury"), the study code derived basically from the "Nature of Injury" cate-

[1] World Health Organization, Geneva, 1949.

TABLE 2. Total episodes of illness by selected types: males under 5 years of age.

A. Rates
Episodes per 100 persons, per period

		Interim period Waves 2–3		"Early after" period Waves 4–7		"Late after" period Waves 8–11	
	N:	Test (113)	Control (113)	Test (113)	Control (113)	Test (113)	Control (113)
(1) Infective and parasitic		41	31	28	18	35	45
(2) Allergic, endocrine, etc.		16	16	23	26	11	19
(3) Respiratory system		137	108	211	221	200	192
(4) Digestive system		32	20	42	41	26	21
(5) Accidents, poisoning, etc.		18	19	30	42	20	24

B. Test-control differences from data above
Difference in rate per 100 persons[a]

	Interim period	"Early after" period	"Late after" period
(1) Infective and parasitic	−10	−10	+10
(2) Allergic, endocrine, etc.	0	+ 3	+ 8
(3) Respiratory system	−29	+10	− 8
(4) Digestive system	−12	− 1	− 5
(5) Accidents, poisoning, etc.	+ 1	+12	+ 4

[a] Plus indicates that test rates were lower; minus, that test rates were higher.

gories. However, each accident was also classified as to external cause (falls, cutting and piercing instruments, fire, etc.) and location of occurrence (inside dwelling unit, not in dwelling unit but in same building, etc.).

For all illnesses mentioned during the course of each of the morbidity surveys, inquiry was made as to whether or not a physician had been consulted. If so, an additional question was asked regarding how the physician had named the condition, and it was this response which subsequently was coded. For illness which did not receive medical attention, detailed information was obtained about its nature, and classification was made on this basis.

Since the detailed classification system gives rise to more than a thousand possible disease entities, it was necessary to reduce the number in order to facilitate analysis of the incidence of illness in the study samples. This was done by combining the detailed categories

TABLE 3. Total episodes of illness by selected types: males 5–9 years of age.

A. Rates

Episodes per 100 persons, per period

	N:	Interim period Waves 2–3		"Early after" period Waves 4–7		"Late after" period Waves 8–11	
		Test (201)	Control (212)	Test (201)	Control (212)	Test (201)	Control (212)
(1) Infective and parasitic		47	38	23	44	20	42
(2) Allergic, endocrine, etc.		11	9	11	17	15	18
(3) Respiratory system		92	95	143	175	166	174
(4) Digestive system		16	10	31	35	19	22
(5) Accidents, poisoning, etc.		21	20	18	31	17	32

B. Test-control differences from data above

Difference in rate per 100 persons[a]

	Interim period	"Early after" period	"Late after" period
(1) Infective and parasitic	−9	+21	+22
(2) Allergic, endocrine, etc.	−2	+ 6	+ 3
(3) Respiratory system	+3	+32	+ 8
(4) Digestive system	−6	+ 4	+ 3
(5) Accidents, poisoning, etc.	−1	+13	+15

[a] Plus indicates that test rates were lower; minus, that test rates were higher.

into 80 groups of conditions which were then further reduced to 18 major categories corresponding to the broad roman numeral groupings of the *International Statistical Classification Manual*. The data of Chapters VII and VIII will concern themselves principally with these broad classifications.

Discussion in this chapter will concentrate on five categories of conditions: (a) infective and parasitic diseases; (b) allergic, endocrine system, metabolic, and nutritional diseases; (c) diseases of the respiratory system; (d) diseases of the digestive system; and (e) accidents, poisoning, and violence.[2] These five categories comprised 90 per cent of all conditions enumerated for persons under 20 years of age in any period of the study. Table 1 gives total episodes

[2] Corresponding to categories I, III, VIII, IX, and XVII of the *International Statistical Classification Manual*.

TABLE 4. Total episodes of illness by selected types: males 10–19 years of age.

A. **Rates**
   Episodes per 100 persons, per period

		Interim period Waves 2–3		"Early after" period Waves 4–7		"Late after" period Waves 8–11	
	N:	Test (98)	Control (124)	Test (98)	Control (124)	Test (98)	Control (124)
(1) Infective and parasitic		8	13	7	18	3	18
(2) Allergic, endocrine, etc.		7	12	11	8	13	11
(3) Respiratory system		53	70	90	124	121	139
(4) Digestive system		12	22	32	49	23	30
(5) Accidents, poisoning, etc.		13	17	27	25	10	25

B. **Test-control differences**
   from data above
   Difference in rate per 100 persons[a]

	Interim period	"Early after" period	"Late after" period
(1) Infective and parasitic	+ 5	+11	+15
(2) Allergic, endocrine, etc.	+ 5	− 3	− 2
(3) Respiratory system	+17	+34	+18
(4) Digestive system	+10	+17	+ 7
(5) Accidents, poisoning, etc.	+ 4	− 2	+15

[a] Plus indicates that test rates were lower; minus, that test rates were higher.

of the various types of illness for ages under 20, boys and girls combined. Findings for more refined age groups of each sex are given in Tables 2 through 7; a test-control difference summary of the same data is provided in Tables 8 and 9.

Types of Illness: All Persons under 20 Years of Age

Table 1 shows that the children as a group, whether test or control, generally tended to suffer most from respiratory infections in all periods; next most frequent were infective and parasitic conditions and complaints of the digestive system; these were followed in over-all frequency by accidents and allergic and allergy-related conditions.

In the "early after" and "late after" periods, test children were generally less likely than control children to be ill of conditions in

TABLE 5. Total episodes of illness by selected types: females under 5 years of age.

A. Rates
Episodes per 100 persons, per period

	N:	Interim period Waves 2–3		"Early after" period Waves 4–7		"Late after" period Waves 8–11	
		Test (138)	Control (134)	Test (138)	Control (134)	Test (138)	Control (134)
(1) Infective and parasitic		33	37	8	22	22	26
(2) Allergic, endocrine, etc.		17	14	23	15	17	19
(3) Respiratory system		124	123	197	213	196	188
(4) Digestive system		20	19	32	32	17	28
(5) Accidents, poisoning, etc.		21	21	22	28	17	32

B. Test-control differences
from data above
Difference in rate per 100 persons[a]

	Interim period	"Early after" period	"Late after" period
(1) Infective and parasitic	+4	+14	+ 4
(2) Allergic, endocrine, etc.	−3	− 8	+ 2
(3) Respiratory system	−1	+16	− 8
(4) Digestive system	−1	0	+11
(5) Accidents, poisoning, etc.	0	+ 6	+15

a Plus indicates that test rates were lower; minus, that test rates were higher.

all five of the disease classifications, with especially consistent regularity in both "after" periods for infective and parasitic conditions,[3] digestive conditions, and accidents. In the "early after" period, the largest test-control difference appeared for respiratory complaints. The largest differences *relative to general incidence in a category* occurred among infective and parasitic conditions and accidents. Other data, not shown, revealed that tests also were less likely than controls to have had attendant disability in each disease category in the two later periods.

[3] One subgroup of conditions among "infective and parasitic" is of special interest, namely the common communicable diseases of childhood, principally measles, mumps, whooping cough, and chicken pox. For both sexes under 20 years of age, the pattern of the total category prevailed; test rates of episodes (and attendant days of disability) were lower than control rates in the "early after" and "late after" periods.

TABLE 6. Total episodes of illness by selected types: females 5–9 years of age.

A. Rates

Episodes per 100 persons, per period

	N:	Interim period Waves 2–3 Test (193)	Control (181)	"Early after" period Waves 4–7 Test (193)	Control (181)	"Late after" period Waves 8–11 Test (193)	Control (181)
(1) Infective and parasitic		34	27	9	17	8	27
(2) Allergic, endocrine, etc.		12	11	20	10	15	14
(3) Respiratory system		93	87	159	172	170	167
(4) Digestive system		21	14	26	31	22	23
(5) Accidents, poisoning, etc.		12	9	16	22	10	20

B. Test-control differences from data above

Difference in rate per 100 persons[a]

	Interim period	"Early after" period	"Late after" period
(1) Infective and parasitic	−7	+ 8	+19
(2) Allergic, endocrine, etc.	− 1	−10	− 1
(3) Respiratory system	−6	+13	− 3
(4) Digestive system	−7	+ 5	+ 1
(5) Accidents, poisoning, etc.	−3	+ 6	+10

[a] Plus indicates that test rates were lower; minus, that test rates were higher.

Types of Illness: Males and Females, Refined Age Groups

The test-control differences of Table 1 derived from pooled information for both sexes and all ages under 20. It is conceivable that only a single age-sex group or a minority of them were responsible for the general trends. Tables 2 through 7 throw light on this possibility by showing detailed age-specific episode rates by type of illness for the "standard" age subdivisions under 20, separately for each sex. Tables 8 and 9 recapitulate the difference summaries provided in each of the preceding tables, but this time assembled by type of illness.

Allowing for sampling variation among subgroups of lesser size, there was general corroboration in the various age-sex groups for the

TABLE 7. Total episodes of illness by selected types: females 10–19 years of age.

A. Rates
Episodes per 100 persons, per period

	N:	Interim period Waves 2–3		"Early after" period Waves 4–7		"Late after" period Waves 8–11	
		Test (113)	Control (109)	Test (113)	Control (109)	Test (113)	Control (109)
(1) Infective and parasitic		15	14	4	8	4	8
(2) Allergic, endocrine, etc.		12	18	14	21	13	18
(3) Respiratory system		85	81	104	124	146	134
(4) Digestive system		25	13	35	25	21	22
(5) Accidents, poisoning, etc.		5	6	10	10	11	12

B. Test-control differences
from data above

Difference in rate per 100 persons[a]

	Interim period	"Early after" period	"Late after" period
(1) Infective and parasitic	− 1	+ 4	+ 4
(2) Allergic, endocrine, etc.	+ 6	+ 7	+ 5
(3) Respiratory system	− 4	+20	−12
(4) Digestive system	−12	−10	+ 1
(5) Accidents, poisoning, etc.	+ 1	0	+ 1

[a] Plus indicates that test rates were lower; minus, that test rates were higher.

over-all findings of Table 1. In the "early after" period, for all but digestive complaints and allergic and allergy-related conditions, the differences for a majority of the six age-sex groups were congruent with the differences for all groups taken together. The findings were particularly consistent in both the "early" and "late after" periods for infective and parasitic illnesses, and accidents. In the "interim" period, also, a majority of the age-sex groups showed consistency with the data for all groups totaled: in particular, three of the illness classifications (infective and parasitic, respiratory, and digestive) bore out the previous finding that overall, test rates were higher than control rates. Thus, it would appear from the foregoing that the data of Table 1, whether confirming or contradicting the study hypothesis, were contributed to by a number of age-sex groups.

TABLE 8. Test-control rate differences for five selected types of illness: males, under 5, 5–9, 10–19 years of age.[a]

Test-control difference in episodes per 100 persons[b]

	Age	Interim period Waves 2–3	"Early after" period Waves 4–7	"Late after" period Waves 8–11
Infective and parasitic	Under 5	− 10	− 10	+ 10
	5–9	− 9	+ 21	+ 22
	10–19	+ 5	+ 11	+ 15
Allergic, endocrine, etc.	Under 5	0	+ 3	+ 8
	5–9	− 2	+ 6	+ 3
	10–19	+ 5	− 3	− 2
Respiratory system	Under 5	− 29	+ 10	− 8
	5–9	+ 3	+ 32	+ 8
	10–19	+ 17	+ 34	+ 18
Digestive system	Under 5	− 12	− 1	− 5
	5–9	− 6	+ 4	+ 3
	10–19	+ 10	+ 17	+ 7
Accidents, poisoning, etc.	Under 5	+ 1	+ 12	+ 4
	5–9	− 1	+ 13	+ 15
	10–19	+ 4	− 2	+ 15

[a] Differences are those shown in Tables 2, 3, 4, above.
[b] Plus indicates that test rates were lower; minus, that test rates were higher.

Accounting for the Morbidity Findings in the "Interim" Period for Persons under 20

In this, and preceding chapters, consistent non-confirmation of the study's hypotheses has occurred in data pertaining to the morbidity experience of children in the "interim" period. Thus, for episodes of illness of all kinds,[4] totaled and subdivided by severity, and for days of disability,[5] test rates uniformly were higher than control rates in the "interim" period for the group under 20 years of age. Data just presented by type of illness have shown this was also the case for three categories of conditions: infective and parasitic, respiratory, and digestive. Consideration of the nature of these types of illness provides a clue which may reasonably account for the lack of con-

[4] First presented and discussed in Chapter V.
[5] First presented and discussed in Chapter VI.

TABLE 9. Test-control rate differences for five selected types of illness: females, under 5, 5–9, 10–19 years of age.[a]

Test-control difference in episodes per 100 persons[b]

	Age	Interim period — Waves 2–3	"Early after" period — Waves 4–7	"Late after" period — Waves 8–11
Infective and parasitic	Under 5	+ 4	+14	+ 4
	5–9	− 7	+ 8	+19
	10–19	− 1	+ 4	+ 4
Allergic, endocrine, etc.	Under 5	− 3	− 8	+ 2
	5–9	− 1	−10	− 1
	10–19	+ 6	+ 7	+ 5
Respiratory system	Under 5	− 1	+16	− 8
	5–9	− 6	+13	− 3
	10–19	− 4	+20	−12
Digestive system	Under 5	− 1	0	+11
	5–9	− 7	+ 5	+ 1
	10–19	−12	−10	+ 1
Accidents, poisoning, etc.	Under 5	0	+ 6	+15
	5–9	− 3	+ 6	+10
	10–19	+ 1	0	+ 1

[a] Differences are those shown in Tables 5, 6, 7, above.
[b] Plus indicates that test rates were lower; minus, that test rates were higher.

firmation of the study's hypotheses among children in the "interim" period. Infective and parasitic diseases (consisting in this group mainly of mumps, measles, chicken pox, etc.), respiratory conditions (consisting largely of minor complaints such as acute nasopharyngitis), and digestive illnesses of bacterial origin, all have one characteristic in common: communicability.

It appears very possible that an upsurge of these communicable types of illnesses occurred among the test children as a consequence of their assembling in large numbers in Lafayette Courts, and of their lacking group immunities to common infections that tend to develop in stable congregations over time. Thus, in the "interim" period, which directly followed the move to the housing development, test children were, in fact, at higher risk of exposure than control children to strains of acute infectious diseases against which they had no natural protection.

Summary

This chapter has presented findings regarding rates of episodes of various types of illness among test and control persons under 20 years of age. The five types of morbidity conditions for which data have been given represented 90 per cent of all the episodes which occurred among children in the study samples. Four of these types were involved in the hypotheses formulated at the outset of the study: it was anticipated that as a consequence of moving to improved housing, test rates would be lower than control rates in the categories of infectious diseases of childhood, acute respiratory conditions, digestive complaints, and accidents.

There was evidence that in the "early after" and "late after" periods of the study, test episode rates were lower than control rates for all five classifications, but with greatest regularity in both periods for infective and parasitic conditions, illnesses referable to the digestive system, and accidents (Table 1). Examination of types of illness by sex and refined age groups revealed that, with some variations attributable probably to sampling fluctuation, almost all age-sex subgroups contributed to the general confirmation of expectation in the "early after" and "late after" periods (Tables 2 through 9).

Morbidity findings for the "interim" period which, among children, were counter to expectations were discussed, and an explanation was offered to account for them. Most of the data pertaining to types of illness, to episodes of illness of all kinds, and to days of disability, had all revealed higher test than control rates among children in the "interim" period. A clue to the explanation of these findings came from the particular types of illness conditions involved: infective and parasitic, respiratory, and digestive. Many of the specific illnesses constituting these categories possess communicability as a characteristic in common. Since the "interim" period was very close to the time of the test population's move into Lafayette Courts, it seemed possible that, as with many newly assembled groups, there was an upsurge in these communicable diseases among the children. Perhaps it was only after the "interim" period that natural, group-protective processes were re-established in the new environment.

CHAPTER VIII

TYPES OF ILLNESS AMONG ADULTS

This chapter deals with morbidity data by type of illness for the adults in the study samples, ages 20-59. Ten major categories accounted for more than 90 per cent of all conditions enumerated for adults in the course of the study.[1] The categories were: (a) infective and parasitic diseases; (b) allergic, endocrine system, metabolic, and nutritional diseases; (c) mental, psychoneurotic, and personality disorders; (d) diseases of the circulatory system; (e) diseases of the respiratory system; (f) diseases of the digestive system; (g) diseases of the genitourinary system; (h) diseases of the bones and organs of movement (mainly arthritis and rheumatism); (i) accidents, poisoning, and violence; (j) other symptoms, senility, and ill-defined conditions.[2]

Types of Illness: Young Adults, Ages 20-34

Rates of episodes for the various types of illness for persons 20-34 years of age are given in Tables 1 through 3. Table 1 shows data for both sexes combined; Tables 2 and 3 give the same information for males and females, respectively. Examination of Table 1 reveals that for both sexes combined, test rates were lower than control rates in a majority of the disease categories. This pervasive accumulation

[1] As with disease categorizations for children, principles of classification followed were those of the *International Statistical Classification Manual*. The technical discussion of these matters in Chapter VII applies, also, to the data of this chapter.

[2] Corresponding to categories I, III, V, VII, VIII, IX, X, XIII, XVII, and XVI, respectively, of the *International Statistical Classification Manual*.

111

TABLE 1. Total episodes of illness by selected types: all persons 20–34 years of age.

		A. Rates					B. Test-control differences from data at left		
		Interim period Waves 2–3		"Early after" period Waves 4–7		"Late after" period Waves 8–11		Interim period	"Early after" period	"Late after" period
	N:	Test (323)	Control (313)	Test (323)	Control (313)	Test (323)	Control (313)	Difference in rate per 100 persons[a]		
		Episodes per 100 persons, per period								
Infective and parasitic		4	2	2	2	2	4	−2	0	+2
Allergic, endo-crine, etc.		13	15	16	19	16	20	+2	+3	+4
Mental, psycho-neurotic, etc.		14	19	25	27	19	25	+5	+2	+6
Circulatory system		22	25	34	45	30	40	+3	+11	+10
Respiratory system		86	90	137	141	157	148	+4	+4	−9
Digestive system		41	41	52	50	37	44	0	−2	+7
Genito-urinary system		26	31	36	46	41	47	+5	+10	+6
Arthritis, rheuma-tism, etc.		23	22	27	27	20	28	−1	0	+8
Accidents, poison-ing, etc.		13	14	17	18	9	16	+1	+1	+7
Other symptoms, etc.		20	17	28	29	25	20	−3	+1	−5

[a] Plus indicates that test rates were lower; minus, that test rates were higher.

across types of illness is best seen in the "late after" period in which 8 out of 10 of the groupings showed lower test than control rates; the two exceptions were respiratory conditions and "other symptoms, etc."

Table 2 shows that for males, 2 out of 10 of the disease categories were in the direction of lower test than control rates in all three "after" periods of the study: allergic and related conditions and circulatory diseases. The remaining categories showed less consistent trends.

TABLE 2. Total episodes of illness by selected types: males 20–34 years of age.

	A. Rates						B. Test-control differences from data at left		
	Interim period Waves 2–3		"Early after" period Waves 4–7		"Late after" period Waves 8–11		Interim period	"Early after" period	"Late after" period
	Test (100)	Control (101)	Test (100)	Control (101)	Test (100)	Control (101)			
N:	Episodes per 100 persons, per period						Difference in rate per 100 persons[a]		
Infective and parasitic	1	2	5	3	1	2	+ 1	− 2	+ 1
Allergic, endo-crine, etc.	2	9	4	9	4	12	+ 7	+ 5	+ 8
Mental, psycho-neurotic, etc.	5	6	7	3	5	7	+ 1	− 4	+ 2
Circulatory system	6	10	4	17	5	6	+ 4	+13	+ 1
Respiratory system	61	71	97	89	115	100	+10	− 8	− 15
Digestive system	16	18	18	26	23	23	+ 2	+ 8	0
Genito-urinary system	1	—	—	1	1	1	− 1	+ 1	0
Arthritis, rheuma-tism, etc.	12	11	14	14	8	12	− 1	0	+ 4
Accidents, poison-ing, etc.	16	13	15	15	5	12	− 3	0	+ 7
Other symptoms, etc.	4	9	3	8	5	2	+ 5	+ 5	− 3

a Plus indicates that test rates were lower; minus, that test rates were higher.

Among females (Table 3), in 5 out of 10 of the major types of illness, test rates were lower than control rates in all three "after" periods. Two of these, as with males, were allergic and related conditions and circulatory diseases; the other three consisted of conditions related to mental illness, genito-urinary diseases,[3] and accidents.

[3] Conditions related to pregnancy are treated in Chapter IX.

TABLE 3. Total episodes of illness by selected types: females 20–34 years of age.

	A. Rates						B. Test-control differences from data at left		
	Interim period Waves 2–3		"Early after" period Waves 4–7		"Late after" period Waves 8–11		Interim period	"Early after" period	"Late after" period
N:	Test (223)	Control (212)	Test (223)	Control (212)	Test (223)	Control (212)			
	Episodes per 100 persons, per period						Difference in rate per 100 persons[a]		
Infective and parasitic	5	2	1	1	2	4	−3	0	+ 2
Allergic, endo-crine, etc.	17	18	22	25	21	24	+1	+ 3	+ 3
Mental, psycho-neurotic, etc.	17	25	33	38	25	33	+8	+ 5	+ 8
Circulatory system	29	33	48	59	42	56	+4	+11	+14
Respiratory system	98	99	154	165	176	171	+1	+11	− 5
Digestive system	53	51	67	61	43	54	−2	− 6	+11
Genito-urinary system	37	45	52	67	59	69	+8	+15	+10
Arthritis, rheuma-tism, etc.	28	27	32	33	26	36	− 1	+ 1	+10
Accidents, poison-ing, etc.	11	15	18	20	11	18	+4	+ 2	+ 7
Other symptoms, etc.	27	20	40	40	34	29	−7	0	− 5

[a] Plus indicates that test rates were lower; minus, that test rates were higher.

Types of Illness: Older Adults, Ages 35-59

Table 4 gives rates of episodes for the various types of illness among all persons 35-59 years of age; Tables 5 and 6 show the same data for the sexes, separately. The tables reveal that there were relatively few instances in which lower test than control rates occurred consistently throughout all three "after" periods of the study. Only for respiratory conditions among both sexes combined, were test rates

TABLE 4. Total episodes of illness by selected types: all persons 35–59 years of age.

	A. Rates						B. Test-control differences from data at left		
	Interim period Waves 2–3		"Early after" period Waves 4–7		"Late after" period Waves 8–11		Interim period	"Early after" period	"Late after" period
N:	Test (142)	Control (148)	Test (142)	Control (148)	Test (142)	Control (148)			
	Episodes per 100 persons, per period						Difference in rate per 100 persons[a]		
Infective and parasitic	1	3	3	4	2	2	+ 2	+ 1	0
Allergic, endocrine, etc.	17	16	37	31	34	29	− 1	− 6	− 5
Mental, psychoneurotic, etc.	19	18	33	35	45	36	− 1	+ 2	− 9
Circulatory system	46	36	98	57	88	51	−10	−41	−37
Respiratory system	75	86	151	158	184	191	+11	+ 7	+ 7
Digestive system	51	51	75	79	76	73	0	+ 4	− 3
Genito-urinary system	25	34	52	45	38	45	+ 9	− 7	+ 7
Arthritis, rheumatism, etc.	66	59	95	80	89	67	− 7	−15	−22
Accidents, poisoning, etc.	16	13	23	16	20	19	− 3	− 7	− 1
Other symptoms, etc.	24	17	33	31	30	33	− 7	− 2	+ 3

[a] Plus indicates that test rates were lower; minus, that test rates were higher.

uniformly lower than control rates during the entire "after" period (Table 4), and this was contributed to largely by the males (Table 5). The only other instances of a similar kind of trend by type of illness for either of the sexes was also found among the males, and occurred for genito-urinary conditions and for episodes referable to the bones and organs of movement (arthritis, rheumatism, etc.).

Of the disease classifications which showed higher test than control rates, three did so most uniformly for all "after" periods for both sexes combined: allergic and related conditions (contributed to by

TABLE 5. Total episodes of illness by selected types: males 35–59 years of age.

	N:	A. Rates						B. Test-control differences from data at left		
		Interim period Waves 2–3		"Early after" period Waves 4–7		"Late after" period Waves 8–11		Interim period	"Early after" period	"Late after" period
		Test (58)	Control (60)	Test (58)	Control (60)	Test (58)	Control (60)	Difference in rate per 100 persons[a]		
		Episodes per 100 persons, per period								
Infective and parasitic		—	—	—	3	5	—	0	+ 3	− 5
Allergic, endo-crine, etc.		12	5	31	7	10	3	− 7	−24	− 7
Mental, psycho-neurotic, etc.		7	5	5	10	9	15	− 2	+ 5	+ 6
Circulatory system		26	7	36	8	34	17	−19	−28	−17
Respiratory system		52	63	121	130	140	162	+11	+ 9	+22
Digestive system		26	30	36	28	29	30	+ 4	− 8	+ 1
Genito-urinary system		—	5	5	8	—	12	+ 5	+ 3	+12
Arthritis, rheuma-tism, etc.		12	38	34	50	17	42	+26	+16	+25
Accidents, poison-ing, etc.		21	10	10	10	17	13	−11	0	− 4
Other symptoms, etc.		14	7	7	12	9	8	− 7	+ 5	− 1

[a] Plus indicates that test rates were lower; minus, that test rates were higher.

the males), circulatory diseases (contributed to by both males and females), and diseases of the bones and organs of movement (contributed to by females).[4] These findings were borne out consistently

[4] A fourth category consisting of accidents, poisoning, and violence, also showed higher test than control rates for both sexes combined during the "after" period (Table 4), but unlike the other three, the size of the test-control differences did not increase steadily as the study progressed, and neither sex contributed as systematically to the combined data.

TABLE 6. Total episodes of illness by selected types: females 35–59 years of age.

	A. Rates						B. Test-control differences from data at left		
	Interim period Waves 2–3		"Early after" period Waves 4–7		"Late after" period Waves 8–11		Interim period	"Early after" period	"Late after" period
	Test (84)	Control (88)	Test (84)	Control (88)	Test (84)	Control (88)			
N:	Episodes per 100 persons, per period						Difference in rate per 100 persons[a]		
Infective and parasitic	2	5	5	5	—	3	+ 3	0	+ 3
Allergic, endocrine, etc.	20	23	40	48	50	47	+ 3	+ 8	− 3
Mental, psychoneurotic, etc.	27	27	52	52	70	50	0	0	−20
Circulatory system	61	57	140	91	125	75	− 4	−49	−50
Respiratory system	92	101	173	177	214	211	+ 9	+ 4	− 3
Digestive system	69	65	102	114	108	102	− 4	+12	− 6
Genito-urinary system	43	53	85	69	64	68	+10	−16	+ 4
Arthritis, rheumatism, etc.	104	73	137	100	138	84	−31	−37	−54
Accidents, poisoning, etc.	13	15	31	20	23	23	+ 2	−11	0
Other symptoms, etc.	31	24	51	44	45	50	− 7	− 7	+ 5

[a] Plus indicates that test rates were lower; minus, that test rates were higher.

in the rates of disability associated with each of the types of illness, as shown by Tables 7 and 8. Higher test than control home disability rates (excluding days hospitalized) occurred in greatest magnitude, among males, in allergic and related conditions and in circulatory diseases; among females, in circulatory conditions and in diseases of the bones and organs of movement.

TABLE 7. Males 35–59 years of age: home days of disability from total episodes of illness by selected types.

		A. Rates						B. Test-control differences from data at left		
		Interim period Waves 2–3		"Early after" period Waves 4–7		"Late after" period Waves 8–11		Interim period	"Early after" period	"Late after" period
	N:	Test (58)	Control (60)	Test (58)	Control (60)	Test (58)	Control (60)			
		Days per 100 persons, per period						Difference in rate per 100 persons[a]		
Infective and parasitic		—	—	—	2	312	—	0	+ 2	−312
Allergic, endocrine, etc.		207	—	416	—	114	—	−207	−416	−114
Mental, psychoneurotic, etc.		2	5	—	—	24	5	+ 3	0	− 19
Circulatory system		924	125	683	—	719	13	−799	−638	−706
Respiratory system		14	340	134	145	293	178	+326	+ 11	−115
Digestive system		110	7	145	47	5	183	−103	− 98	+178
Genito-urinary system		—	—	7	8	—	3	0	+ 1	+ 3
Arthritis, rheumatism, etc.		7	108	134	17	81	23	+101	−117	− 58
Accidents, poisoning, etc.		203	80	117	65	52	215	−123	− 52	+163
Other symptoms, etc.		5	7	9	—	9	—	+ 2	− 9	− 9

[a] Plus indicates that test rates were lower; minus, that test rates were higher.

Accounting for the Morbidity Findings in the "After" Period for Older Adults, Ages 35-59

Findings just presented, and those of preceding chapters as well, have revealed several puzzling instances in which the morbidity data for the age group 35-59 consistently contradicted the expectation that, as a consequence of improved housing, test rates would be lower than control rates. Among the 35-59 year-old *females,* it has been

TABLE 8. Females 35–59 years of age: home days of disability from total episodes of illness by selected types.

		A. Rates					B. Test-control differences from data at left		
		Interim period Waves 2–3		"Early after" period Waves 4–7		"Late after" period Waves 8–11		Interim period	"Early after" period	"Late after" period
		Test (84)	Control (88)	Test (84)	Control (88)	Test (84)	Control (88)			
	N:	Days per 100 persons, per period						Difference in rate per 100 persons[a]		
Infective and parasitic		—	5	1	69	—	—	+ 5	+ 68	0
Allergic, endocrine, etc.		10	50	29	368	94	300	+ 40	+339	+206
Mental, psychoneurotic, etc.		30	68	89	322	280	76	+ 38	+233	−204
Circulatory system		238	236	915	151	694	264	− 2	−764	−430
Respiratory system		44	36	274	153	533	491	− 8	−121	− 42
Digestive system		230	36	225	44	192	60	−194	−181	−132
Genito-urinary system		50	217	90	231	74	65	+167	+141	− 9
Arthritis, rheumatism, etc.		364	239	501	425	575	317	−125	− 76	−258
Accidents, poisoning, etc.		55	78	70	94	35	41	+ 23	+ 24	+ 6
Other symptoms, etc.		35	17	144	42	93	147	− 18	−102	+ 54

[a] Plus indicates that test rates were lower; minus, that test rates were higher.

shown that for the entire "after" period, test rates were uniformly higher than control rates for episodes of illness of all kinds,[5] totaled and subdivided by severity, and for days of disability.[6] Among *males* of the same age group, similar findings counter to the hypothesis occurred in connection with serious episodes of illness and with days of disability. Data in this chapter have shown that among persons

[5] First presented and discussed in Chapter V.
[6] First presented and discussed in Chapter VI.

TABLE 9. Persons 35–59 years of age: distribution of number of serious episodes of illness for males and females.

Number of episodes	Interim period Waves 2–3		"Early after" period Waves 4–7		"Late after" period Waves 8–11	
	Test	Control	Test	Control	Test	Control
			Number of persons, per period			
Males:						
0	34	39	24	35	25	26
1–3	18	17	24	19	24	27
4–6	5	4	8	6	6	5
7–9	1	—	2	—	2	2
10–12	—	—	—	—	1	—
Total	58	60	58	60	58	60
Females:						
0	34	36	21	20	18	23
1–3	33	33	29	38	37	35
4–6	7	16	21	18	12	15
7–9	7	2	7	7	7	10
10–12	—	—	1	2	2	3
13–15	3	1	1	1	4	1
16–18	—	—	1	1	3	—
19–21	—	—	1	—	—	—
22–24	—	—	1	—	—	1
25–28	—	—	1	1	1	—
Total	84	88	84	88	84	88

35-59 years of age (both in episodes and disability), higher test than control rates occurred notably for three types of illness, all of them chronic in nature: allergic and related conditions, circulatory diseases, and diseases of the bones and organs of movement.

Efforts to account for these findings led to speculation that the higher test morbidity rates might be due to a relatively small number of persons who had experienced frequent exacerbations of conditions probably chronic in character, which had perhaps existed even before the study began. Tables 9 and 10 present data which explore

TABLE 10.   Persons 35–59 years of age: distribution of total number of   days of disability for males and females.

Total number of days of disability	Interim period Waves 2–3		"Early after" period Waves 4–7		"Late after" period Waves 8–11	
	Test	Control	Test	Control	Test	Control
			Number of persons, per period			
Males:						
0	40	44	31	41	31	27
1–9	10	10	14	12	17	20
10–19	—	—	5	—	4	5
20–29	1	2	2	2	2	3
30–59	—	1	—	3	1	2
60–99	2	2	4	1	2	2
100–199	5	1	1	1	—	1
200–242	—	—	1	—	1	—
Total	58	60	58	60	58	60
Females:						
0	42	44	31	29	28	28
1–9	24	28	19	34	24	32
10–19	5	4	10	8	9	10
20–29	4	2	10	7	9	7
30–59	2	7	5	1	6	6
60–99	6	2	4	7	2	3
100–199	1	1	4	—	5	—
200–242	—	—	1	2	1	2
Total	84	88	84	88	84	88

these possibilities. The tables show the frequency of persons who experienced varying numbers of serious episodes of illness and varying total numbers of days of disability. At each period and for each kind of data, it was apparent that a few persons at the high end of the distributions accounted for most of the larger test variance; this was most clearly the case for days of disability among males, and for both serious episodes and days of disability for females.

Examination of the individual cases revealed further that it was generally the same persons who were responsible for the high rates wave after wave and period after period. Thus, among females, Table 9 shows that in the "interim" period there were 10 tests and 3 controls, each with 7 or more serious conditions; these same persons also had the highest rates of disability in the "interim" period. Analysis of the "early after" and "late after" periods revealed that these 13 persons were responsible in the succeeding periods for the largest test and control episode and disability rates recorded. A similar analysis for *males* showed that in the "interim" period there were 6 tests and 4 controls who had 4 or more episodes of serious illness. These 10 persons accounted for the greatest test and control episode and disability rates in the "early after" and "late after" periods. Finally, examination of the Wave 1, "before" data for these persons, both male and female, indicated higher than ordinary incidence of chronic conditions to be existent at the outset of the study.

It seems, then, that in the 35-59 year-old group there were a few persons who had especially large episode and disability rates in the entire "after" period of the study, and that their morbidity pattern was established even before the study began. Of considerable consequence was the fact that there was a small excess of these persons among the test group. Apparently this test-control inequality arose through sampling variation, despite the high quality of matching observed for the samples as a whole. In order to investigate the effects on the data of taking the inequality into account, an adjustment was made on the basis of dividing the individuals into two groups according to high and low incidence of serious episodes in the *"interim"* period. The high incidence group consisted, among males, of those who had 4 or more episodes; among females, of those who had 7 or more episodes (Table 9, "interim" period). Tables 11 and 12 show for males and females, respectively, the rates for the high and low incidence groups, together with the final adjusted differences which are averages of the group differences weighted according to the numbers in the groups.

The tables show that, whereas the original episode and disability data revealed consistently higher test than control rates in the "early after" and "late after" periods for each age-sex group, the adjusted data resulted, for males, in lower test than control disability rates in the "late after" period; for females, adjustment resulted in lower test than control episode and disability rates in both of the later periods.

TABLE 11. Males 35–59 years of age: serious episodes of illness and total days of disability adjusted for initial illness level.

A. Rates

(Episodes) (days) per 100 persons, per period

	"Early after" period Waves 4–7		"Late after" period Waves 8–11	
	Test	Control	Test	Control
(1) Episodes				
Serious episodes as reported in Chapter V, Table 7[a]	162	102	152	133
Serious episodes for males who in "interim" period had:[b]				
Fewer than 4 episodes of illness	119	82	96	114
4 or more episodes of illness	533	375	633	400
(2) Days of disability				
Total days as reported in Chapter VI, Table 2[a]	1395	708	1000	930
Total days for males who in "interim" period had:[b]				
Fewer than 4 episodes of illness	856	486	438	566
4 or more episodes of illness	6067	3825	5867	6025

B. Test-control differences
from data above

Difference in rate per 100 persons[c]

	"Early after" period	"Late after" period
(1) Episodes		
Serious episodes of illness as reported in Chapter V, Table 7	− 60	− 19
Adjusted	− 47	− 3
(2) Days of disability		
Total days as reported in Chapter VI, Table 2	−687	− 70
Adjusted	−523	+ 105

[a] For N's on which rates are based, see Appendix 9, or Table 9, "Total," this chapter.
[b] For N's on which rates are based, see Table 9, "Interim," this chapter.
[c] Plus indicates that test rates were lower; minus, that test rates were higher.

TABLE 12.   Females 35–59 years of age: serious episodes of illness and total days
of disability adjusted for initial illness level.

A. Rates

(Episodes) (days) per 100 persons, per period

	"Early after" period Waves 4–7		"Late after" period Waves 8–11	
	Test	Control	Test	Control
(1) Episodes				
Serious episodes as reported in Chapter V, Table 8[a]	385	334	399	320
Serious episodes for females who in "interim" period had:[b]				
Fewer than 7 episodes of illness	259	293	272	288
7 or more episodes of illness	1310	1500	1340	1233
(2) Days of disability				
Total days as reported in Chapter VI, Table 3[a]	1971	1664	2001	1666
Total days for females who in "interim" period had:[b]				
Fewer than 7 episodes of illness	1282	1581	1165	1498
7 or more episodes of illness	7070	4000	8190	6433

B. Test–control differences from data above

Difference in rate per 100 persons[c]

	"Early after" period	"Late after" period
(1) Episodes		
Serious episodes of illness as reported in Chapter V, Table 8	− 51	− 79
Adjusted	+ 43	+ 9
(2) Days of disability		
Total days as reported in Chapter VI, Table 3	−307	−335
Adjusted	+113	+218

[a] For N's on which rates are based, see Appendix 9, or Table 9, "Total," this chapter.
[b] For N's on which rates are based, see Table 9, "Interim," this chapter.
[c] Plus indicates that test rates were lower; minus, that test rates were higher.

Summary

This chapter has presented rates of episodes of various types of illness incurred by persons 20-59 years of age. Data have been given for ten types of morbidity conditions which included 90 per cent of all episodes among persons of this age category.

For young adults, ages 20-34, test rates were lower than control rates in a majority of the disease categories for both sexes combined, particularly in the "late after" period of the study (Table 1). Somewhat more of the types of illness among females (Table 3) than among males (Table 2) showed consistently lower test than control rates throughout all three "after" periods.

For older adults of ages 35-59, respiratory conditions constituted the only category of illness in which uniformly lower test than control rates occurred throughout the entire "after" period for both sexes combined (Table 4). Higher test than control rates, both in episodes (Tables 4 through 6) and in home days of disability (Tables 7 and 8), were most marked and consistent for three types of illness, all of them chronic in nature: allergic and related conditions, circulatory diseases, and diseases of the bones and organs of movement.

A review was made of the morbidity findings for older adults, ages 35-59, which throughout the entire "after" period were counter to the hypothesis that due to differential quality of housing, test rates would be lower than control rates. Efforts to account for these findings revealed that there was a small number of persons who had higher than ordinary rates of serious episodes and total days of disability in the "interim" period and in both later periods as well (Tables 9 and 10); these persons, also, were found to have had an unusually high incidence of chronic conditions in the Wave 1, "before" period. A small excess of such persons occurred among the test group, apparently in spite of the quality of the matching of the test and control samples as a whole. Adjustment of the "after" period rates of serious episodes of illness and total days of disability resulted in lower test than control disability rates in the "late after" period for males; for episode and disability rates in the two later periods for females (Tables 11 and 12). Because of their high episode and disability rates, this small number of persons was apparently able to affect markedly the direction of the differences between test and control groups in this age bracket.

CHAPTER IX

CHILDBEARING EXPERIENCE

The statements of hypotheses and expectations reviewed in preceding chapters, especially in Chapters II and IV, made no reference to the possible differential effects of housing on childbearing experience. The reason for this omission stemmed from the difficulty in singling out the specific elements of housing that might be directly connected with the process of pregnancy, the *a priori* reasoning not being as clear as, for example, that regarding communicable diseases and accidents. Nevertheless, it was expected that the general character of good housing together with its anticipated effects on health, would result in benefits for the test women during pregnancy.

The following sections compare the test and control women as to various matters concerning the outcomes of pregnancy and the incidence of major and minor complaints associated with the pregnancies. The data were obtained in the course of the regular morbidity surveys, and subsequently supplemented by information from health department records.

Number of Pregnancies and Age of Mother at Outcome

There were 405 pregnancies enumerated in the period covered by the study, evenly divided among test and control women as shown by Table 1. This number represented a very high pregnancy rate, but not extraordinary when it is considered that more than 70 per cent of adult females in both test and control groups were between 20 and 34 years of age.

To assess the possible role of housing quality in the outcomes of pregnancy, it was necessary to make several partitions of total preg-

TABLE 1. Number of pregnancies.

Wave of outcome	Test			Control		
	Number of pregnancies					
1–2	55			35		
3–5	45	134	189	47	140	175
6–11	89			93		
Still pregnant, Wave 11	14			27		
Total pregnancies	203			202		

nancies observed. Fourteen, and 27 pregnancies among test and control groups, respectively, were still in progress at Wave 11, the terminal wave of the study, and being without outcome, were set aside as not germane to the inquiry. A second group of pregnancies was also set aside, not for lack of outcome, but for a reason having to do with the study design. It was felt that the proper test of the effects of housing on pregnancy outcome involved consideration only of those pregnancies in which the full term occurred under differential housing circumstances. Thus, as can be seen from Table 1, 55 of the pregnancies among test women occurred in the period following Wave 1 through Wave 2. The majority of test pregnancies with outcomes in that time span were begun in slum housing, and therefore would not constitute a group clearly relevant to an investigation of the study hypotheses. Among control women, 35 pregnancies had outcome in the same time period, and, although those pregnancies were begun and terminated in generally similar housing, they were set aside in the interest of temporal correspondence between test and control groups. There remained 134 test and 140 control pregnancies with outcomes in the periods covered by the morbidity surveys of Waves 3 through 11.

Table 2 shows maternal age distributions of test and control pregnancies that had outcomes during Waves 3 through 11. The two groups were very similar in the per cent of pregnancies that had outcome among very young women (mother's age less than 20 years) and among older women (mother's age 35 years and older). A somewhat greater proportion of test than control women had outcomes in the age range 25-29; conversely, a greater proportion of control women had outcomes in the age range 30-34.

TABLE 2. Age of mother at outcome of pregnancy (pregnancies with outcome at Waves 3–11, inclusive).

Age at outcome	No. of pregnancies:	Test (134)	Control (140)
		Per cent of pregnancies	
Under 15		—	—
15–19		4	6
20–24		31	29
25–29		37	27
30–34		20	28
35–39		7	9
40 and over		1	1

Outcomes of Pregnancy

The average number of outcomes per pregnant woman was very similar in both groups, with slightly different patterning, as revealed in Table 3. A somewhat greater proportion of control than test women had a single outcome in the period of Waves 3 through 11 (82 per cent compared to 72 per cent) ; but two control women (2 per cent) also had three outcomes.

The actual results of the 134 test and 140 control pregnancies are given in Table 4. Because of twins (2 sets among the test and 4 sets among the controls), there were 136 and 144 total outcomes among the test and control group, respectively. Perinatal casualties occurred among 16 per cent of the test and 13 per cent of the control total

TABLE 3. Number of outcomes per woman pregnant (pregnancies with outcome at Waves 3–11, inclusive).

No. of outcomes	No. of pregnant women:	Test (105)	Control (117)
		Per cent of pregnant women	
1		72	82
2		28	16
3		—	2

TABLE 4. Outcomes of pregnancy, including birth weight[a] of live births (pregnancies with outcome at Waves 3–11, inclusive).

	Test		Control	
	Number	Per cent	Number	Per cent
Perinatal mortality				
Fetal deaths	(20)	15	(14)	10
Live births, subsequent deaths	(1)	1	(4)	3
Live births, surviving: birth weight records	(106)		(118)	
Birth weight: 1500 gms. or less	—	—	(2)	1
1501–2000	(2)	1	(3)	2
2001–2500	(2)	1	(10)	7
2501–3000	(32)	24	(45)	31
3001–3500	(48)	35 } 77	(42)	29 } 81
3501–4000	(18)	13	(14)	10
4001–4500	(3)	2	(2)	1
4501–5000	(1)	1	—	—
5001 and more	—	—	—	—
Live births, surviving: incomplete records	(9)	7	(8)	6
Total outcomes	(136)	100	(144)	100
Number of sets of twins	(2)		(4)	
Total number of pregnancies	(134)		(140)	

a From birth certificates on file with the Bureau of Vital Statistics, Baltimore City Health Department.

outcomes. Most of these were fetal deaths (stillbirths, miscarriages, or abortions), a slight excess of which took place among the tests. Live births, surviving, constituted 84 per cent and 87 per cent of test and control outcomes, respectively. Birth weight information was sought on these infants from birth certificate records[1] and was obtained on all but a relatively small number—fewer than 10—of test and control births. The data show (Table 4) a trend toward lower birth weights among control infants successfully coming to term, including an excess of control births in the premature range (2500 grams or less in weight). Overall, control infants surviving were on the average 200 grams lighter than test infants. Even when the larger number of control-to-test twins was taken into account, control infants were found to be 170 grams (on the average) lighter than test infants.

[1] Bureau of Vital Statistics, Baltimore City Health Department.

TABLE 5. Outcomes of pregnancy, including birth weight[a] of live births, by age of mother at outcome (pregnancies with outcome at Waves 3–11, inclusive).

	Test			Control		
Age at outcome:	Under 25	25–29	30 and over	Under 25	25–29	30 and over
	Per cent of pregnancies					
Perinatal mortality						
Fetal deaths	11	14	20	10	8	11
Live births, subsequent deaths	—	2	—	6	—	2
Live births, surviving: birth weight records						
Birth weight: 2500 gms. or less	2	—	8	—	15	16
2501–3000	29	20	20	39	33	23
3001–3500	28	44	35	35	30	24
3501 and more	21	14	12	6	12	15
Live births, surviving: incomplete records	9	6	5	4	2	9
Total number of outcomes	(47)	(49)	(40)	(49)	(40)	(55)
Number of sets of twins	(—)	(—)	(2)	(—)	(2)	(2)
Total number of pregnancies	(47)	(49)	(38)	(49)	(38)	(53)

a From birth certificates on file with the Bureau of Vital Statistics, Baltimore City Health Department.

In an effort to gain a clearer understanding of the possible influences on various results of pregnancy, the data in Table 4 were examined in the light of age of the mother at outcome. Table 5 indicates that for perinatal mortality and prematurity combined, twice as many of these outcomes occurred among mothers 30 years and over as occurred among mothers under 25, but this applied almost equally to both tests and controls. In general, there appeared to be no age clue to the test-control differences that were summarized above in connection with Table 4.

Complaints during Pregnancy

Data regarding complications and minor complaints of pregnancy as enumerated during the regular morbidity surveys, are shown in Table 6. A slightly smaller proportion of test than control pregnancies

TABLE 6. Complications and minor complaints during pregnancy (pregnancies with outcome at Waves 3—11, inclusive).

	Test (134)	Control (140)
No. of pregnancies:		
	Per cent of pregnancies	
Pregnancies with complications	30	28
Minor complaints, only	51	49
Neither complications nor complaints	19	23

were *free* of episodes of illness related to pregnancy, the test-control difference being equally distributed among major and minor complaints. In two per cent more test than control pregnancies, there were reports of minor complaints exclusively, such as nausea, dizziness, and headaches. Also, in two per cent more test than control pregnancies, there were reports of more serious complaints, including toxemias, ectopic pregnancies, *ante partum* hemorrhage, and breast abscesses after birth.

Summary

The data presented in this chapter revealed little to suggest that differential housing quality affected, in any significant way, the outcomes of pregnancies. The test and control groups were found to be similar in several respects: in the number of pregnancies that occurred (Table 1); in the ages of the mothers at outcome (Table 2); and in the average number of outcomes per mother, although the patterning of frequency of outcome was somewhat different (Table 3). The actual outcomes themselves showed a complex situation: there was a slight excess of perinatal mortality among test outcomes, but there was somewhat greater incidence of prematurity among control live outcomes (Table 4), a situation which was not illuminated by examination of the data by the age of the mother (Table 5). Morbidity data showed little difference between the two groups in the incidence of either minor or more serious complaints during the pregnancies, although a slightly smaller proportion of the test than control pregnancies were *free* of episodes of illness related to childbearing (Table 6).

PART 3

SOCIAL PSYCHOLOGICAL ADJUSTMENT

Introduction

Development of the social adjustment chapters

Each of the social adjustment chapters follows a similar mode of development. First, the relevant hypotheses and general expectations originally specified in Chapter II are recapitulated and elaborated. The general content of the chapter also is outlined.

Second, there is an assessment of the *comparability* of the test and control families on the relevant dependent variable measures that were made during the initial interview. Presentation in each chapter of the "before" data makes possible a detailed description of the initial similarity of the two groups on the issues covered by the chapter, and, in addition, provides base lines for comparison of test and control families in the "after" period.

Third, *the "after" findings* of the study are discussed. In general, all questions asked on Wave 1 were also asked in the "after" period at least once, either in the "18-month after" interview (Wave 5 or Wave 7) or in the "3-year after" interview (Wave 10 or Wave 11). A number of items, because of special interest, were pursued at three points in time: in the "before" period and in both "after" periods. Finally, because of limitations of space and time in the initial survey, a number of items were inquired about only in one of the "after" periods, without a Wave 1, initial measure.

Tabular presentation

The tabular presentation of data in *all* of the social adjustment chapters has the following characteristics:

(a) Data presented are for the reduced effective samples of 300 test and 300 control families, unless otherwise specified within the table itself.

(b) For any item on which an initial measure was obtained, the "before" data always accompany the "after" data.

(c) Data for which no initial, "before" measures were obtained are presented as "after, only."

134

In addition to these characteristics, the tables in Chapters X through XIV, and XVI have the following properties:

(a)   Any item which was asked only of a subsample of the total reduced effective test and control groups is indicated by a footnote in the table; the number of cases involved in such an item appears in Appendix 13.

(b)   For items that were inquired about at three points in time, the "before" and the most recent (3-year) "after" data are shown.

(c)   Data collected at the 18-month, "early after" period appear in the tables in italics; data collected at the 3-year, "late after" period are shown in roman type. In Chapter XVI, all of the "after" data were obtained in the "late after" period.

(d)   Most of the items are presented in abbreviated form, only a single line being given for the full distribution. This is solely a device for economy of presentation; the "sense" of the distribution is communicated by the line presented.

The tabular presentation of data in Chapter XV, because of its special characteristics, is somewhat different from that of the other social adjustment chapters. First, the "before" and both the "early after" and "late after" data are shown for items that were obtained at all three points in time. Second, in addition to the single-line summary, the full distribution is given for each item.

Statistical summaries

At the conclusion of each of Chapters X through XV, a chart is presented which summarizes the direction and statistical significance of the data shown in the tables for the chapter. For completeness, every test-control comparison presented earlier in a chapter is represented in the summary. This results in occasional overlap of information: for example, in some tables, a series of items has been presented together with an index summarizing the sense of the total set; in such cases, both the individual items *and* the index are represented in the summary.

Direction.   The term "direction" in the chart should be taken to indicate confirmation of hypotheses and expectations (tests more "positive" than controls), or non-confirmation (no difference, or controls more "positive" than tests). The hypotheses referred to apply to the "after" period, but since it is helpful to have a concise assessment of test-control initial comparability, the same "directional" criteria have also been applied to the "before" measures. On a majority of items, the "positive" direction of differences describes attitudes, outlook, or behavior which most observers would tend to agree represent a happier or healthier state of affairs for the population in question. On some items, the social desirability of the "positive" direction may not have such wide acceptability. The assigned direction is referable, however, to the reasoning that underlay the framing of the hypotheses about a population having the social characteristics of these study groups. Finally, there are a few items in various chapters for which the choice of the "positive" direction of differences, as denoting a happier or healthier state of affairs, does not rest necessarily on either common agreement or on the hypotheses.

Statistical significance. The statistical assessment of the significance of test-control differences for the data of Chapters X through XVI was accomplished with the aid of a set of nomographs prepared by Dr. Joseph Zubin.[1] The Zubin nomographs permit close visual comparison of the observed normal deviate with the critical ratios for significance levels $P<0.05$ and $P<0.01$ and are of great aid in the calculation of the statistical significance of large bodies of dichotomous data. The statistical appraisal in Chapters X through XVI are for the segments of distributions presented in the tables. The nomographs were used conservatively; that is, a difference between test and control groups had to be clearly significant at the 1 or 5 per cent level before being so labeled. Borderline cases were considered to be directional only.

---

[1] J. Zubin. "Nomographs for Determining the Significance of the Differences between the Frequencies of Events in Two Contrasted Series or Groups," *Journal of the American Statistical Association,* **34** (1939), 539-544.

CHAPTER X

REACTIONS TO HOUSING AND SPACE

It will be recalled that "before" measurements of housing quality revealed both test and control families to be living, initially, in dwelling units of poor quality. With the move to good housing, quality of the housing environs improved markedly for the test families. Former deficiencies such as the sharing of facilities, crowding, dilapidation, lack of space, lack of hot water, and lack of central heating were wiped out. The intention in measuring reactions to housing and space was to discover the extent to which test respondents, in contrast to controls, manifested conscious recognition of their improved housing circumstances. There was, of course, the possibility that sizeable effects on substantive matters might be experienced without conscious awareness of the altered environment. Yet it seemed likely that the objective facts of the housing improvement would be reflected in the housewives' reactions to specific elements of their housing, and would have discernible consequences in certain pragmatic and psychological areas.

The subject matter of this chapter will pertain, first, to reactions to the dwelling unit, building maintenance, and play facilities for children; second, to the issue of space and some of its consequences for individual privacy, entertaining, and certain psychological reactions. The data are shown in Tables 1 through 7.

Initial Comparability of Test and Control Groups at Wave 1

"Before" measurements were obtained on almost all the items pertaining to reactions to housing and space. A general review of these

137

TABLE 1. The apartment.

	Before		After	
	Test	Control	Test	Control
		Per cent		
a. How do you like your apartment? "A lot"	14	25[a]	60	33[a]
b. What do you like **most**?				
"Likes" most frequently mentioned:[b]				
Living space	24	27	48	46
Water supply; kitchen, bathroom facilities	14	13	47	22[a]
Storage space	1	c	34	4[a]
Proximity to public facilities, desired social contacts; privacy	23	30	23	30
Nothing liked	23	15[d]	1	8[a]
c. What do you like **least**?				
"Dislikes" most frequently mentioned:[b]				
Not enough living or storage space	33	27	9	26[a]
Structural deterioration	32	31	1	24[a]
Deficiencies in architectural design	24	17[d]	18	23
Nothing disliked	6	14[a]	58	21[a]

[a] Test-control difference significant at level of .01 or less.
[b] The categories of responses shown are those mentioned most frequently by test and control in the "after" period.
[c] Less than one-half of one per cent.
[d] Test-control difference significant at level of .02 to .05.

measures, shown in Tables 1 through 7, reveals a moderate degree of comparability between the test and control groups initially. Responses to approximately half the principal "before" measures showed no marked differences between test and control families, although there was a tendency for these minor inequalities, where they did occur, to consist of more favorable reactions among controls than among tests. The remaining measures of initial reactions to housing and space showed more marked test-control differences, some of them greater than 10 per cent; again, controls were more likely than tests to have favorable reactions.

The over-all housing quality score of test families in both the intact and the reduced samples was somewhat worse than that of the controls; in fact, 10 per cent more reduced test than control families lived in initially "bad" housing as measured by the index of all housing components combined.[1] The direction and consistency of differences noted in the initial measurements of reactions to housing and space were congruent with this initial housing "handicap" of the test families. Almost all the initial inequalities noted in Tables 1 through 7 showed the test respondents reflecting this initial deficit; they reported somewhat less liking for the dwelling unit, expressed less satisfaction with children's play places, and indicated less space and privacy, etc., than did the controls.

Reactions to Housing

The apartment

Respondents were asked at Wave 1, and again after 18 months, and 36 months, "How do you like your apartment?" Table 1a shows that by the end of three years, having started with an 11 per cent handicap, approximately twice as many test as control housewives said they liked their apartment "a lot" (60 per cent compared to 33 per cent). The 18-month data, not shown, indicated differences of corresponding magnitude and direction.

The two groups were also asked both "before" and 18 months later to describe the characteristics they liked most and liked least about their apartments. Table 1 (b and c) shows this information. From near equality on a number of items at Wave 1, the "most *liked*" housing aspects which distinguished markedly between tests and controls in the "after" period were water supply, kitchen and bathroom facilities, and storage space: a larger proportion of tests than controls mentioned these as the characteristics they liked most about their apartments. Just as striking were the greater proportions of controls than of tests who mentioned aspects "most *disliked*"; these consisted of insufficient living or storage space and structural deterioration. Finally, test families were about three times as likely as controls to find *nothing* they disliked about their apartments (58 per cent compared to 21 per cent).

[1] See Appendix 8, Table 3.

The building, maintenance, and value received

Questions were asked in the "after" period about the exterior appearance of the building, attention paid to maintenance and repair by the landlord and management, and the value of the apartment for the money. On all three items (Table 2), test families showed substantial advantage over control families. Forty-two per cent more test respondents than controls thought the outside of the building looked "very nice," 54 per cent more tests asserted that management took care of all needed repairs, and 19 per cent more tests thought that for what they were getting, the rent they paid was "about right." These are further data supplementing the notion that rehoused persons in markedly improved housing circumstances do, in fact, recognize the improvement they enjoy.

Play facilities for children

An important correlate of housing quality is that of play facilities for children. In crowded slum areas, even very young children are found playing in the street where automobile traffic and other hazards exist. At Wave 1 and again in the "after" period, mothers of children between three and sixteen years of age were asked to enumerate from a list the places where their children played, to indicate their satis-

TABLE 2. The building, maintenance, and value received.

		Before		After	
		Test	Con-trol	Test	Con-trol
			Per cent		
a. How does this building look on the outside?	"Very nice"			54	12[a]
b. What does landlord do about needed repairs?	Takes care of all			80	26[a]
c. For what you are getting, is your rent high, about right, or low?	"About right"	39	49[b]	77	58[a]

[a] Test-control difference significant at level of .01 or less.
[b] Test-control difference significant at level of .02 to .05.

faction with the play locations, and to give in their own words the positive and negative reasons for their evaluations.

The responses to these inquiries are given in Table 3. From essential similarity at Wave 1, sharp differences emerged in the "after" period. Almost none of the test mothers compared to approximately half of the control mothers (Table 3a) indicated that their children played in *unsafe* places. This actual difference was reflected in the respondents' *expressions of satisfaction* with the play locations. Table 3b shows that 29 per cent more test than control women viewed their

TABLE 3. Play facilities for children.[a]

		Before		After	
		Test	Con-trol	Test	Con-trol
		Per cent			
a. Safety of places where children play[b]	Not safe	32	32	1	53[c]
b. How satisfactory are the places where your children play?	"Very satisfactory"	22	24	68	39[c]
c. **Positive** reasons for evaluation of play facilities					
Most frequently mentioned:[d]					
Adequate safety		20	15	43	28[c]
Adequate facilities		8	11	33	22[e]
Adequate supervision		10	13	26	16[e]
Negative responses, only		54	44[e]	20	38[c]
d. **Negative** reasons for evaluation of play facilities					
Most frequently mentioned:[d]					
Lack of safety		39	37	6	28[c]
Inadequate or no facilities		18	13	7	15[e]
Interpersonal contacts		15	14	13	7[e]
Positive responses, only		29	37	69	47[c]

[a] Among families who had at least one child between 3 and 16 years of age; for N's, see Appendix 13.
[b] The "not safe" category consists of public streets.
[c] Test-control difference significant at level of .01 or less.
[d] The categories of responses shown are those mentioned most frequently by test and control in the "after" period.
[e] Test-control difference significant at level of .02 to .05.

children's respective play places as "very satisfactory." The positive and negative reasons (Table 3, c and d) distinguishing between the two groups provided further evidence of the relative difference, particularly in the factors of safety and supervision.

Various unique aspects of the housing development undoubtedly accounted for the test mothers' feelings of greater security about the safety of their children. The buildings of the housing project were, in general, set back from the streets and surrounded by walks, terraces, and play areas so that there were ample places, other than the street, for children to play. In addition, some of the structural features of the buildings themselves undoubtedly played a role. It will be recalled that the "high-rise" buildings had long corridors on each floor running the length of the building which themselves were used as play areas. Of even greater importance was the fact that on each floor there was a 16x30-foot play area which was observed to be used extensively by the test children, particularly those under seven or eight years of age.

Reactions to Space

Occupancy standards of the Baltimore Housing Authority applying to Lafayette Courts and other projects were as follows: one-bedroom apartments housed not fewer than two nor more than three persons; two-bedroom apartments, three to five persons; three-bedroom apartments, four to seven persons; and four-bedroom apartments, five to nine persons. Further enforced standards applied to occupancy of bedrooms by children and other unmarried persons of different sex, depending on age. The resulting low over-all number of persons per room could be expected to result in adequate space for movement about the apartment, privacy from other family members when needed, space for storage of clothes and placement of personal articles, use of different rooms for their intended functions, etc. Facilities were ample for storage and preparation of food, as well as for maintaining personal cleanliness.

Space in dwelling units in the slum was, of course, more limited. While there was some variability, in general the number of persons per room was higher than in Lafayette Courts and other housing projects, and many of the space-related benefits were lacking.

A number of matters pertaining to space were pursued on Wave 1 and again in the "after" period: privacy, invitations to the home, appraisal of adequacy of space-related facilities, and possible discomforts and minor frictions related to space limitations. The findings are given in Tables 4 through 7, and will be discussed in the following sections.

Individual privacy

It was reasoned that the ability to withdraw from the noise and demands of children might be an important element in the lives of mothers of the study. Respondents were asked to comment on the likelihood of their being able to be alone somewhere in the apartment if they so desired. Table 4a shows test women only slightly more likely than control women to be able to do this "very easily." The gain over time in this respect is more substantial, however, when the initial "handicap" of test respondents is taken into account.

Table 4 (b and c) shows the responses for several relevant questions regarding the "work" and play of children. Eleven per cent more test than control respondents in the "after" period answered "Yes" to the question, "Do children have a place to do homework in the apartment without being bothered by anyone else?"; and 9 per cent more

TABLE 4.   Individual privacy.[a]

		Before		After	
		Test	Con-trol	Test	Con-trol
		Per cent			
a. Can you be by yourself in the apartment if you want to?[b]	Very easily	27	43[c]	60	56
b. Do children have a place to do homework in the apartment without being bothered by anyone else?[d]	"Yes"	64	78[e]	95	84[e]
c. Can children's friends come in without getting in anyone's way?[f]	"Yes"	65	70	91	82[e]

[a] For N's on which per cents are based, see Appendix 13.

[b] Among families of appropriate family composition: at least two adults, or if one adult, at least one child 10 years of age or older.

[c] Test-control difference significant at level of .01 or less.

[d] Among families who had at least one child between 6 and 16 years of age.

[e] Test-control difference significant at level of .02 to .05.

[f] Among families who had at least one child between 3 and 16 years of age.

test than control women answered affirmatively to the question: "Can children's friends come in without getting in anyone's way?" On both of these items, test gains from "before" to "after" were more marked than control gains.

Inviting friends and neighbors in

Preliminary considerations of space and the character of the dwelling units suggested the possibility that these factors would play a role in the social lives of the families in the study. In particular, two items were asked having to do with spatial and esthetic inhibitions to sociality.

The first question was: "Sometimes people don't invite their friends to their home as often as they would like, because they feel they don't *have enough space to entertain* them. Have you ever felt this way about your present apartment?" Table 5a reveals that in the "after" period, 22 per cent more test than control householders replied "No" (do not feel that way) in answer to the question.

The second question was: "Sometimes people don't invite other people into their home because they feel their home doesn't *look quite nice enough*. Have you ever felt this way about your present apartment?" Table 5b shows that in the "after" period 18 per cent more test than control women were undeterred by this factor.

TABLE 5. Inviting friends and neighbors in.

		Before		After	
		Test	Control	Test	Control
		Per cent			
a. Don't invite because not enough space	Don't feel that way	42	54[a]	90	68[b]
b. Don't invite because home doesn't look quite nice enough	Don't feel that way	51	55	82	64[b]
c. **Index of above two items**	Neither factor deters	30	37	75	50[b]

[a] Test-control difference significant at level of .02 to .05.
[b] Test-control difference significant at level of .01 or less.

Table 5c shows the proportions of respondents who said "No" to both questions. In the "after" period, three-quarters of the test women compared to one-half of the control women felt that neither factor—space nor appearance—prevented them from inviting others into their homes.

"Personal" space

In comprehensive evaluations of housing quality, the measures of space most emphasized are those describing person-room density and the extent of sharing of facilities with non-family members. From the social psychological standpoint, relatively more minor elements of space, usually neglected, may also be of some consequence.

During Wave 1 and again in the "after" period, inquiry was made about a few of these minor space-related factors. The respondents were asked whether or not there was enough closet space, drawer, shelf, and comfortable sitting space in the apartment for all members of the family. Table 6 (parts a through d) shows that on these items, from 11 per cent to 38 per cent more test than control women reported having enough of the kinds of space indicated. Table 6e describes the result of an index made up of all four "personal space" items: approximately 40 per cent more test than control women reported enough of all four kinds of space in the "after" period.

TABLE 6.   Personal space.

		Before		After	
		Test	Con-trol	Test	Con-trol
			Per cent		
a. Enough closet space?	"Yes"	23	40[a]	95	57[a]
b. Enough drawer space?	"Yes"	40	64[a]	87	70[a]
c. Enough shelf space?	"Yes"	27	49[a]	98	65[a]
d. Enough comfortable sitting space?	"Yes"	68	82[a]	98	87[a]
e. **Index of above four items**	All four: enough space	14	30[a]	85	46[a]

[a] Test-control difference significant at level of .01 or less.

Psychological consequences

While many psychological issues covered in succeeding chapters undoubtedly can be related to spatial characteristics of the dwelling units, two matters of psychological import were inquired about at Wave 1 and again in the "after" period which were phrased directly in a spatial context. Table 7a shows that, starting from a sizeable initial "handicap" in the "before" period, 8 per cent more test than control respondents stated that no one in the family was bothered by insufficient space in the "after" period.

The second item (Table 7b) carried the matter a step further. Among families of appropriate composition, the question was asked: "Do bad feelings ever arise between any members of the family who live here because of the amount of space in the apartment?" Again, 8 per cent more test than control women said that space was not an issue in intra-family dissension. As with the preceding item, the difference is considerably emphasized when the fact of the initial test "handicap" is taken into account.

Statistical Summary for Data on Reaction to Housing and Space

Level of significance	Direction	No. of test-control comparisons	
		Before	After
	Confirming the "after" expectations		
.01 or less	Tests more "positive" than controls	—	27
.02 to .05	" " " " "	—	4
Greater than .05	" " " " "	3	3
	Counter to the "after" expectations		
No difference:	Identical percentages	1	—
Greater than .05	Controls more "positive" than tests	14	1
.02 to .05	" " " " "	6	1
.01 or less	" " " " "	10	—

The summary chart above indicates the direction and magnitude of differences for the test-control data presented in this chapter. In 31 of the comparisons in the "after" period, the test group was significantly more positive than the control group; only 3 items had the

TABLE 7. Psychological consequences of space.

		Before		After	
		Test	Con-trol	Test	Con-trol
		Per cent			
a. Anyone in family bothered by lack of space?	"No"	62	74ᵃ	94	86ᵃ
b. Do bad feelings arise because of amount of space?ᵇ	"No"	72	85ᵃ	96	88ᵃ

ᵃ Test-control difference significant at level of .01 or less.
ᵇ Among families of appropriate family composition: at least two adults, or if one adult, at least one child 10 years of age or older; for N's, see Appendix 13.

same direction in the "before" period, and none reached the 5 per cent level. On the contrary, in 30 of the "before" comparisons, controls were in fact more likely than the tests to be positive, 16 of the comparisons showing differences of at least the 5 per cent level; these data summarize the test housing "handicap" referred to earlier.

It is thus clear that in contrast to the control women, the housewives in the rehoused setting were conscious of the improvements in their living circumstances (Tables 1 and 2), were sensitive to the safety of the places where their children now played (Table 3), reported somewhat increased opportunity for privacy for themselves and for their children (Table 4), and also reported diminution of spatial and esthetic barriers to sociality (Table 5), increments in items of "personal" space (Table 6), and reductions in psychological discomfort directly related to space (Table 7).

CHAPTER XI

PERSONAL AND FAMILY RELATIONS

One set of study hypotheses suggested that because of such factors as increased space and other improvements in housing, patterns of within-family activities and quality of family-member relationships might be expected to undergo alterations in the rehoused, test group. In order to investigate these suppositions, two major subjects will be examined in this chapter.

The first pertains to the more behavioral aspect of family relations, particularly in connection with certain common activities about the home which persons have the option of doing together or not. Among these common activities are:

(a) The day-to-day, routine tasks that are necessary to maintain housekeeping. Among deprived families these activities are generally handled in one of two ways: either the family members help, or the woman of the house does them alone.

(b) Mutual leisure-time pursuits including those which specifically involve parents and children. These are of importance in a group which, for reasons of cultural and economic background, has difficulty in undertaking such activities as a family unit.

The second major subject deals with the *quality* of the behavior among family members. It involves such matters as warmth and compatability, and the confidence which children manifest in parents by bringing personal problems to them. Although the mother's role in relation to her children is generally well defined, that of the father is apt to be less clear cut, and the degree of his interest in and concern for the children is likely to be a contributing factor to the

148

general quality of relations within the family. Finally, in addition to positive elements, it would be a rare family that did not have some negative aspects to its relationships. In this connection, the frequency and nature of quarrels, arguments, and hard feelings are relevant, as well as the mother's reactions to the problem behavior of the children.

An important element in the supposition of improved test family relations was the anticipation that the rehoused persons would be more likely than those in the slum to spend their free time—after work, after school, and on week ends—in the dwelling unit. This expectation was based on the proposition that severely limited space and physically unattractive quarters would provide less incentive to pursue activities about the house than would the more spacious and more attractive quarters of the housing development. This should apply with special force to adult males and adolescent children who have neither the culturally defined bond with the dwelling unit, nor the dependency upon it which, for example, young children have.

Initial Comparability of Test and Control Groups at Wave 1

Tables 1 through 6 contain in abbreviated form the data covering selected items of personal and family relations. Approximately half of the items asked in the "after" period were also asked in the "before" period. The Wave 1 measures on these variables may be used to estimate the initial comparability of test and control groups on the entire battery of questions.

A review of the "before" measures reveals that the maximum test-control difference, on one item, was 10 per cent. On about half of the items, the difference was 5 per cent or less. The conclusion seems justified that the two groups were initially very similar on the issues dealt with in the present chapter.

Intrafamilial Activities and Cooperation

If the preceding hypotheses regarding home-centeredness are sound, it is reasonable to expect that certain activities which family members may undertake together would be less likely to occur in the slum than in Lafayette Courts. In the slum, for instance, some factors tending to deter mutual activity might be the relative physical and psychological unattractiveness of the dwelling unit, or the sheer physical difficulty in pursuing such activity. Thus, obtaining assistance for certain necessary activities may be a rare occurrence because family members simply are not around enough. Or, meals may not be taken together if available dining space is not adequate to accommodate the entire family. Husbands or children may not volunteer help with the dishes or be asked to help (especially if water supply is irregular) in a kitchen that is big enough for only one person. A father (or mother) may find it difficult to help a child with homework in the presence of other children or otherwise occupied adults. More and larger rooms and lessened density per room may conceivably affect mutual activity and cooperation among family members.

Common family activities

In pursuing evidence for the foregoing speculations, families of appropriate family composition were asked to indicate from a brief

TABE 1. Common family activities.[a]

		Before		After	
		Test	Con-trol	Test	Con-trol
		Per cent			
Family members do things together, for example:					
a. Go shopping?	"Often"	38	45	46	42
b. Sit and talk?	"Often"	76	80	84	82
c. Go for walks?	"Often"	28	29	31	29
d. Go to the movies?	"Often"	17	23	24	21
e. Listen to the radio or watch TV?	"Often"	80	81	89	86
f. **Index of above five items**	Three or more: "Often"	45	50	55	52
g. Everyone takes evening meal together?	"Always"	50	57	45	38

[a] Among families of appropriate family composition: at least two adults, or if one adult, at least one child 10 years of age or older; for N's, see Appendix 13.

check list how often family members took part in mutual activities. The items included were "go shopping together," "sit and talk in the apartment," "go for walks," "go to the movies," and "listen to the radio or watch TV together." Table 1 (parts a through e) gives the answers to these items. In the "after" period, slightly more test than control respondents stated that each activity was undertaken "often." The range of differences was only from 2 per cent to 4 per cent for each item. An index of all five activities taken together showed a 3 per cent difference in the same direction (Table 1f).

A question on the frequency of taking the evening meal together (Table 1g) revealed that in the "after" period, 7 per cent more test than control families "always" did so.

It will be observed in Table 1 that for all the items just discussed, a slight test handicap existed at Wave 1, ranging from 1 per cent to 7 per cent. The "after" differences are, as a consequence, somewhat enhanced, more pronounced test gains on some items having been made between "before" and "after."

Parental interest in children's activities

Three questions asked of families with appropriate family composition in the "after" period dealt with parental interest in children's activities. In the first, inquiry was made about the extent to which parents helped children with homework, played with them, read aloud,

TABLE 2. Parental interest in children's activities.[a]

		Before		After	
		Test	Con-trol	Test	Con-trol
			Per cent		
a. Time parent(s) spend with children in helping with homework, playing, reading aloud, telling stories[b]	"A lot"			35	40
b. **During present school year:** parent(s) attended a program at child's school?[c]	"Yes"			41	44
c. **During present school year:** parent(s) visited a class at child's school?[c]	"Yes"			71	64

[a] For N's on which per cents are based, see Appendix 13.
[b] Among families who had at least one child between 6 and 16 years of age.
[c] Among families who had at least one child 6 years of age, or older, attending school.

and told stories. Table 2a shows that 5 per cent *fewer* test than control parents helped their children "a lot" in the ways specified.

The next two questions had to do with parents' participation with children in school activities. The questions, asked of families with at least one child attending school, were:

"During the present school year, that is since September, have you (or your husband) —
Attended a program put on by the children at (_____'s) school?
Visited a class at (his) (her) school?"

Table 2 (b and c) shows that 3 per cent *fewer* test than control parents had attended a school program, but 7 per cent *more* tests than controls had visited a class.

Assistance given housewife around the home

To pursue the issues related to assistance tendered the woman of the house in performing chores about the apartment, the question was asked in the "after" period:

TABLE 3.   Assistance given housewife around the home.[a]

		Before		After	
		Test	Con-trol	Test	Con-trol
			Per cent		
Do family members usually help you:[b]					
a. With the dishes?	"Yes"			81	84
b. To clean the apartment?	"Yes"			84	84
c. With the shopping?	"Yes"			81	79
d. With the laundry?	"Yes"			56	57
e. With the cooking?	"Yes"			54	53
f. **Index of above five items**	Four or more: "Yes"			62	59
g. Does husband help you out around the house?[c]	"A lot" or "Quite a bit"	56	62	59	65

[a] For N's on which per cents are based, see Appendix 13.
[b] Among families of appropriate family composition: at least two adults, or if one adult, at least one child 10 years of age or older.
[c] Among families with husband present.

"Do the members of your family who live here usually help *you*: with the dishes? to clean the apartment? with the shopping? with the laundry? with the cooking?"

Table 3 (parts a through e) shows the proportions of women in the test and control groups answering "yes" to each question. Responses were in general very similar to one another, without a trend in direction. An index of the five items taken together also revealed only a 3 per cent difference between the groups (Table 3f).

A final item in this section dealt with the extent to which husbands helped wives around the house (Table 3g). In the "after" period, 6 per cent *fewer* test than control women reported that husbands helped out to an appreciable extent ("a lot" or "quite a bit"). This item was also asked during Wave 1, at which time 6 per cent *fewer* test than control husbands were reported to be a help around the house; there was apparently no test-control differential change on this issue over a period of time.

TABLE 4. Relationships among family members.[a]

		Before		After	
		Test	Con-trol	Test	Con-trol
			Per cent		
a. Do family members enjoy being together?[b]	"A lot"			63	65
b. How do you and husband get along compared to other couples?[c]	"About as well as other couples"	78	74	77	78
c. Do you and husband go out together socially?[c]	"Very often" or "Fairly often"	61	65	77	75
d. Do children bring personal problems to parent(s) for help or advice?[d]	"Yes"			70	72
e. How much concern and interest does husband show in children?[e]	"A lot"			56	59

a For N's on which per cents are based, see Appendix 13.
b Among families of appropriate family composition: at least two adults, or if one adult, at least one child 10 years of age or older.
c Among families with husband present.
d Among families who had at least one child between 10 and 19 years of age.
e Among families with husband present and who had at least one child 16 years of age or younger.

Friction and Compatibility

One possible consequence of differences in the housing environment is the level of the generally minor and sometimes more serious frictions that may arise out of competition for limited facilities. There are the resentments and bickerings generated by the necessity for sharing limited closet space, sitting space, and sleeping quarters. There are the frictions due to lack of privacy for both adults and children; for parents in pursuit of conjugal relationships; for women who wish to sew undisturbed; for adults of both sexes who wish to talk, figure how their income is spent, or entertain guests; for children who wish to do homework or play. The differences between the rehoused and slum environments may, by virtue of the factors cited above, provide differential opportunities for frictions to arise on these counts between family members. It was expected that there would be less friction within the family in Lafayette Courts than in the slum.

Better feelings toward other family members is a conceivable outcome of good housing. Greater compatibility was expected in the rehoused than in the control group between husband and wife, between parents and children, and among children themselves.

Relations among family members

At various points in the study, five questions were asked of families of appropriate family composition about relationships among various family members. The questions covered:

How much family members enjoy being together,
How well husband and wife get along with one another,
How often husband and wife go out together socially,
Whether the children bring personal problems to parents,
Husband's concern for and interest in the children.

Table 4 gives the results of these inquiries in the "after" period and shows the close similarity of test and control responses on each item. The two groups differed at most by 3 per cent on any question. Two of the questions, how husband and wife get along and how often they go out together socially, were also asked at Wave 1. Only in the extent of going out together socially was there somewhat more positive gain for tests than for controls from the "before" to the "after" period.

Quarrels, arguments, and hard feelings

The possibility that variations in housing quality give rise to differential amounts of quarreling and arguing has been mentioned in statements of the expectations for these issues. Table 5 shows data for questions dealing with:

The frequency of quarrels, arguments, or hard feelings among family members (asked at Wave 1 and again in the "after" period)

Between which family members friction occurred (asked at Wave 1 and again in the "after" period)

The reasons for the friction between husband and wife (asked in the "after" period, only)

From Table 5a it will be seen that in the "after" period, 9 per cent fewer test than control respondents reported that intra-family friction arose "often" or "sometimes." The *relative* reduction in friction is small, however, when the Wave 1 responses are taken into account: 7 per cent fewer test than control respondents reported friction among family members in the "before" measure.

Table 5b shows the family members between whom friction occurred. While friction involving children showed a *relative* rise among test families compared to controls, disagreements involving husband and wife underwent a relative decline among test families compared to controls. In the "after" period, 3 per cent more test than control children were given to quarreling and arguments, but test children were 4 per cent *less* given to friction at Wave 1; the net *rise* in friction among children for test families was 7 per cent. Among husbands and wives, however, 3 per cent fewer test than control couples showed friction in the "after" period, but 5 per cent *more* of the test than of the control group showed similar behavior at Wave 1; the net *reduction* in husband-wife friction was 8 per cent.

The most frequently mentioned reasons for quarrels and arguments between husband and wife were (Table 5c):

Money and/or job ("spending too much," "thinks I should work")

Children ("care of children," "discipline")

Personality traits and/or behavior patterns ("I am mouthy," "nasty," "drinking," "jealousy," "gambling")

TABLE 5.   Quarrels, arguments, and hard feelings.[a]

		Before		After	
		Test	Con-trol	Test	Con-trol
			Per cent		
a. How often do quarrels, arguments, or hard feelings happen among family members?[b]	"Often" or "Sometimes"	52	59	58	67
b. Between what family members do quarrels, etc., happen?[c]	Children	29	33	58	55
	Wife and children	24	34[d]	19	18
	Wife and husband	69	64	49	52
c. Topics of friction between husband and wife:[e]					
Money and/or job				37	37
Children				17	22
Personality traits and/or behavior patterns				20	17
Services rendered				20	12
Going out				19	18

[a] For N's on which per cents are based, see Appendix 13.

[b] Among families of appropriate family composition: at least two adults, or if one adult, at least one child 10 years of age or older.

[c] Among families consisting of at least two adults, or if one adult, at least one child 10 years of age or older and who reported any quarrels, arguments, or hard feelings. The categories of responses shown are those mentioned most frequently by test and control in both the "before" and "after" periods.

[d] Test-control difference significant at level of .02 to .05.

[e] Among families with husband present, and who reported any quarrels, arguments, or hard feelings between husband and wife. The categories of responses shown are those mentioned most frequently by test and control in the "after" period.

Services rendered ("way I fix his food," "not helping around the house," "way I iron his shirts")

Going out ("which one goes out," "going out alone," "staying out late")

On only two of the five types of reasons given did the difference between test and control families exceed 3 per cent. One of these had to do with children; 5 per cent *fewer* test than control respondents reported that husband-wife friction was over the children. The other had to do with services rendered; 8 per cent *more* test than control families reported friction over spouses' contributions to necessary services about the house.

Reaction to and discipline of children

The final aspect of family relations explored in the study had to do with the mothers' reactions to their children's behavior and experiences with possible problems of discipline. The general propositions being tested were that the rehoused setting, for the various reasons already set forth would give rise to behavior less upsetting to parents and would lead to lessened necessity to control undesirable actions of the children. The items of Table 6, asked of families of appropriate family composition at various periods, throw light on these possibilities.

TABLE 6. Reactions to and discipline of children.[a]

		Before		After	
		Test	Con-trol	Test	Con-trol
		Per cent			
a. Are you seriously bothered or upset by children's behavior?[b]	"Very often" or "Fairly often"			57	58
b. Do you have to discipline or correct children?[c]	"Very often" or "Fairly often"	80	84	83	87
Do you have to scold or fuss with children about:[d]					
c. Not helping out around the apartment?	"Yes"			66	76
d. Too much time spent away from home?	"Yes"			23	37[e]
e. Their activities outside the home?	"Yes"			19	28
f. Kind of friends they go around with?	"Yes"			23	33
g. **Index of above four items**	Two or more: "Yes"			43	52

a For N's on which per cents are based, see Appendix 13.
b Among families who had at least one child between 6 and 19 years of age.
c Among families who had at least one child between 3 and 16 years of age.
d Among families who had at least one child between 10 and 19 years of age.
e Test-control difference significant at level of .02 to .05.

Table 6a gives the answers to the question: "How often do you feel seriously bothered or upset by the behavior of your (child) (children)?" The data showed almost no difference between test and control families: about three-fifths of the mothers in each group reported being "very often" or "fairly often" upset by their children's behavior.

Table 6b gives the responses to the question: "How often do you have to discipline or correct (this child) (these children)?" In the "after" period, only 4 per cent fewer test than control mothers answered, "very often" or "fairly often" to this question. The item had also been asked at Wave 1 with corresponding test-control differences in response.

In the "after" period, a series of four items was asked pertaining to kinds of behavior among children which might cause their mothers to "scold or fuss." The behavior items were: not helping out around the apartment, too much time spent away from home, activities outside the home, and kinds of friends the children went around with. Table 6 (parts c through f) gives the data for these matters. From 9 per cent to 14 per cent *fewer* test than control parents reported they had to take corrective steps to limit these activities, the largest difference occurring in connection with "too much time spent away from home." An index of all four items showed 9 per cent fewer test than control mothers having to scold their children about two or more of the activities (Table 6g).

Statistical Summary for Data on Personal and Family Relations

Level of significance	Direction	No. of test-control comparisons	
		Before	After
	Confirming the "after" expectations		
.01 or less	Tests more "positive" than controls	—	—
.02 to .05	" " " " "	1	1
Greater than .05	" " " " "	4	21
	Counter to the "after" expectations		
No difference:	Identical percentages	—	2
Greater than .05	Controls more "positive" than tests	10	14
.02 to .05	" " " " "	—	—
.01 or less	" " " " "	—	—

The summary chart above shows that one comparison in the "after" period was statistically significant at the 5 per cent level of confidence: control parents, significantly more than test parents, had to remonstrate with their children about too much time spent away from home. Aside from this one issue, no comparisons made in the "after" period reached a satisfactory level of statistical confirmation, either in a direction confirming the hypotheses covering this chapter, or counter to them.

In two sections of the chapter, those dealing with common family activities and with reactions to and discipline of children, there is consistent, but not significant, confirmation of the hypotheses.

In general, the data are inconclusive. It is not clear from the material presented that the change from bad to good housing has brought with it distinguishable alteration in relations among persons within the family.

CHAPTER XII

RELATIONS WITH NEIGHBORS

Neighbors may serve as sources of social nutrition for one another in many ways and provide outlets for mutual needs for general sociality. The probable social process through which relations among neighbors develop and achieve a degree of closeness may be described in a series of identifiable steps. The first step is likely to be the exchange of casual greetings in the course of incidental encounters outside the home. Through repetition of more casual contacts, neighbors get to know one another better. Common interests and concerns become evident. Visits back and forth within the home may be undertaken, both on a casual, dropping-in basis, and by more formal prearrangement. Interaction may begin to manifest more pragmatic elements: guidance and assistance may be offered and received on a reciprocal basis in connection with minor problems of the day or even more serious problems and in times of crisis. Eventually, acquaintanceships may begin to assume the characteristics of more enduring friendships.

Certain sets of circumstances may facilitate, while others may impede, the process just described through which relations among neighbors develop. Among the factors that are apt to be conducive to the formation of neighborly relations are:

(a) A type of dwelling architecture which automatically provides many opportunities for contacts among a large number of persons.

(b) A dwelling unit which possesses some esthetic qualities and a sufficient amount of room space.

(c) The existence of facilities which are used in common by persons in nearby dwelling units.

(d) A degree of homogeneity in the social and demographic characteristics of the people living near one another.

(e) Some permanency of residence among contiguous families.

It was expected that a greater number of these factors would be found in Lafayette Courts than in the slum. As a consequence, it was anticipated that the test families, to a greater extent than the controls, would be provided with the optimal conditions to encourage the formation of close and amicable relations with neighbors. In comparison to the slum, the architecture of the project was expected to facilitate interaction considerably. Additional opportunities for increased neighborly contacts were expected to result from the provision of certain service and recreational facilities in the project, and it was anticipated that their common use would encourage socializing. The facilities would be sufficient in number and of such a nature that competition for them would be avoided or at least minimized. Generally greater homogeneity of population was expected to occur in Lafayette Courts than in the slum. Due to the regulations governing admission to public housing, there was a considerable likelihood of similarity in such factors as family composition, ages and numbers of children, and ages of the female heads of households. These similarities might, in turn, be expected to be associated with certain common interests. Finally, it was expected that project living would be viewed by the test families as having sufficient advantages to entice them to remain, thus providing the stability and permanence needed for the formation of neighborly relations. The greater spaciousness and attractiveness of the dwelling unit itself was also expected to play a role in fostering these relations. Chapter X has already shown that the test respondents, after moving to the project, were markedly less reluctant to invite others in because of lack of space or unattractiveness of their homes. This fact in itself would foster some sociality with neighbors.

The possibility that there might be some negative components to the expected heightened interaction between test families and their neighbors was not overlooked. Neighbors may be sources of irritation and annoyance as well as sources of sociality and help. However, it was hypothesized that, compared to the slum, amiable relations would predominate in the project and acrimony would be minimized.

The major sections of this chapter will compare the test and control groups as to the general extent of daytime interaction with neighbors and the specific ways in which neighbors helped one another. Whether or not infringement on privacy was perceived as a consequence of interaction with neighbors will also be discussed. There will be accounts of the extent of visiting back and forth in the evening, test and control respondents' views of some of the characteristics of their respective neighbors, the quality of the associations with them, and the extent of new friendship formations. The data are shown in Tables 1 through 6.

Initial Comparability of Test and Control Groups at Wave 1

Of the items asked in the "after" period pertaining to relations with neighbors, approximately two-thirds were also asked in the "before" period. Tables 1 through 6 show very close comparability between the test and control groups in their responses to the "before," Wave 1 measures. No initial test-control difference exceeded 9 per cent, and in half the instances, the difference was less than 5 per cent. It may be concluded that, at the outset, the two groups were very similar to one another on the topic of the present chapter.

Daytime Interaction with Neighbors

Improvements for the test families in physical and "personal" space have already been noted in preceding chapters, and the relationship of these factors to sociality has been suggested. Pertaining to associations with neighbors, the general expectation was that the improved housing, by virtue of enhanced *interior space* and general esthetic improvement, would give rise to increased social interaction. Another contributing factor was expected to be the general architecture and layout of dwelling units in Lafayette Courts. A number of studies have shown the role played by physical proximity of dwelling units in providing the setting in which casual contacts take place between neighbors. However, proximity itself is not the only factor. The presence of commonly used facilities which result in the opportunity for neighbors to be in contact for more or less prolonged time periods, also provides the occasion for mutual recognition, exchange of greetings, and conversation.

The differences between Lafayette Courts and many slum dwellings, in regard to architecture and commonly used facilities, were striking. Particularly in the eleven-story, "high-rise" buildings in Lafayette

Courts, the families on each floor lived physically near to one another. They had a common corridor, elevator, and play area for the children. In the basement of each building, automatic laundry facilities were available for the use of all occupants. The expectation was that the close physical proximity of dwelling units and their commonly used facilities would provide numerous opportunities for initial neighborly contact, and that the context of the meetings would be fairly pleasant and would permit conversational acquaintance. As acquaintance developed, it was reasoned, the housewives would become sources of mutual assistance for one another in time of need, they would exchange services, and borrow and lend household items possessed by one family but not by another.

In the slum, opportunities for casual interaction with neighbors were likely to be less numerous than for the rehoused group. While the physical distance between nearby occupants was apt to be no greater than in Lafayette Courts, the actual number of families per floor was considerably fewer, especially in contrast to the "high-rise" buildings of Lafayette Courts. Thus, in the slum there were literally *not as many neighbors* conveniently located with whom contacts could occur. The number of facilities to be used in common also were fewer in the slum than in Lafayette Courts, so that some of the opportunities for neighborly contacts were lacking. The character of the contacts that did occur in connection with the use of common facilities might not be expected necessarily to have pleasant connotations, inasmuch as they were likely to be competitive rather than facilitative. For example, for some of the slum families, bathing, toilet, or cooking facilities were used in common with neighbors. This, it was suspected, would lead to considerable interaction with one or two neighbors, but under circumstances possibly not always pleasant, especially if facilities were inadequate and dilapidated, as was likely to be the case.

To test the hypotheses regarding the nature of the contacts among neighbors, a series of questions was asked about daytime interaction between the housewife and neighboring women. Two levels of contact were distinguished: the more casual kind in which interaction is limited primarily to greeting, and the more intimate variety involving visits back and forth.

In the "before" and again in the "after" period, test and control housewives were asked: "How many women around here do you know well enough to say 'hello' to?" Table 1a shows that in the "after" period approximately 20 per cent more test than control respondents reported knowing at least ten neighboring women that well. The two groups were very nearly equal in this respect in the "before" period.

Table 1b gives the data for answers to the question: "How many women around here do you visit back and forth with in the daytime?" The table shows that in the "before" period, slightly more than half of both groups did no visiting back and forth. In the "after" period, this proportion dropped to about a quarter for the test housewives, but remained very nearly at the Wave 1 level for the control respondents. In other words, in the "after" period, approximately twice as many control as test women had *no* visiting contacts with their neighbors.

The preceding suggests that test families were more likely than controls to undertake both casual and more intimate daytime contacts with neighbors. Through additional probing it was possible to establish where neighbors lived with whom the more intimate contacts occurred. Table 1c shows that at Wave 1, for both test and control families alike, approximately one-quarter of their close daytime contacts took place with neighbors in their own buildings. In the "after" period, while control interaction with same-building neighbors remained at the "before" level, the proportion among test families rose to 72 per cent. In short, in the "after" period, more than three times as many test as control families reported other than casual daytime contacts with neighbors in the same building.

TABLE 1. Daytime interaction with neighbors.

		Before		After	
		Test	Con-trol	Test	Con-trol
			Per cent		
a. Number of women you know well enough to say "hello" to?	Ten or more	42	44	51	32[a]
b. Number of women visit back and forth with?	"None"	57	58	27	50[a]
c. Where contacts live with whom there is daytime interaction?	"In this building"	27	20	72	20[a]

[a] Test-control difference significant at level of .01 or less.

Helping One Another

In order to investigate the kinds of activities that took place in the daytime contacts among neighbors, a checklist was used in the "before" interview and again in the "after" period which inquired whether the respondent and her neighbors ever helped one another with meals or housework, picking up things at the store, with children, when someone was sick, and with lending of groceries and other household articles.

Table 2 shows how test and control groups compared in the "before" and in the "after" periods. The two groups were very similar on each item at Wave 1. In the "after" period, test families in each instance gave greater evidence of neighborly interaction than did control families. The differences ranged from 4 per cent (helping with meals or housework) to 24 per cent (picking things up at a store, and borrowing and lending). An index of all items taken together showed that 24 per cent more test than control respondents engaged in at least three kinds of salutary interchanges with neighbors.

TABLE 2. Helping one another out.

| | | Before | | After | |
		Test	Con-trol	Test	Con-trol
			Per cent		
Do you help one another out in any way like:					
a. With meals or housework?	"Yes"	14	17	14	10
b. Picking things up at a store?	"Yes"	29	32	58	34[a]
c. With children?	"Yes"	49	52	66	45[a]
d. When someone is sick?	"Yes"	62	67	75	59[a]
e. Borrowing and lending groceries, etc.?	"Yes"	28	32	51	27[a]
f. **Index of above five items**	Three or more: "Yes"	35	39	59	35[a]

[a] Test-control difference significant at level of .01 or less.

The data of Tables 1 and 2 lend substantial support to the hypotheses enumerated above regarding the outcome of differences in architectural layout of apartments and common facilities in Lafayette Courts in contrast to those in the slum. Daytime interaction among neighbors may sometimes have purely social connotations, but, as with neighborly exchanges, there appears to be a strong element of reciprocation of services for the benefit of all concerned.

Infringement on Privacy

A question now arises as to whether this increase in social interaction in Lafayette Courts may not have produced some negative results. Two items inquired about in the "after" period yield information on this point. The housewives were asked: "How often do neighbors drop in when you'd rather they would not?"; and for those who indicated any frequency to the preceding: "How much does their dropping in bother you?"

Table 3a shows almost no difference between the groups: only about a quarter of both the test and control respondents indicated that neighbors dropped in unwanted "very often" or "fairly often." Among those who reported any unwanted dropping in, similar proportions of the tests and controls, about two-thirds in each group, said they were "not at all" bothered by unwished-for neighborly calls (Table 3b).

Evening Visiting Back and Forth

Social interaction in the neighborhood may consist of more than daytime visiting. Another gauge of relations with neighbors is the extent and locus of evening interaction. Respondents were asked: "About how often do people—not counting relatives—visit you for an evening?" Table 4a shows very little difference between the two groups: in the "after" period, only 3 per cent more test than control respondents reported being visited at least once a week; exactly this difference existed in the "before" period as well.

People are not only visited; they may also initiate the interaction. Respondents were asked: "About how many times a week do you visit people—not counting relatives—for an evening?" Table 4b

TABLE 3. Infringement on privacy.

		Before		After	
		Test	Con-trol	Test	Con-trol
			Per cent		
a. Neighbors drop in when you'd rather they wouldn't?	"Very often" or "Fairly often"			25	26
b. Does their dropping in bother you?[a]	"Not at all"			66	66

[a] Among respondents who reported any unwanted dropping in by neighbors; for N's, see Appendix 13.

shows that 4 per cent more test than control women reported visiting others at least once a week. In contrast, 7 per cent *fewer* test than control respondents reported this frequency of paying visits in the "before" period.

As with daytime interaction, it was of some consequence to discover where the people lived with whom evening social contacts were undertaken. Table 4c gives the data for responses to a question on this subject. In the "after" period, 66 per cent of the test compared to 10 per cent of the control respondents indicated that evening interaction was undertaken with families in the building. The same-building evening contacts at Wave 1 were approximately 10 per cent for both groups.

TABLE 4. Evening visiting back and forth.

		Before		After	
		Test	Con-trol	Test	Con-trol
			Per cent		
a. Do other people visit you?	At least once a week	61	58	74	71
b. Do you visit other people?	At least once a week	42	49	57	53
c. Where contacts live with whom evening visiting is done?[a]	"In this building"	9	6	66	10[b]

[a] Among respondents who reported any evening visiting; for N's, see Appendix 13.
[b] Test-control difference significant at level of .01 or less.

Evaluation of Neighbors

A series of items inquired about some general affective qualities of the interaction thus far discussed in terms of frequency. Respondents were asked for an over-all evaluation of their neighbors: "In general, how well do you like the people who live around here?" Table 5a shows that in the "after" period, 6 per cent more test than control respondents answered, "a lot" or "quite a bit," compared to the "before" period in which 6 per cent *fewer* test than control housewives answered in the same manner.

Table 5 (parts b through e) gives the answers to a brief checklist of four characteristics of neighbors; the characteristics had to do with noise, interference, drinking, and behavior of children. In the "before" period, for each item, test respondents were less likely than controls to report favorable characteristics ("quiet," "minding own

TABLE 5. Evaluation of neighbors.

		Before		After	
		Test	Con-trol	Test	Con-trol
			Per cent		
a. Do you like the people who live around here?	"A lot" or "Quite a bit"	70	76	79	73
Would you describe the people around here as:					
b. Loud and noisy, or quiet?	"Quiet"	68	77[a]	85	79
c. Tending to be nosey or minding own business?	"Minding own business"	59	65	79	74
d. Doing quite a bit or not much drinking?	"Not much drinking"	63	68	80	74
e. Having badly or well-behaved children?	"Well-behaved"	65	73	77	78
f. **Index of above four items**	All four: favorable attributes	36	44	56	51

[a] Test-control difference significant at level of .02 to .05.

business," etc.). For each item there was greater *relative* gain for test than for control families from the "before" to the "after" period. In the "after" period itself, with the exception of behavior of children, 5 per cent or 6 per cent more test than control respondents attributed favorable characteristics to their neighbors. An index (Table 5f) comprising the favorable attitude on all items taken together shows, in summary, an initial test "handicap" of 8 per cent, and a later "favorable" difference of 5 per cent.

Pleasant and Unpleasant Experiences and New Friendships

The preceding section describes some general affective reactions to people in the neighborhood. More particular reactions apply to neighbors with whom housewives have had direct experience, and to the formation of new friendships.

In the "after" period, respondents were asked to indicate whether they had had any especially pleasant experiences with women in the neighborhood. Table 6a indicates that 6 per cent more test than control women reported such pleasant experiences. Table 6b gives the data for the question: "Have you had any unpleasant experiences at all with the women who live around here?" In the "after" period, 8 per cent *fewer* test than control respondents denied having had any

TABLE 6. Pleasant and unpleasant experiences and new friendships.

		Before		After	
		Test	Con-trol	Test	Con-trol
			Per cent		
a. Any especially pleasant experiences with other women around here?	"Yes"			31	25
b. Any unpleasant experiences at all?	"No"			83	91[a]
c. Have you made any new, really good friends in the past three years?	"Yes"			68	53[b]
d. New friend(s) live in immediate neighbor-hood?[c]	"Yes"			88	56[b]

[a] Test-control difference significant at level of .02 to .05.
[b] Test-control difference significant at level of .01 or less.
[c] Among respondents who said they had made any new friends in the past three years; for N's, see Appendix 13

unpleasant experiences with neighboring women. Thus, it would appear that the test housewives, compared to the controls, were more likely to have had both pleasant and unpleasant experiences with other women nearby.

One natural outcome of increased interaction, especially if the exchanges have a generally positive quality, is the development of new friendships. Table 6c gives the responses in the "after" period to the question: "Have you made any *new,* really good friends in the past three years?" The table shows that 15 per cent more test than control respondents said they had made new friends. What is the locus of the new friendships? Table 6d indicates that among those who had made any new friends, 32 per cent more of tests' than of the controls' friendships had been formed in the immediate neighborhood.

Statistical Summary for Data on Relations with Neighbors

Level of significance	Direction	No. of test-control comparisons	
		Before	After
	Confirming the "after" expectations		
.01 or less	Tests more "positive" than controls	—	11
.02 to .05	” ” ” ” ”	—	—
Greater than .05	” ” ” ” ”	4	10
	Counter to the "after" expectations		
No difference:	Identical percentages	—	1
Greater than .05	Controls more "positive" than tests	13	1
.02 to .05	” ” ” ” ”	1	1
.01 or less	” ” ” ” ”	—	—

The statistical summary above shows that of the 24 comparisons in the "after" period, 21 were in a direction confirming the hypotheses and expectations of the chapter, 11 of the comparisons reaching the 1 per cent level of confidence. These data are the more striking when it is considered that of the 18 "before" comparisons, 14 indicated an initial test "handicap."

The data thus revealed that, relative to controls, families in the rehoused circumstances had more to do with their immediate neighbors than previously (Table 1), that this interaction included helpful, mutually supportive daytime behavior (Table 2), and that this increased neighborly activity was not resented nor considered an infringement on privacy (Table 3). There was some evidence (though considerably less marked) that evening social behavior followed the pattern of daytime activities. The data revealed that rehoused families, in comparison to controls, were somewhat more likely (though not significantly) to hold benign views of their neighbors (Table 5). There was evidence (Table 6) that test women were more likely than controls to have had both pleasant experiences (not significantly) and unpleasant experiences (significantly) with nearby women. Finally, test respondents were more likely than controls to have made *"new,* really good friends," and to have made most of these new friendships in the immediate neighborhood (in both instances, significantly).

CHAPTER XIII

SOCIAL SELF-CONCEPT AND ASPIRATIONS

Objective measures of social class and status identification traditionally include such factors as education, housing, source of income, amount of income, and occupation. It will be recalled that at the outset of the study, test and control groups were very similar in educational level and types of occupations, and that the test families suffered a small handicap in income and housing quality. Chapters III and XVI[1] present background and other data related to such correlates of social class for the populations of the study.

The present chapter deals with the more subjective elements of social class: self-perceived class membership and level of aspiration for self and for children. The basic expectation for the subject matter of this chapter was that the move from bad to good housing would, in and of itself, suggest enhancement in personal circumstances and would thus give rise to upgrading of self and of aspirations.

Improved personal circumstances is traditionally a consequence of altered occupation and income. Increased income ordinarily leads to better housing and, perhaps in a generation, to the attainment of a higher educational level. However, it was reasoned, to members of certain groups, particularly those most deprived socially and economically, a change in housing quality, alone, without attendant rise in income, might conceivably result in a change in perceived social status.

---

[1] See also Appendix 8.

172

It was anticipated that this would possibly be the case for members of the rehoused, test population of the study, coming as they did from the privations of the Negro slum. The crucial question is whether or not good housing alone is sufficiently highly valued and psychologically enhancing to lead to an alteration in self-perceived social status and aspirations.

Is good housing valued highly by members of generally deprived groups? Some evidence of the high valuation placed on the good housing of Lafayette Courts by the test families has already been shown. It will be recalled that Chapter X revealed marked differences between the test and control groups in the extent of liking their apartments, in the appraisal of the appearance of their buildings, and in the assessment of the value of their apartments for the rent paid.

Among Negroes in Baltimore, generally, there is some additional evidence of the valuation placed on good housing. Studies of tenant turnover in public housing in the past ten years tend to reveal that move-out rates of Negro residents are considerably lower than the rates for white residents. Furthermore, white families are less likely to apply for public housing, and, when they do, they tend to become inactive as applicants sooner. Several factors may be adduced to account for the apparent higher consideration placed on good, public housing by Negro families than by white families. The first has to do with access to good *private housing*. In general, due to various restrictions, Negro families in most border or northern cities of the United States are less able to obtain suitable dwellings outside of public housing. A second factor has to do with income limitations on tenants in public housing. Since there are legal upper income limits for admission to and continued residence in public housing, Negroes, whose family incomes tend to be less than those of whites, are more often eligible to enter and to remain. It is fair to say that for Negroes in Baltimore and in other northern cities, public housing represents an extraordinary bargain.

Based on the foregoing evidence that good housing does, indeed, appear to be valued highly by low-income Negro families, it was hypothesized that the acquisition of good public housing might itself be considered a mark of social achievement. Since the test group was to acquire good housing and the control group was not, it was felt that differential feelings of social accomplishment would arise, and that these feelings would be reflected in different levels of aspirations for other social and economic benefits.

Initial Comparability of Test and Control Groups at Wave 1

Tables 1 through 8 contain in abbreviated form the data covering social self-concept and aspirations. About a third of the items asked in the "after" period were also asked at Wave 1. The tables show general close comparability between test and control groups in the "before" period. No initial test-control difference exceeds 8 per cent. The supposition is that the two groups were at the outset very similar in regard to the factors considered in this chapter.

TABLE 1.   Current status compared to past.

| | | Before | | After | |
		Test	Con-trol	Test	Con-trol
			Per cent		
a. Compared to (5) (3) years ago, how do you feel?[a]	"Better off" (now)	55	60	77	60[b]
b. Reasons for improvement in present status					
Most frequently mentioned:[c] Income, job, etc.				42	51
Life cycle of family, change in composition, etc.				29	41[d]
Ownership, consumption of goods, facilities, services				26	30
Psychological or social aspects of housing				36	10[b]
Spatial and density aspects of housing				31	25
Economic aspects of housing				16	1[b]

[a] In the "before" period, respondents were asked to compare their current status to "five years ago"; in the "early-after" period, they were asked to compare their current status to "three years ago," i.e., a point in time before any test families had moved into the public housing project.

[b] Test-control difference significant at level of .01 or less.

[c] Among respondents who considered themselves "better off in life" by the "early-after" period than they were "three years ago"; for N's, see Appendix 13. The categories of responses shown are those mentioned most frequently by test and control in the "early-after" period.

[d] Test-control difference significant at level of .02 to .05.

Social Self-Concept

Two general questions were designed to throw light on the proposition that housing improvement suggests to the individual a general rise in position in life. The first of these questions dealt with a self-evaluation of current status in life compared to several years before; the second required the respondent to indicate the degree of upward mobility of the family.

Current status compared to past

At Wave 1, respondents were asked: "Compared to, say, five years ago, do you feel you are: better off in life now than you were then, about the same now as then, or worse off in life now than you were then?" Table 1a shows that, initially, the two groups were fairly similar, although 5 per cent fewer test than control respondents thought they were "better off" (now).

The same question was asked again in the "after" period, but this time the comparison was between the situation "now" and "three years ago," the latter being a point in time before any test families had moved into Lafayette Courts. Table 1a shows that 17 per cent more test families than control families reported being "better off" at the time of the "after" interview than they had been three years earlier. When the initial test "handicap" is taken into account, the relative gain for test over control respondents is 22 per cent.

The respondents also were asked to give the reasons for their answers to the comparison question. The comments of those respondents who considered themselves "better off" in the "after" period than three years before were grouped under six category headings as follows:

Non-housing related
- —Income, job (wages, bills, savings, welfare)
- —Life cycle of family, change in family composition (birth or growth of children, marital status)
- —Clothes, food, furniture, other possessions

Housing-related
- —Psychological or social aspects (environment, neighborhood, privacy, living conditions)
- —Spatial and density aspects (space, crowding, sharing)
- —Economic aspects (rent, utilities)

Table 1b shows that tests were less likely than controls to give non-housing related reasons, and considerably more likely to mention some aspect of housing, *per se,* as the reason for their belief in their general progress.

"Going up in the world"

Both in the "before" and "after" periods, respondents were asked: "Which of these groups of people would you say you belong to: people who are going up in the world, people who are not really going up or going down, or people who have gone somewhat down in the world?" Table 2a shows that 9 per cent more test than control respondents in the "after" period indicated they felt they were "going up in the world." The "gain" of the test families from "before" to "after" was smaller

TABLE 2. "Going up in the world".

		Before		After	
		Test	Con-trol	Test	Con-trol
			Per cent		
a. What group belong to?	"People going up in the world"	68	62	72	63[a]
b. Reasons for self-assignment to group "going up in the world"					
Most frequently mentioned:[b] Income, job, etc.				33	43[a]
Life cycle of family, changes in composition, etc.				32	40
Ownership, consumption of goods, facilities, services				35	38
Psychological or social aspects of housing				35	14[c]
Spatial and density aspects of housing				27	20
Economic aspects of housing				7	2[a]

[a] Test-control difference significant at level of .02 to .05.

[b] Among respondents who considered themselves as belonging to the group of "people who are going up in the world"; for N's, see Appendix 13. The categories of responses shown are those mentioned most frequently by test and control in the "after" period.

[c] Test-control difference significant at level of .01 or less.

than this, however, since at Wave 1, 6 per cent more test than control respondents had already felt they were on the way up.

As with the "reasons" question of the preceding section, the reasons for self-assignment to the group "going up in the world" were classified into three housing and three non-housing categories. The data are given in Table 2b. Again, test respondents were somewhat more likely to mention reasons related to housing, and controls were more likely to mention reasons pertaining to matters other than housing.

Social Aspirations

For upwardly mobile groups, perceived social status and aspirations are likely to work in a cyclical fashion—a step up the social ladder heightening aspirations for the acquisition of cultural and material possessions that would in turn symbolize the next step up. For the test group, it was expected that if, as a consequence of the acquisition of good housing (a mark of upward class affiliation) there was felt an improvement in position in life, then aspirations would be congruent with this perceived betterment. Inquiry was directed toward aspira-

TABLE 3.   Aspirations for children's education.[a, b]

| | | Before | | After | |
| | | Test | Con-trol | Test | Con-trol |
			Per cent		
a. Through what grade do you hope to be able to send children?	Twelfth grade	48	56	54	59
b. How good are chances for sending children through twelfth grade?[c]	"Very good"	32	31	44	40
c. Through what grade do you hope to be able to send children?	Through college	44	37	42	37
d. How good are chances for sending children through college?[d]	"Very good"	22	28	25	28

a For N's on which per cents are based, see Appendix 13.
b Among families who had at least one child 16 years of age or younger.
c Among respondents who hoped to send children through twelfth grade.
d Among respondents who hoped to send children through college.

tions regarding a number of matters on which the test and control samples were known to rank low, when compared with other segments of society. The subjects investigated were the respondents' anticipation of educational, occupational, and other future benefits for their children, as well as housing and job betterment for the adults.

Aspirations for children's education

In the "before" and again in the "after" period, mothers of children less than seventeen years of age were asked: "Through what grade in school do you hope to be able to send your (child) (children)?" Table 3 (a and c) gives the proportion of women who hoped to send their children through high school and through college, respectively. The data show that for both items there was little *relative* change over time between test and control groups. On Wave 1, 8 per cent fewer test than control respondents hoped to be able to send their children through high school. In the "after" period, the difference was 5 per cent in the same direction. There was similar close correspondence over time in the proportions who hoped to send their children through college. At Wave 1, 7 per cent more test than control mothers expressed this hope; in the "after" period, the difference was 5 per cent.

Table 3 (b and d) shows the answers to a question concerning the respondents' own evaluation of their hopes for their children's education. In this instance also, there was great similarity between the test and control groups over time. In the "before" period, only 1 per cent more test than control respondents thought chances for a high school education were "very good," compared to 4 per cent more tests than controls in the "after" period. Regarding aspirations for college, in both the "before" and "after" periods, slightly fewer test than control respondents thought their children's chances of going that far were "very good."

Aspirations for jobs and professions for boys and girls

In the "after" period, mothers were asked how good they thought their children's future chances were for obtaining certain professional, business, and government jobs. As in the education questions, the jobs described were of higher status than those held by a majority of adult males or females in the sample. A series of questions was asked of mothers who had at least one child under seventeen years of age; first, about the oldest boy, then about the oldest girl.

The basic data for boys' jobs are given in Table 4 (parts a through c). On two of the items, "a professional job" and "being in business," there was virtually no difference between test and control responses. On the third, "having a government job," 10 per cent more test than control respondents reported they thought their boys' chances were "very good" for having such a job. An index of the three items together, given in Table 4d, showed test mothers 4 per cent more likely than control mothers to report belief that children's chances were "very good" for one or more of the professions or jobs.

The findings for girls are given in Table 4 (parts e through g).

TABLE 4. Aspirations for jobs and professions for boys and girls.[a]

		Before		After	
		Test	Con-trol	Test	Con-trol
			Per cent		
Oldest (or only) boy— **How good are his chances for:**[b]					
a. A professional job like a lawyer, doctor, teacher?	"Very good"			26	25
b. Being in business for himself?	"Very good"			23	24
c. Having a government job?	"Very good"			36	26
d. **Index of above three items**	One or more: "very good"			46	42
Oldest (or only) girl— **How good are her chances for:**[c]					
e. A professional job like a nurse, social worker, teacher?	"Very good"			53	44
f. Being a secretary?	"Very good"			41	30
g. Having a government job?	"Very good"			43	31[d]
h. **Index of above three items**	Two or more: "very good"			45	34

[a] For N's on which per cents are based, see Appendix 13.
[b] Among families who had a boy 16 years of age or younger.
[c] Among families who had a girl 16 years of age or younger.
[d] Test-control difference significant at level of .02 to .05.

The question pertained to the chances for obtaining a professional job (nurse, social worker, or teacher), a government job, or a secretarial job. On each item, approximately 10 per cent more test than control parents felt chances were "very good" for their girls to attain these job levels. An index of the three girls' jobs taken together (Table 4h) showed 11 per cent more test than control respondents saying chances were "very good" for two or more of the jobs listed.

General aspirations for children's future

In addition to aspirations for children's education and jobs, three questions were asked about the possibility of other kinds of future benefits for children. The topics covered "a nice place to live," "owning nice things," and "staying healthy." Table 5 shows that 4 per cent more test than control respondents thought children's future chances were "very good" for getting each of the first two items. On the third item, "staying healthy," 8 per cent more test than control mothers thought this was a "very good" future possibility for their children. An index of all three items together showed a small test-control difference in the same direction as the individual items.

Aspirations for home ownership; husband's job aspirations

Aspirations regarding housing, and husband's aspirations regarding

TABLE 5.   General aspirations for children's future.[a]

		Before		After	
		Test	Con-trol	Test	Con-trol
			Per cent		
How good are your children's future chances for:					
a. Getting a nice place to live?	"Very good"			44	40
b. Owning nice things?	"Very good"			43	39
c. Staying healthy?	"Very good"			64	56
d. **Index of above three items**	Two or more: "very good"			46	43

[a] Among families who had at least one child 16 years of age or younger; for N's, see Appendix 13.

his job were asked about at various points in the study. In connection with housing, the question at Wave 1 was: "If you could really have your choice, which would you rather do: *rent* an apartment, or *own* your own home?" Table 6a shows that at Wave 1, approximately 90 per cent of the women of both groups expressed a preference for owning a home, with somewhat more control respondents indicating this preference. Thus, at the outset, almost all the women in the study aspired to that mark of higher status, home ownership.

The next question investigated the reality of this dream. At Wave 1, respondents who aspired to "owning" were asked: "How good do you think the chances are of your owning your own home some day?" Table 6b shows that about half of both groups (with a 6 per cent excess among control respondents) thought their chances were "very good" or "fairly good." The *relative* change from "before" to "after" was identical for the two groups: in the "after" period, slightly more than half of all respondents considered future home ownership as a "very good" or "fairly good" possibility, again with 6 per cent fewer tests than controls answering in this manner.

In the "after" period, respondents were asked whether their husbands were "thinking or doing anything about getting a better job than the one he has now?" Among wives whose husbands were em-

TABLE 6. Aspirations for home ownership; husband's job aspirations.

		Before		After	
		Test	Con-trol	Test	Con-trol
		Per cent			
a. Would you rather rent an apartment or own your own home?	"Own home"	88	94[a]		
b. How good are your chances for owning own home?[b]	"Very good" or "Fairly good"	45	51	52	58
c. Is husband thinking or doing anything about getting a better job?[c]	"Yes"			27	31

[a] Test-control difference significant at level of .02 to .05.
[b] In the "before" period, only: among respondents who said they wanted to own their own home; for N's, see Appendix 13.
[c] Among families with husband present and employed; for N's, see Appendix 13.

ployed, 4 per cent fewer test than control respondents reported some thought or action on the part of their husbands regarding a change to a better job.

Statistical Summary for Data on Social Self-Concept and Aspirations

Level of significance	Direction	No. of test-control comparisons	
		Before	After
	Confirming the "after" expectations		
.01 or less	Tests more "positive" than controls	—	4
.02 to .05	" " " " "	—	3
Greater than .05	" " " " "	3	14
	Counter to the "after" expectations		
No difference:	Identical percentages	—	—
Greater than .05	Controls more "positive" than tests	4	9
.02 to .05	" " " " "	1	2
.01 or less	" " " " "	—	—

The statistical summary immediately above shows that of 32 comparisons in the "after" period, 21 were in a direction confirming the general expectations regarding the material covered by this chapter; 7 of the 21 showed significance at least at the 5 per cent level. Eleven "after" comparisons were in a direction contrary to expectation, 2 of them significant at the 5 per cent level. The "before" picture is different: of the 8 comparisons, 5 showed an initial test "handicap," 1 being significant at the 5 per cent level.

In general, it may be said that the chapter presents partial confirmation of the hypotheses of the study. Analysis of the issues confirming expectations showed that test respondents, more than controls, were likely to view themselves as better off now than formerly, and to report themselves as rising in the world (Tables 1 and 2). The pattern of reasons for the answers to both items revealed that tests were more likely than controls to attribute their upward movement to housing-related factors. There was very little difference between the test and control groups with respect to aspirations for children's education (Table 3), or for jobs and professions for boys (Table 4), the one exception of any magnitude being chances for boys' having a government job (but the difference was not significant). Among the remaining items pertaining to aspirations for children's future, the largest test-control differences in the hypothesized direction were in connection with jobs for girls (Table 4), and children's future possession of good health (Table 5). However, for the most part these were not statistically significant differences. Aspirations for home ownership and husbands' job aspirations generally did not confirm expectations.

CHAPTER XIV

ATTITUDES AND BEHAVIOR TOWARD NEIGHBORHOOD AND COMMUNITY

When the test families moved to Lafayette Courts, the project, in effect, became their new neighborhood. Findings regarding the consequences for the test group of living in the particular kind of neighborhood that the project provided constitute the subject matter of this chapter.

It was expected that the project and the slum environments would exert different behavioral and attitudinal influences upon their respective residents. This possibility was suggested largely by several kinds of differences that were observed to exist between the two types of neighborhoods.

First, the project and the slum neighborhoods differed from one another in general physical characteristics. Some of the specific physical elements which distinguished Lafayette Courts from the slum have already been alluded to in Chapter II. In the slum, dwellings which were dilapidated and in other ways of low quality (as measured by the indices of housing quality) tended to exist throughout the area. Perhaps 85 per cent to 90 per cent of dwelling units and buildings occupied by both test and control groups at the outset of the study may be said to have been in slum neighborhoods. Lafayette Courts, although set within a general slum area, in no way resembled the adjacent surroundings. The distinction was achieved by such factors as the project's conspicuously different architectural pattern and its building arrangement on contiguous plots of grounds. The fact that it was bounded by busy main streets carrying heavy traffic also served

184

as demarcation from the larger area. The general expectation was that for Lafayette Courts residents, consciousness of this difference in physical characteristics between the project and the slum would imbue the test families with pride in their surroundings. Control families, in general still living in slum quarters, were not expected to share these feelings.

A second difference observed to exist between project and slum neighborhoods had to do with community facilities. Insofar as certain facilities were available or not, or at least were more accessible in the project environment than in the slum, there should have been differential use made of them by the test and control groups. If the facilities were valued, it might be expected that altered behavior and attitudes toward the neighborhood as a whole would occur among the test group.

A third distinguishing element between project and slum neighborhoods pertained to people, and the concept of neighborliness. This matter has already been explored in Chapter XII where there was revealed a sharp relative increment for test families in the project in the extent of neighborly interaction of both a social and utilitarian nature. These circumstances might well be expected to influence affective appraisal of the neighborhood.

Finally, the character of the interior of the dwellings constituted a notable difference between the project and slum neighborhoods. Chapter X has already indicated the extent to which the test families, in contrast to controls, recognized the improvements in the quality of their dwelling units and expressed satisfaction with numerous specific aspects. It was anticipated that these perceived benefits might, independently of the project's appearance or resources, affect identification with and favorable reactions toward the project community.

It was expected that the foregoing factors, in some combinations, would give rise to differences between test and control groups in feelings of allegiance to the neighborhood, interest in its physical maintenance, extent of participation in community and neighborhood activities, and in other indicators of good citizenship.

Initial Comparability of Test and Control Groups at Wave 1

Tables 1 through 8 contain in abbreviated form the data concerning attitudes and behavior regarding neighborhood and community. Of the total items asked in the "after" period, approximately half were also asked at Wave 1. There was general close comparability between test and control groups on these items. All but two of the Wave 1 comparisons showed no more than a 6 per cent difference between the two groups. It may be concluded that the two groups were very similar in regard to the content of the present chapter.

Physical Aspects of the Neighborhood

The presence, absence, or varying quality of certain "public" features of a neighborhood may conceivably affect the residents' feelings toward the neighborhood. The next three sections present comparative test-control data touching on these topics.

Evaluation of specific aspects of the neighborhood

The study samples were asked in the "before" period and again in the "after" period to evaluate the neighborhood from the standpoint of shopping, public transportation, and street lighting. The data are given in Table 1 (parts a through c). On two of the items, public transportation and street lighting, there was virtually no difference between test and control groups in the "after" period. On the third, shopping, 12 per cent more test than control respondents indicated

TABLE 1. Evaluation of specific aspects of the neighborhood.

		Before		After	
		Test	Con-trol	Test	Con-trol
			Per cent		
How good is the neighborhood for					
a. Shopping?	"Very good"	38	36	54	42[a]
b. Public transportation?	"Very good"	52	48	46	46
c. Street lighting?[b]	"Very good"	43	43	57	56
d. **Index of above three items**	Two or more: "very good"	44	41	51	47

[a] Test-control difference significant at level of .02 to .05.
[b] In the "after" period, this question was asked of test respondents in terms of "this project" rather than "this neighborhood."

that shopping was "very good" in the neighborhood. The test women's point of reference was very likely a public market not far from Lafayette Courts; similar facilities this close were not likely to be available to all control respondents.

An index of the three items taken together showed that in the "after" period, about half of both the test and control groups judged two or more of the facilities to be "very good" in their respective types of neighborhood (Table 1d). The *relative* change from "before" to "after" also was similar for the two groups.

Neighborhood annoyances

Urban neighborhoods, especially those in slum districts, are sometimes characterized by annoyances and disturbances caused by children or adults fighting, and drunkenness. In the neighborhoods with which the present study was concerned, bars and taverns were numerous both in the slum and on the outskirts of Lafayette Courts. In both kinds of neighborhoods there were large numbers of children.

TABLE 2. Neighborhood annoyances.

| | | Before | | After | |
		Test	Con-trol	Test	Con-trol
			Per cent		
a. Any annoyances in this neighborhood like noisy bars or taverns or people hanging around street corners?	"Yes"	42	33[a]	24	27
Other (project) (neighborhood) annoyances:					
b. Gangs of children or teenagers misbehaving?	"Yes"			54	37[b]
c. Fights between adults or between children?	"Yes"			25	21
d. Drunks?	"Yes"			12	21[a]
e. Index of above three items	One or more: "yes"			60	49[a]

[a] Test-control difference significant at level of .02 to .05.
[b] Test-control difference significant at level of .01 or less.

Respondents were asked at various points in the study whether they had observed several kinds of annoyance in the environs. The first question, asked in the "before" and in the "after" period, had to do with annoyances experienced because of noisy bars or taverns or people hanging around street corners. Table 2a shows that slightly fewer (3 per cent) test than control respondents were aware of such annoyances in the "after" period. The *relative* difference between the two groups was larger, however, due to the fact that 9 per cent more test than controls had observed these annoyances in the neighborhoods where they had lived during the "before" period.

Three other sources of annoyance were inquired about in the "after" period, only. The reactions elicited by these questions are given in Table 2 (b, c, and d). Seventeen per cent *more* test than control women reported having sometimes been annoyed by "gangs of children or teen-agers misbehaving." The test excess was in all likelihood related to the even higher density of children in the project than in any section of the slum. The second item, "fights between adults or between children," also showed a higher proportion of annoyance among tests than among controls, but in this instance the difference was small (4 per cent). Nine per cent *fewer* test than control respondents reported "drunks" in the neighborhood. An index of all three of these items, Table 2e, showed 11 per cent more tests than controls reporting one or more of the annoyances.

Distance from facilities and relatives

A neighborhood in a modern city is not apt to provide all the economic, social, or cultural facilities that might be needed or desired by its residents. However, there may be differences between neighborhoods as to the degree of their adequacy in these respects. A final component of the inquiry about test and control evaluation of the physical aspects of their respective neighborhoods pertained to feelings regarding relative distance from desired elements of community and social life.

In the "after" period, the study respondents were asked whether they were about as close as they would like to be to: recreation places, church, relatives, a hospital or clinic, a community center, and schools. As shown by Table 3, test respondents were *more* likely than controls to express dissatisfaction with their location in relation to recreation places (like movies and parks), church, and relatives, but *less* likely to express dissatisfaction with regard to a hospital or clinic, a community center, and schools.

Project residents' degree of satisfaction with the convenience of location of particular facilities was likely, of course, to be affected by the location of the housing project. Thus, the greater test than control group dissatisfaction with distance from relatives may have been related to Lafayette Courts' location in the eastern part of the city. Although its residents tended to come from that section of the city, a number originated in west and north-central districts, so that for such families the new neighborhood was a considerable distance from the old. To the extent that relatives tend to settle near one another within a fairly circumscribed area, this would be a "missed" characteristic among the test families. Another effect of the project's location was apparent with respect to recreation places, church, and hospital or clinic. The first two kinds of facilities were not as indigenous to the immediate Lafayette Courts' surroundings as they were to some other areas in the city; on the other hand, the project was within eight to ten blocks of both Johns Hopkins Hospital and the Eastern Health District Building where hospital and clinic services were available to low-income groups. Finally, Lafayette Courts provided its own community center, so that this particular facility was

TABLE 3.   Distance from facilities and relatives.

		Before		After	
		Test	Con-trol	Test	Con-trol
		Per cent			
Are you about as close as you would like to be to:					
a. Recreation places like movies, parks?	No			50	24[a]
b. Church?	No			28	21
c. Relatives?	No			39	24[a]
d. A hospital or clinic?	No			8	20[a]
e. A community center?	No			4	39[a]
f. Schools?[b]	No			5	12[c]

[a] Test-control difference significant at level of .01 or less.
[b] Among families who had at least one child between 6 and 16 years of age; for N's, see Appendix 13.
[c] Test-control difference significant at level of .02 to .05.

located considerably closer to most of the project residents than a
similar facility was for the residents of any non-project neighborhood.

Group Memberships and Attendance at Community Centers

In formulating the study hypotheses, it was considered that the immediate neighborhood might play a role in membership and extent
of activity in both formal and informal organizations and groups.
The following sections compare the test and control groups as to their
participation in various group activities, including attendance at local
community centers.

Respondent's church attendance and group activities

Church attendance.   At Wave 1 and again in the "after" period,
respondents were asked: "About how many times during the month
do you go to church services, including week days as well as Sundays?"
Table 4a shows that in the "after" period, virtually the same proportion (about three-fifths) of test and control women reported attending church at least two or three times a month. Both groups underwent a small decline in frequency of church attendance from the
"before" to the "after" period.

Participation in formal clubs or groups.   Respondents were asked
to indicate from a checklist, the formal clubs or groups they belonged
to; Table 4b shows the proportions who belonged to one or more.
There was some increase in the extent of affiliation from the "before"
to the "after" period, but it occurred equally for the test and control
groups. By the "after" period, 58 per cent of each group belonged to
one or more organizations.

Membership in a Parent-Teacher Association (Table 4c) was mentioned considerably more frequently than membership in any other
type of group, again by similar proportions of tests and controls (about
two-fifths in the "after" period). Fewer than one-tenth of each group,
both "before" and "after," indicated membership in the two major
Negro service organizations: the N.A.A.C.P. or the Urban League.

Table 4 (d and e) shows, for respondents who belonged to one or
more of the formal clubs or groups, the extent of attending meetings
and holding official posts. In the "after" period, 6 per cent more tests
than controls reported that they "usually" or "always" attended the

meetings of at least one of the organizations to which they belonged, and the *relative* change in extent of attendance from "before" to "after" was considerably greater for the test than for the control group. Extent of holding office or committee membership was the same for both groups in the "after" period: 38 per cent of tests and controls reported holding a post in one or more of their organizations.

Attendance at a community center. As will be seen from the account in Appendix 14, the community center in Lafayette Courts

TABLE 4. Respondents' church attendance and group activities.

		Before		After	
		Test	Con-trol	Test	Con-trol
			Per cent		
a. How often do you go to church services?	At least two or three times a month	69	66	61	60
b. Do you belong to or take part in any clubs or groups?	One or more	49	49	58	58
c. Participation in selected organizations:					
Parent-Teacher Association	"Yes"	30	30	38	39
Religious group like Ladies Aid, Sodality, or Missionary	"Yes"	12	6[a]	14	9
Church singing group or choir	"Yes"	9	11	10	11
N.A.A.C.P. or Urban League	"Yes"	6	6	7	7
d. Number of organizations whose meetings respondent attends "usually" or "always"[b]	One or more	58	64	72	66
e. Number of organizations in which respondent is officer or committee member[b]	One or more	31	29	38	38
f. Do you ever go to community center in this (project) (neighborhood) for meetings or social activities?	"Yes"			90	11[c]

[a] Test-control difference significant at level of .02 to .05.
[b] Among respondents who belonged to one or more clubs or groups; for N's, see Appendix 13.
[c] Test-control difference significant at level of .01 or less.

provided space and facilities for meetings and a variety of activities for both adults and children. In non-project neighborhoods, a community facility of this kind was generally not so readily available. Test and control respondents were asked to indicate whether they ever attended community centers in their respective neighborhoods for meetings or social activities. Table 4f indicates that in the "after" period, 90 per cent of the test group, compared to 11 per cent of the control group, made use of a community center. When asked in the "after" period how often they had been to the center, almost three-quarters of the test women who "ever" went indicated they had been there once or twice or more often in the past two months.[1] A brief description of the activities provided at the community center for the adult residents of Lafayette Courts will be found in Appendix 14.

From the foregoing, it would appear that, although there was little test-control difference in the "after" period in the extent of respondent participation in the formal types of organizations apt to be found in the "larger" community, there was considerable difference in the extent to which they participated in the kinds of activities provided in a local neighborhood community center.

Children's Sunday School attendance and group activities

Information was also sought from respondents regarding their children's organizational memberships. Data for Sunday School attendance, and for a summary of the number of group memberships, are given in Table 5. Table 5a shows close similarity in the "after" period in the proportion of test and control children attending Sunday School once a week, but there was slightly more *relative* gain for controls than for tests from "before" to "after." Table 5b gives data for extent of children's memberships in various relatively formal clubs or groups. In the "after" period, 14 per cent fewer tests than controls indicated membership in one or more organizations. At Wave 1, also, tests were somewhat less likely (by 9 per cent) than controls to report organizational memberships among their children.

As with adults, children's attendance at neighborhood community

---

[1] Similar questions were asked of appropriate families in the "after" period regarding husband's attendance at a neighborhood community center. Half the test husbands were reported attending; of these, three-fifths had been there once or twice or more often in the past two months. Only 5 per cent of control husbands were reported as "ever" attending a community center.

TABLE 5. Children's Sunday School attendance and group activities.[a]

		Before		After	
		Test	Con-trol	Test	Con-trol
			Per	cent	
a. How often do children go to Sunday School?[b]	Once a week	53	48	55	54
b. Do children belong to or take part in any clubs or groups?[b]	One or more	38	47	36	50[c]
c. Do children ever go to community center in this (project) (neighborhood) for meetings or social activities?[d]	"Yes"			84	32[e]

[a] For N's on which per cents are based, see Appendix 13.
[b] Among families who had at least one child between 6 and 16 years of age.
[c] Test-control difference significant at level of .02 to .05.
[d] Among families who had at least one child between 6 and 19 years of age.
[e] Test-control difference significant at level of .01 or less.

centers was inquired about in both groups. Mothers of children of appropriate ages were asked whether the children ever went to a community center in the neighborhood for meetings or for social activities. Table 5c shows that in the "after" period, 84 per cent of test mothers reported that their children attended, compared to 32 per cent of control mothers. *Frequency* of children's attendance also was probed: about two-thirds of the test women who reported that their children went to the community center also said they had done so three or more times in the past two months; about two-fifths reported once a week or more. A brief description of the activities provided for children at the Lafayette Courts Community Center will be found in Appendix 14.

Attitudes and Activities Regarding the Immediate Neighborhood and the Larger Community

In the earlier section of this chapter dealing with physical aspects of the neighborhood, the test-control reactions pertained to a number of specific environmental features which were largely chance outcomes of location and over which, therefore, the respondent had little or no control. A portion of the following section deals with some of those aspects of the neighborhood in which there was greater possibility for the respondents to play a role, personally, if they so desired. The remainder of the section discusses respondents' more general affective reactions to the immediate neighborhood, and their attitudes and activities regarding the "larger" community. In formulating the study's hypotheses, the expectation was that as a consequence of the various intrinsic differences between the project and slum neighborhoods, test respondents would be more likely than controls to assume an active role in neighborhood maintenance, and to manifest positive affective reactions to several general topics essentially divorced from the project neighborhood's location. If the hypothesized test-control differences did arise on these subjects pertaining to the groups' respective local neighborhoods, it was felt that corresponding differences might also be found in the realm of attitudes and activities regarding the "larger" community.

Keeping up the neighborhood

Respondents were asked in the "after" period how well their immediate environs were kept up. Table 6a shows that 35 per cent more test than control respondents considered their neighborhood to be maintained "very well."

In the "before" and again in the "after" period, respondents were asked to indicate their *own* interest in keeping up the neighborhood. Table 6b indicates that in the "after" period, 21 per cent more test than control respondents reported that they were "very interested" in keeping up their surroundings.

Of those showing some interest in neighborhood upkeep in the "after" period, the question was asked: "What have you done to keep it up?" Table 6c indicates that 12 per cent more test than control respondents reported that they had taken some specific type of action in this regard. The activities undertaken are shown in Table 6d. Test women were less likely than controls to indicate participation in two of the activities, both of which were somewhat less relevant for the test than for the control group: "keeping the front yard, steps, and pavement clean," and "participation in the 'clean block' campaign" (a non-housing-project organized effort at community self-improvement). For the other three activities shown, test women were more likely than controls to report participation: "keeping up the grounds,"

TABLE 6.   Keeping up the neighborhood.

		Before		After	
		Test	Con-trol	Test	Con-trol
		Per cent			
a. How well is this (project) (neighborhood) kept up?	"Very well"			59	24[a]
b. Are you interested in keeping up the neighborhood?[b]	"Very interested"	56	51	84	63[a]
c. Activities undertaken to keep it up?[c]	Some action taken			90	78[a]
d. Types of action most frequently mentioned:[d]					
Keep front, yard, steps, pavement clean				67	76[e]
Participation in "clean block" campaign				9	25[a]
Controlling destructive behavior of children				28	3[a]
Proper garbage disposal				26	16[e]
Keep grounds up				18	8[a]

[a] Test-control difference significant at level of .01 or less.

[b] In the "after" period, this question was asked of test respondents in terms of "this project" rather than "this neighborhood."

[c] Among respondents who said they were "very interested" or "fairly interested" in keeping up the (project) (neighborhood); for N's, see Appendix 13.

[d] Among respondents who said they were "very interested" or "fairly interested" in keeping up the (project) (neighborhood) and who indicated they had taken some action to keep it up; for N's, see Appendix 13. The categories of responses shown are those mentioned most frequently by test and control in the "after" period.

[e] Test-control difference significant at level of .02 to .05.

"proper garbage disposal," and "control of destructive behavior of children."

General point of view toward the neighborhood

The preceding findings indicate a heightened interest in their neighborhood on the part of the project residents. Is this interest accompanied by affect and pride? Table 7 gives the data for some relevant items.

The first three questions reported in Table 7 (parts a through c)

TABLE 7. General point of view toward neighborhood.

		Before		After	
		Test	Con-trol	Test	Con-trol
			Per cent		
a. How is this neighborhood as a place to live?[a]	"Very good"	27	27	66	30[b]
b. Is this neighborhood a good place to raise children?[a]	"Very good"	18	22	59	23[b]
c. How proud are you of this neighborhood?	"Very proud"			42	27[b]
d. Which neighborhood do you think of as your real home?	This one			55	66[c]
e. Have you ever thought of moving out of this neighborhood?	"Never" or "Only occasionally"			71	47[b]

[a] In the "after" period, this question was asked of test respondents in terms of "this project" rather than "this neighborhood."
[b] Test-control difference significant at level of .01 or less.
[c] Test-control difference significant at level of .02 to .05.

deal with general attitudes: evaluation of the neighborhood as a place to live, as a place to raise children, and degree of pride in the neighborhood. In the "after" period, tests were considerably more likely than controls to say the neighborhood was "very good" as a place to live and as a place to raise children, the test-control differences being 36 per cent for each item. For these items in the "before" period, there was little or no difference between the groups. On the third question which inquired about pride in neighborhood, 15 per cent more test than control respondents said, in the "after" period, that they felt "very proud."

The remaining two items, Table 7 (d and e), provide some indication of neighborhood affiliation or "rootedness." In the "after" period, respondents were asked: "Which neighborhood do you think of as your real home—that is, where you feel you really belong—would you say: this neighborhood, some other neighborhood in Baltimore, or some neighborhood outside of Baltimore?" Eleven per cent *fewer* test than control respondents felt they belonged in their present neighborhood (Table 7d). Evidence of greater test than control group attachment to an "old" neighborhood is shown by other data

TABLE 8. Attitudes and activities regarding the larger community.

		Before		After	
		Test	Con-trol	Test	Con-trol
				Per cent	
a. How is Baltimore as a place to live?	"Very good"			63	59
Baltimore newspaper reading during the week:					
b. Read any?	One or more read			80	87[a]
c. Which ones?[b]					
News Post				59	65
Afro-American				34	40
Sun				23	27
d. Are you interested in and concerned about "larger issues"?	"Very interested"			50	41[a]
e. Compared to 4 or 5 years ago, how interested are you in "larger issues"?	"More interested now"			70	66
f. Did you vote in the last (national) election?	"Yes"			34	31

[a] Test-control difference significant at level of .02 to .05.
[b] Percentages exceed 100 because some respondents mentioned more than one newspaper.

not given in the table: 40 per cent of the tests compared to 29 per cent of the controls considered "some other neighborhood in Baltimore" as their real home. However, a different view from the foregoing is provided by the data in Table 7e for the question: "How often have you thought of moving out of this neighborhood altogether?" The table shows that 24 per cent *more* test than control women reported they had "never" thought of it, or at most, "only occasionally."

The larger community

The preceding sections have dealt primarily with actions and attitudes regarding fairly circumscribed areas: the test and control groups' more or less immediate neighborhoods. In addition, a series of items was asked in the "after" period touching on issues related to the much broader surroundings, the expectation being that concern about local matters might extend to the "larger" community.

Table 8a shows that only 4 per cent more test than control respondents believed Baltimore to be "very good" as a place to live. Inquiry about readership of Baltimore newspapers revealed that test families were less likely than controls to read *any* newspaper (Table 8b), and also less likely to read each of the three principal local papers that were inquired about (Table 8c).

Table 8d indicates the results of a question about respondents' interest in larger issues "that affect many people, like: politics, national defense and crime and delinquency." Nine per cent more test than control respondents indicated they were "very interested" in such matters; 4 per cent more tests than controls indicated they had greater interest "now" than "four or five years ago." Finally, Table 8f shows that only 3 per cent more test than control respondents reported they had voted in the 1956 national elections.

Statistical Summary for Data on Neighborhood and Community

Level of significance	Direction	No. of test-control comparisons	
		Before	After
	Confirming the "after" expectations		
.01 or less	Tests more "positive" than controls	—	13
.02 to .05	" " " " "	1	5
Greater than .05	" " " " "	7	10
	Counter to the "after" expectations		
No difference:	Identical percentages	5	4
Greater than .05	Controls more "positive" than tests	4	7
.02 to .05	" " " " "	1	5
.01 or less	" " " " "	—	4

The summary chart above reveals that of 48 comparisons in the "after" period, 28 showed findings in a direction confirming the hypotheses, 18 of these significant at least at the 5 per cent level. In the "before" period, 5 out of 18 comparisons indicated an initial test "handicap"; in 8 of the comparisons, tests were more likely than controls to express an initially "positive" attitude.

Analysis of the material in the chapter by content reveals generally mixed findings regarding "public" aspects of the neighborhood. For those aspects involving *human elements* (Table 2), tests were more likely than controls to be bothered by gangs of children or teen-agers misbehaving, and by fights between adults or between children; however, they were less likely to be bothered by drunks, noisy bars or taverns, and street corner loafers. For those aspects involving *physical elements* of the neighborhood (Tables 1 and 3), the test group was less likely than the control to be satisfied with proximity to public recreation places and to churches, but more apt to be satisfied with location in relation to hospital or clinic, community center, and schools, and to evaluate the local shopping facilities favorably. The groups showed no difference in their evaluation of the quality of their respective street lighting or public transportation. For both groups, most of these physical aspects of their neighborhoods were a consequence of chance geographic location. All of the test families were subject to whatever facilities pre-existed in the environs around the project. Although the controls also were subject to pre-existing neighborhood conditions, there was somewhat greater possibility for variation in this respect, since the control families were scattered throughout the city.

Formal organizational memberships showed no systematic differences between test and control groups (Tables 4 and 5). While there was some test gain from "before" to "after" in memberships in formal groups for adults, there was similar gain among the controls. Test respondents were somewhat more likely than controls to report consistent attendance at the meetings of the organizations to which they belonged, but they were no more likely to hold an official post in these organizations. Fewer test than control children took part in clubs or groups in the "after" period.

On those matters which were most intimately neighborhood-centered, several notable test-control differences emerged. Attendance at the project community center was markedly greater for all members of the test families than was control family attendance at community centers in any of their own neighborhoods (Tables 4 and 5). Interest in keeping up the project was high among test families, and reports of activities in maintenance substantiated these expressions of concern; of special interest were reports among test respondents of efforts to control destructive behavior of children (Table 6). The test women were also more likely than the controls to express a favorable over-all reaction to the way their project-neighborhood was kept up (Table 6), to view the neighborhood as a good place to live, to consider it a good place to raise children, and to evince pride in the neighborhood (Table 7).

The geographic dislocation which the test respondents underwent when they moved to Lafayette Courts was mirrored in two findings: first, in contrast to the controls, they were less likely to think of the project-neighborhood as their "real home" (Table 7); second, they were less likely to report being as close to relatives as they wished to be (Table 3). However, neither of these factors was apparently a serious deterrent to the test respondents' generally favorable reactions to their immediate neighborhood. This has been indicated by the data summarized in the preceding paragraph and is further substantiated by one additional finding: compared to controls, considerably fewer test women had ever thought seriously of moving out of their neighborhood altogether (Table 7).

Expectations regarding a possible extension of attitudes and activities from the immediate neighborhood to the "larger" community were borne out only slightly (Table 8). Test respondents were more likely than controls to express an interest in "larger issues," but only a slightly larger proportion of tests than controls stated they were more interested "now" than "four or five years ago." The test women, to only a slightly greater extent than the controls, considered Baltimore as a "very good" place to live, and reported having voted in the 1956 national elections. Newspaper readership was less extensive among the test than among the control respondents.

CHAPTER XV

PSYCHOLOGICAL STATE

Chapters X through XIV have dealt mainly with behavior and attitudes involving the social and familial settings in which the members of the test and control groups lived. Inferences have been drawn regarding advantages and disadvantages accruing from the alteration in the quality of housing and in the larger housing environment. Where possible, environmental factors have been suggested which might play a role in differences emerging over time between the test and control groups.

This chapter considers a number of psychological variables dealing more with the *self* than with attitudes and behavior relative to social settings. Attention will be given to matters related to inner-personal tension and distress, and to psychological subjects related to outlook on life. In describing expectations and findings, some attempt will be made to link responses to housing variables, although, as was indicated in the brief statement of the hypotheses in Chapter II, effects of housing quality on these matters are likely to involve intermediary processes.

In choosing the variables to pursue, four criteria were kept in mind: (a) the concepts should be related to psychosocial functioning rather than to more complex psychodynamic issues; (b) the concepts should have relevance to the social characteristics of a deprived, minority population; (c) the measurements should be amenable to repetition in the context and tempo of the other aspects of the study; and (d) the instruments should be applicable to the adult female heads of households, the "respondents" in the study.

Ten psychological variables were eventually singled out for investigation: *mood, control of temper* (as a component of adequacy of emotionality), *nervousness, potency* (feelings about the efficacy

201

of one's own exertions), *optimism-pessimism, satisfaction with personal state of affairs* ("status quo"), *authoritarianism, aggression toward authority figures, self-esteem,* and *general anxiety.*

In general, these topics met the criteria enumerated above. All the topics have psychosocial elements. All are relevant to the fact that the study population was Negro, and of generally low socioeconomic status, with severe limitations upon participation in ego-gratifications more available to other populations. All, moreover, have been the subject of investigation by psychologists for several decades, and for all, large-scale measurement appeared to be feasible.

In deciding on the measurement procedures to be used, a review was made of a variety of extant scales and instruments. From the point of view of requirements of the present research, several factors militated against the direct adoption of existing schemes. First, not all topics had been previously pursued in unidimensional fashion. Second, few scales had been standardized with low income, Negro subjects. Third, few scales had been developed to be used in personal interview, a matter of some importance with a study population of limited literacy.

The outcome was a decision to construct afresh the ten scales on the issues mentioned above. The scaling method used was that devised by Louis Guttman, employing only the first, or direction, component. The scales were developed prior to their use with actual study respondents on a sample of 100 persons: 50 women living in a housing project (simulating the test sample) and 50 women living in the slum (simulating the controls); in performing the scaling, the two samples were pooled. Comments on some additional technical matters related to the construction of the scales, an enumeration of the items included in the final scales, and the direction of scoring for each item are given in Appendix 15.

Tables 1 through 8 contain the entire distributions of responses for each of the ten scales. These tables show, as well, an abbreviated (one-line) summary that divides the distribution into a dichotomy as close to the 50 per cent point as possible. The one-line summary communicates the numerical sense of each distribution. Six of the scales (Tables 1 through 6) were administered in the "before" period and twice in the "after" period: at Wave 7 and at Wave 11. Because these data differ markedly in content from those of the preceding chapters, the distribution of responses for all three points in time will be given for these scales. The Authoritarianism scale was administered in the two "after" periods, only; both distributions are

TABLE 1. Mood scale.

		Before		Early after		Late after	
		Test	Control	Test	Control	Test	Control
	Number of scale items			Per cent			
Least moody	4	9	9	17	15	22	19
	3	28	28	33	31	34	33
	2	31	31	28	26	23	27
	1	25	22	15	20	15	14
Most moody	0	7	10	7	8	6	7
	Three or more in positive (least moody) direction	37	37	50	46	56	52

given in Table 7a. The remaining scales were administered in the "late after" period, only.

Initial Comparability of Test and Control Groups at Wave 1

There was close comparability on five of the six "before" scales at Wave 1. The one-line summary shows that on these five, tests and controls were at most 3 per cent different at the outset. On one scale, Potency (Table 4), the full distribution shows that 12 per cent more tests than controls gave responses in the top three positive categories. On the standard one-line comparison for this scale, 7 per cent more tests than controls answered in the positive direction.

Mood, Control of Temper, and Nervousness

The scales of Mood, Control of Temper, and Nervousness were intended to tap a constellation of personal reactions and feeling states related to stressful living circumstances. The specific expectations regarding change over time on the issues covered by these scales stemmed from observations of several characteristics of the general population from which the study groups came.

Generally, the women whose attitudes were to be tapped had a difficult life, financially, trying to make ends meet. Overwork was likely to be common among mothers of large families, especially when

TABLE 2.   Control of temper scale.

	Number of scale items	Before		Early after		Late after	
		Test	Con-trol	Test	Con-trol	Test	Con-trol
			Per cent				
Most adequate control	5	13	15	14	11	14	15
	4	33	32	33	28	33	30
	3	28	28	30	33	32	29
	2	15	16	13	17	10	13
	1	8	7	6	7	8	8
Least adequate control	0	3	2	4	4	3	5
	Four or more in positive (most adequate) direction	46	47	47	39	47	45

the mother worked outside the home. Crowding, sharing, and inadequate housekeeping facilities were some of the components of bad housing which might, in particular, be expected to affect the female heads of the households. Expectations regarding the role of these housing factors in connection with social friction in the dwelling unit already have been discussed in Chapters X and XI. The psychological outcomes were expected to be consonant with the interpersonal consequences. In general, bad housing was expected to contribute to feelings of despondency and depression (Mood), to impulsiveness and poorly controlled anger (Control of Temper), to over-sensitivity to upset, and lack of equilibrium (Nervousness).

The test move to good housing was not expected to alter completely the pattern of life presumably related to these psychological constructs, but it did appear to provide a potential for eventually alleviating some of the situational pressures. For example, finances might be as tight as ever, but overwork might be alleviated by hypothesized additional assistance received around the house from family members, and by the additional friendly and mutually supportive help obtained from neighbors. Adequate space, with its potential for reducing quarreling and bickering and making the day-to-day routine easier might have further advantageous psychological effects.

TABLE 3. Nervousness scale.

	Number of scale items	Before		Early after		Late after	
		Test	Control	Test	Control	Test	Control
				Per cent			
Least nervous	5	11	9	7	5	4	7
	4	33	32	36	36	39	34
	3	22	23	25	23	25	25
	2	15	18	17	18	14	16
	1	12	10	9	13	11	13
Most nervous	0	7	8	6	5	7	5
	Four or more in direction of least nervous	44	41	43	41	43	41

The data of Tables 1, 2, and 3 show the extent of change over time for test and control samples on the three variables under discussion. There was very little difference in the distribution of scores at the three periods of inquiry for any of the scales. The one-line summary of Table 1 (Mood) shows that, starting from no difference between the groups at Wave 1, 4 per cent more test than control respondents scored in the positive direction in each of the "after" periods. The summary of Table 2 (Control of Temper) shows 8 per cent and 2 per cent more tests than controls at Waves 7 and 11, respectively, answering in the positive direction. Table 3 shows that in each "after" period, as in the "before" period, both groups showed virtually identical distributions on the scale of Nervousness.

From these three tables it is apparent that only on the scale of Mood was there any shift over time, *both* groups gradually moving in the more positive (less moody) direction during the three-year period.

Potency, Optimism-Pessimism, and Satisfaction with Personal State of Affairs

The scales of Potency, Optimism-Pessimism, and Satisfaction with Personal State of Affairs ("status quo") were designed to tap a somewhat different constellation from those presented in the preceding sec-

TABLE 4.   Potency scale (efficacy of self-help).

	Number of scale items	Before		Early after		Late after	
		Test	Control	Test	Control	Test	Control
				Per cent			
Most committed to efficacy of self-help	5	21	21	25	26	25	23
	4	28	21	28	26	28	23
	3	25	20	21	18	20	19
	2	15	21	16	16	19	21
	1	10	15	8	13	7	14
Least committed to efficacy of self-help	0	1	2	2	1	1	a
	Four or more in positive (most committed) direction	49	42	. 53	52	53	46

a Less than one-half of one per cent.

tion. Unlike the latter, these three scales are more nearly related to general morale.

In constructing these particular scales, it was reasoned that people at the lower rungs of the social ladder, especially with the ethnic and economically marginal characteristics of the study samples, may feel they are unable to accomplish appreciable personal and social gains through their own efforts. In general, this social group has little contact with those personal and social pressures that bring about improvement in life. They have many handicaps: subsistence finances, low level of literacy, and caste characteristics which seriously limit the preparation and carrying out of plans for social ascent. The outcome, it was expected, might be general frustration and dissatisfaction, thus adversely affecting general outlook on life.

It was in the light of the foregoing that certain alterations were expected to attend the test respondents' move to Lafayette Courts. For the test group, it was thought that the fact of being accepted for admission to the project might well be a symbol of personal and social accomplishment. Both test and control respondents had applied for

TABLE 5. Optimism-pessimism scale.

	Number of scale items	Before		Early after		Late after	
		Test	Control	Test	Control	Test	Control
				Per cent			
Most optimistic	4	13	14	18	19	19	20
	3	26	22	31	27	29	19
	2	33	28	29	21	29	25
	1	19	25	16	23	13	20
Least optimistic	0	9	11	6	10	10	16
	Three or more in positive (most optimistic) direction	39	36	49	46	48	39[a]

[a] Test-control difference significant at level of .02 to .05.

public housing, but only the test families were successful. It was this successful culmination of a social venture, self-instigated in large part and resulting in an improved physical and social environment, that was expected to confirm feelings of increased social power (Potency) for the test women. A further expected consequence was an increase in positive feelings regarding personal and social expectations for the future (Optimism-Pessimism). Finally, it was felt that satisfaction with the general tenor of life would be enhanced (Satisfaction with Personal State of Affairs).

The data bearing on these expectations are given in Tables 4, 5, and 6. The scale of Potency (Table 4) shows no *relative* difference at all between test and control when the single-line summary is considered: 7 per cent more test than control women answered in the positive direction both at Wave 1 and at Wave 11.

There was greater relative test improvement on the other two scales. The one-line summary of Table 5 shows that 9 per cent more test than control women responded in the "most optimistic" direction at Wave 11 compared to 3 per cent more tests than controls in the same direction at Wave 1. The scale of Satisfaction with Personal State of Affairs (Table 6) reveals that, at Wave 11 for the one-line summary, 10 per cent more test than control respondents answered in the positive direction. At Wave 1, there was a 3 per cent "handicap"

TABLE 6. Scale of satisfaction with personal state of affairs (status quo).

		Before		Early after		Late after	
	Number of scale items	Test	Control	Test	Control	Test	Control
					Per cent		
Most satisfied	4	37	40	60	58	59	49
	3	20	22	15	14	17	19
	2	18	12	15	11	12	13
	1	11	11	5	8	6	9
Least satisfied	0	14	15	5	9	6	10
	All four in positive (most satisfied) direction	37	40	60	58	59	49 [a]

[a] Test-control difference significant at level of .02 to .05.

for the test women, so that *relatively* they achieved a larger gain than did the controls.

Authoritarianism and Aggression toward Authority Figures

Two scales touched on hierarchical relationships in which the population of the study is likely to be involved. The Authoritarianism scale has abstracted from more generalized scales on the same subject, elements of strictness of obedience to personal authority; the items chosen refer to discipline of children and to strictness of leadership. In arriving at the rationale for the use of these concepts, it was considered that, whatever the psychodynamic origin of authoritarian attitudes, condition of life probably plays a role in their maintenance. Thus, it was felt that the frustrations of daily life among harassed mothers might well reinforce demands for unquestioning obedience and the wish for subservience to maternal authority. It was anticipated that the improvement in general conditions of life accruing for the test families upon moving into the project would result in lesser emphasis on these attitudes. In other words, a less exacting existence might well lead to less exacting demands on the behavior of others.

TABLE 7. Scales of authoritarianism and aggression toward authority figures.

		Early after		Late after	
		Test	Control	Test	Control
	Number of scale items		Per cent		
a. Authoritarianism					
Least authoritarian	4	12	13	9	12
	3	14	13	14	8
	2	16	17	20	21
	1	34	34	33	36
Most authoritarian	0	24	23	24	23
	Two or more in positive (least authoritarian) direction	42	43	43	41
b. Aggression toward authority figures					
Least aggressive	5			4	3
	4			11	6
	3			23	21
	2			28	24
	1			31	37
Most aggressive	0			3	9
	Two or more in positive (least aggressive) direction			66	54 [a]

[a] Test-control difference significant at level of .02 to .05.

The Authoritarianism scale was administered at two points in the "after" period, without Wave 1 data on the same topic. From Table 7a it may be seen that the total distributions show virtually identical responses among test and control respondents at each point in time. The single-line summary reveals that about two-fifths of each group gave two or more responses in the "least authoritarian" direction.

The scale of Aggression toward Authority Figures taps a different aspect of reactions toward authority; an aspect which is much more social in nature. The socioeconomic-ethnic population from which the study samples derive have, in general, experiences with social authority figures that do not always lead to happy outcomes. Often the context of interaction is one of distress, particularly when the authority figures are police, court, and welfare officials. It was reasoned that there is, in general, for this population a lack of interchange with institutional figures in which there are positive benefits in a happy context. One psychological outcome for the study population, it was anticipated, might be an unreasoning antagonism toward apparently detrimental or unjust "official" actions. It was felt that the move to the project would provide, for the test families, at least one major positive interchange in which the outcome provided major social benefits for the recipient. One possible psychological consequence might be a lessened tendency to react in unequivocally negative fashion to seemingly "bad" official acts, and to proceed more cautiously in arriving at final judgments.

To test these speculations, the scale of Aggression toward Authority Figures contained items in which "bad" acts were attributed to police, employer, doctor, welfare official, and judge; the respondent was asked to indicate the degree of retribution each "bad" act warranted. Table 7b gives the data for responses to this scale at Wave 11, the only time these items were asked. The one-line summary shows that 12 per cent more test than control respondents answered in the "least aggressive" direction; the trend was consistent throughout the distribution of scores.

Self-Esteem and General Anxiety

The concepts of self-esteem and anxiety were viewed as the psychological analogue of the concept of general social self-confidence which has been considered in previous chapters and in earlier sections of the present chapter. The scale of Self-Esteem pertains to the element of appraisal of personal worth. The supposition was that populations with few of life's attainments and with dim outlook on the future would be likely to downgrade their attainments and the degree of their worth to others. The scale of General Anxiety is to some extent the other side of this coin, although such anxiety involves psychodynamic elements as well. The rationale in connection with the formulation of this scale was that the general conditions of slum life for the study population would be conducive to evocation and prolongation

TABLE 8. Scales of self-esteem and general anxiety.

		Late after	
		Test	Control
	Number of scale items	Per cent	
a. Self-esteem			
Least self-depreciating	5	51	46
	4	21	24
	3	15	14
	2	7	8
	1	3	4
Most self-depreciating	0	3	4
All five in positive (least self-depreciating) direction		51	46
b. General anxiety			
Least anxious	5	26	24
	4	20	14
	3	16	20
	2	20	18
	1	12	14
Most anxious	0	6	10
Four or more in positive (least anxious) direction		46	38

of anxiety. It was anticipated that, for the test women, the improvements experienced as a consequence of the move to Lafayette Courts might be reflected in a degree of higher self-assessment and in a reduced general anxiety level.

Table 8 gives the data on responses to these two scales, both of which were administered in the "late after" period (Wave 11), only. The one-line summary for the Self-Esteem scale (Table 8a) shows that 5 per cent more test than control respondents answered in the "least self-depreciating" direction. Table 8b, which shows the data for the General Anxiety scale, also reveals a somewhat higher proportion of positive responses among the tests than among the controls. The single-line summary indicates that 8 per cent more test than control women responded in the "least anxious" direction.

Statistical Summary for Data
on Psychological State

Level of significance	Direction	No. of test-control comparisons		
		Before	Early After	Late After
	Confirming the "after" expectations			
.01 or less	Tests more "positive" than controls	–	–	–
.02 to .05	" " " " "	–	–	3
Greater than .05	" " " " "	3	6	7
	Counter to the "after" expectations			
No difference:	Identical percentages	1	–	–
Greater than .05	Controls more "positive" than tests	2	1	–
.02 to .05	" " " " "	–	–	–
.01 or less	" " " " "	–	–	–

The statistical summary above shows partial confirmation of the expectations for the material in this chapter. Although of the six "before"-"after" scales, three showed that a somewhat larger proportion of test than control respondents were "positive" on the Wave 1 measures (by 3 per cent or 7 per cent), the remaining three scales showed either no difference or an initial test "handicap." By the "late after" period (Wave 11), more test than control women scored in the "positive" direction on all ten of the psychological-state scales, but the amount of difference fluctuated. Three of the scales showed a test-control differential significant at the 5 per cent level of confidence: Optimism-Pessimism, Satisfaction with Personal State of Affairs, and Aggression toward Authority Figures. The remaining seven scales revealed more test than control respondents scoring "positively" by proportions of from 2 per cent to 8 per cent.

CHAPTER XVI

STYLE OF LIFE

Several additional characteristics of the test and control families were investigated in the social-psychological adjustment phase of the study that were not conveniently classifiable in the various sections of Chapters X to XV. These characteristics had to do with interviewer ratings of various aspects of the appearance of the apartment and of the respondent; activities—self-promotive and otherwise—of the woman of the house, and of the husband; and a canvass of the possession of various kinds of consumer goods. As indicated in Chapter II, there were no specific hypotheses formulated at the outset of the study regarding possible changes these characteristics might undergo among the test families as a consequence of their move to good housing. The items enumerated above were included mainly for descriptive purposes and to provide some supplementary information on the nature of the groups with which the study was concerned. It was considered reasonable, however, to expect that the differences between the test and control groups in the quality of their respective physical and social environments might be reflected in differential elements characterizing their styles of life.

Initial Comparability of Test and Control Groups at Wave 1

Tables 1 through 5 present the findings for the subject matter of this chapter. Initial measures of the test and control groups were obtained only on the items involving the interviewers' ratings of the appearance of the apartment and of the respondent (Table 1), and on the ownership of "common items" (Table 5, parts a through e). The interviewers' ratings showed general close comparability. The largest difference was a 6 per cent initial "handicap" for the test group in connection with the ratings of furnishings as being in "good repair"; the remaining differences were of the magnitude of 3 per cent or 1 per cent. Somewhat larger variations were apparent in connection with the possession of "common items," mainly television sets, washing machines, and cars. In each instance, fewer test than control families owned these items (by 9 per cent, 7 per cent, and 5 per cent, respectively).

Interviewer's Ratings of Home and Respondent

The ratings of various aspects of the apartment and of the respondent were made by the interviewers directly after an interview but not in the presence of the respondent. During good weather, the rating forms were filled out immediately outside the dwelling unit; in inclement weather, they were completed at a convenient place during the post-interview break.

There were three ratings of the dwelling units: "cleanliness" of the furnishings, "orderliness" of the room and furnishings, and "condition of repair" of the furnishings. The "cleanliness" ratings considered the presence or absence of dust, spots, and stains. "Orderliness" involved a distinction between whether articles were neat, in place, and in usable order, or cluttered and in great disorder. "Condition of repair" took into account whether articles were fixed, sewed, and mended, or broken, ripped, frayed, and torn. Table 1 (parts a through c) shows the "positive" ratings for each of the categories. On all three items, there were *relative* gains in the ratings of test over control families from the "before" to the "after" period. On "cleanliness" in the "after" period, the furnishings of 11 per cent more test than control families were rated "clean," in contrast to 3 per cent fewer test "clean" ratings in the "before" period. On "orderliness," the test gain was less marked: 9 per cent more test than control rooms and furnishings were rated as "neat and uncluttered" in the "after" period; at Wave 1 the ratings were almost identical. On "condition of repair" in the "after" period, 11 per cent more test than control families were rated as having articles in "good repair," in contrast to 6 per cent fewer in the "before" period.

There were two ratings of the personal appearance of the adult woman of the house (the respondent), one having to do with cleanli-

TABLE 1. Interviewers' ratings of home and respondent.

| | | Before | | After | |
		Test	Con-trol	Test	Con-trol
		Per cent			
a. Ratings of cleanliness of furnishings	Clean	54	57	68	57[a]
b. Ratings of orderliness of room and furnishings	Neat and uncluttered	57	56	70	61[a]
c. Ratings of repair of furnishings	Good repair	62	68	73	62[a]
d. Ratings of cleanliness of woman of the house	Very clean	58	55	67	61
e. Ratings of neatness of woman of the house	Very neat	55	52	59	57

[a] Test-control difference significant at level of .02 to .05.

ness, the other pertaining to neatness. "Cleanliness" depended primarily on observations of the presence or absence of spots and stains on clothing. "Neatness" depended on condition of the clothing (presence or absence of holes or rips) and on condition of the hair (well arranged or in disarray). Table 1 (parts d and e) gives the data for these ratings. On respondent "cleanliness," 6 per cent more test than control respondents were rated as "very clean," but there was a 3 per cent difference in the same direction at Wave 1. The ratings of "neatness" of the respondent show that both groups were very similar to one another both in the "after" and in the "before" periods.

From the foregoing, it is apparent that of the five interviewers' ratings, those pertaining to the dwelling unit showed the most marked test-control differences. Although on any of these ratings in the "after" period about three-fifths or more of each group received a "positive" evaluation, the proportion of test respondents so rated was systematically larger than that of the controls, and test gains from "before" to "after" were uniformly greater. This finding is congruent with the hypotheses advanced and the findings reported in connection with the subject matter of some of the preceding chapters. Thus, it has been shown that in the "after" period, test respondents were markedly more likely than controls to show high regard for their apartments and the appearance of their buildings, and to view themselves as having improved their status. The improved dwelling units may have inspired the test respondents to improve in cleanliness, orderliness, and repair of furnishings. The perceived rise in social status attending the move to the project for the test families also might have influenced efforts to bring household articles into line or acquire more fitting household equipment.

Self-Promotive and Other Activities

Characteristic personal and social activities are determined to a large extent by social and cultural training and habit, by availability of resources, by economic circumstances, and by personal aspiration. For the husbands and wives of the study, it could be expected that their typical personal and social activities were well established at the start of the study. Whether or not these behavior patterns would undergo any changes among the test group would depend upon the pervasiveness of the influence of the new housing environment.

Two kinds of activities were singled out for examination in the "after" period: the first may be considered self-promotive in the sense of enhancing self-maintenance and raising social, educational, or cultural levels; the second is apt to be characterized mainly by self-enjoyment with fewer elements of self-enhancement involved.

Respondents' activities

Table 2 (parts a through f) shows the data for the self-promotive types of activities among the women: activities involving needlework; attendance at museums, concerts, libraries; and a class or course of instruction. The table shows that 3 per cent fewer test than control respondents engaged in sewing, knitting, and like activities. On each of the next three "educational" items, only 3 or 4 per cent more test than control respondents indicated they went to a museum, concerts, or a library. An index of all four items taken together (Table 2e) showed that 7 per cent more test than control women participated in two or more of the activities. The remaining "educational" type of activity in this series was that of taking a course or class at school. Table 2f reveals that 9 per cent more test than control respondents indicated participation.

Table 2 (parts g through k) gives the extent of participation in

TABLE 2. Self-promotive and other activities: woman of the house.

		Before		After	
		Test	Con-trol	Test	Con-trol
			Per cent		
Self-promotive activities indicated					
a. Sew, knit, crochet or embroider				54	57
b. Go to a museum				14	11
c. Go to concerts				19	16
d. Go to a library to get own books				26	22
e. **Index of above four items**	Two or more			31	24
f. Taken a course at school or gone to a class of any kind during the past year?	"Yes"			20	11[a]
Other activities indicated					
g. Go to the movies				56	61
h. Go to a bar or night club				31	32
i. Play cards				38	43
j. Go to dances or parties				52	52
k. Go to watch sports events				32	32
l. **Index of above five items**	Three or more			41	45

[a] Test-control difference significant at level of .01 or less.

the other types of activities. Although the differences were small, the test women were *less* likely than the controls to undertake three out of the five activities: go to the movies, go to a bar or night club, or play cards. One to 5 per cent fewer test than control respondents engaged in these pastimes; there was no difference between the groups in the extent of going to dances or parties, or to watch sports events. An index of all five items (Table 2, part 1) indicates that 4 per cent fewer tests than controls took part in three or more of these activities.

Husbands' activities

Table 3 (parts a through f) reports the extent of self-promotive activities among the adult males of the study as mentioned by their

TABLE 3. Self-promotive and other activities: husband.[a]

		Before		After	
		Test	Con- trol	Test	Con- trol
			Per cent		
Husband's self-promotive activities indicated					
a. Work on a hobby				21	28
b. Play a musical instrument				7	8
c. Take part in any sports activities				18	18
d. Go to a library to get own books				11	12
e. Index of above four items	One or more			43	47
f. Taken a course at school or gone to a class of any kind during the past year?	"Yes"			7	7
Husband's other activities indicated					
g. Go to a bar or night club				55	58
h. Play cards				51	60
i. Go to watch sports events				52	63[b]
j. Index of above three items	Two or more			56	63

[a] Among families with husband present; for N's, see Appendix 13.
[b] Test-control difference significant at level of .02 to .05.

wives. Seven per cent fewer test than control husbands worked on hobbies; there was little or no difference between the groups on the other three items: playing a musical instrument, taking part in sports activities, or going to a library. An index of the four items taken together showed 4 per cent fewer tests than controls took part in one or more of the self-promotive kinds of activities. Furthermore, fewer than one-tenth of the husbands in each group had taken a course at school or attended a class.

Test husbands were somewhat less likely than controls to engage in each of the three other types of activities inquired about (Table 3, parts g through i). Going to a bar or night club, playing cards, and going to watch sports events were less frequently reported as activities of test than of control husbands by 3 per cent, 9 per cent, and 11 per cent, respectively. An index of the items showed a 7 per cent test-control differential in the same direction (Table 3j).

Summary of respondents' and husbands' activities

It would appear from the foregoing that the change in the housing environment had, in general, no marked influence upon the behavior patterns of adult members of the test group, in contrast to those of the controls, as measured by the series of self-promotive and self-enjoyment types of activities. The most notable difference in the "after" period was a slight tendency on the part of both test husbands and wives, in comparison to controls, to refrain from the less self-promotive kinds of activities, and for test respondents to be a little more likely to engage in self-promotive activities.

Magazine Readership and Possessions

Magazine readership was canvassed in the "after" period among both test and control respondents. Table 4 shows that about two-fifths of each group read none. More than a quarter of each group read "slick" picture magazines directed to Negro readership; slightly

TABLE 4. Magazine readership.

	Before		After	
	Test	Control	Test	Control
		Per cent		
What magazines do you read most regularly?				
Most frequently mentioned:[a]				
Negro emphasis				
"Slick": picture			29	27
General emphasis				
"Slick": picture			25	22
"Pulp": romance			17	16
"Slick": home			13	12
"Slick": fiction and feature			12	11
No magazines read			37	37

[a] The categories of responses shown are those mentioned most frequently by test and control samples.

TABLE 5. Ownership of consumer goods.

	Before		After	
	Test	Control	Test	Control
		Per cent		
Common items: possession indicated				
a. T.V. set	58	67[a]	87	79[a]
b. Radio	89	87	92	87
c. Washing machine	37	44	38	54[b]
d. Telephone	17	19	44	30[b]
e. Car	12	17	21	21
Electrical utility items: possession indicated				
f. Electric iron			98	95
g. Electric mixer			18	17
h. Electric sewing machine			13	13
i. Electric toaster			48	47
"Luxury" items: possession indicated				
j. Record player or phonograph			62	54
k. Camera			40	40
l. Wrist watch			61	62

[a] Test-control difference significant at level of .02 to .05.
[b] Test-control difference significant at level of .01 or less.

fewer read other "slick" picture magazines. Smaller percentages read "pulp" romance and "slick" home, fiction, and feature magazines.

Data regarding possessions are shown in Table 5. The first five items, asked in both the "before" and "after" periods, pertained to television sets, radios, washing machines, telephones, and cars. The items most likely to be owned in the "after" period by each group were radios and T.V. sets; the item least likely to be owned was a car. From the "before" to the "after" period, there was *relatively* greater test than control acquisition of four of the five items, notably in connection with T.V. sets and telephones, and considerably less in connection with radios and cars. There was relatively less test than control acquisition of washing machines from "before" to "after," undoubtedly accounted for by the fact that test families had less need for this utility since washing machines were available for the use of the project residents.

The remainder of Table 5 shows the extent of ownership in the "after" period, only, of four electrical utility items (iron, mixer, sewing machine, and toaster) and three "luxury" items (record player, camera, and wrist watch). Half or more of each group possessed electric irons, record players, and wrist watches. Comparison of the test and control groups showed close similarity in the ownership of every article listed, with the exception of record players. These were reported by 8 per cent more test than control respondents.

In summary, a review of all the kinds of consumer goods reported in Table 5 reveals that test families possessed only four of the total of twelve items to any noticeably greater extent than did the controls in the "after" period. These items were: telephones (possessed by 14 per cent more tests than controls), television sets (by 8 per cent), record players (by 8 per cent), and radios (by 5 per cent).

PART **4**

SCHOOL PERFORMANCE

CHAPTER XVII

SCHOOL PERFORMANCE OF CHILDREN

Children in their period of rapid growth and development might be expected to be sensitive indicators of environmental influences. The change of housing in the test families, with its altering of morbidity and social adjustment patterns, might be expected to produce secondary effects on the experience and performance of the children in school. This chapter describes the results of the study of the school records of the children in the test and control families. Composition of the school samples will be presented briefly. Next will be examined several variables characterizing the performance tests to which the children were exposed. Finally, the results will be shown of the measures of the children's performance in school before and after the rehousing of test families.

General expectations were that the test and control children would be similar in the "before" period and that the test children would, in the "after" period, show somewhat better school performance than the control children. The expectation of differential school performance was based on various considerations thought to be directly or indirectly related to the quality of the housing which distinguished the test and control groups. First, there was the possible influence of dwelling unit density and the opportunity to read and to do homework unhampered by interruptions from other family members. In the slum, homework and study are made especially difficult if there are infants and small children in the household. For the rehoused school child, not only is there lessened person density, but there are also more actual rooms in the dwelling unit in which a child can do homework undisturbed.

225

Second, the possible indirect influence of several psychological factors suggested that rehoused children might, in time, do better in school than slum children. For example, heightened general morale, increased educational aspirations of parents for their children, and more parental participation in educationally promotive activities with children were viewed as possible consequences of improved housing, and these factors in turn were suspected of influencing educational achievement of the children.

Finally, there was the possibility that health status might play a role in school performance. It had been hypothesized that illness rates and rates of attendant disability would be substantially lower among test than among control children. In this event, a test-control differential might be expected to arise in connection with elements of school behavior conceivably influenced by state of health, attendance being perhaps foremost among these.

In general, the hypotheses in connection with school performance of children were somewhat more tenuous than was the case with other substantive areas of the study. There were two principal reasons for this. First, as was apparent from the preceding discussion, a number of the hypotheses were of a secondary rather than a primary order, i.e., housing would need to have a discernible effect in a given area and this effect in turn might then influence school performance. Second, it was recognized that although the social, psychological, and health characteristics of the home might be influenced by the quality of housing, these influences might not extend sufficiently into the relatively independent environment of the school. There were clearly a number of factors within the school itself that influenced a child's school performance quite apart from his home and the housing quality characterizing it.

Composition of the School Samples

Number and types of children followed up

Information on the status of the test and control school-age children during the period of the school performance study is given in Table 1.

The whereabouts of all school-age children was established as of September, 1956, a date which, for the purpose of assessing the school

TABLE 1. Status of school records samples, September, 1956, and June, 1958.

	Test	Control
		Number
Total number of children of school age, September, 1956	486	510
Excluded from follow-up because in September, 1956, children were:	(147)	(148)
In grade 1	100	103
In grades 10–12	6	5
In vocational school	17	15
In parochial school	11	11
In college or secretarial school	2	1
In an institution	1	2
Not in school	10	11
Included in follow-up: children who in September, 1956, were in grades 2–9	(339)	(362)
Follow-up completed	293	287
Unable to locate by September, 1958	40	69
Miscellaneous losses by September, 1958 (moved from city, not in school, etc.)	6	6

data, may be considered as ending the "before" period of the study. A total of 486 school-age children were identified among the 300 test families (1.62 per family) and 510 children among the 300 control families (1.70 per family).

Follow-up into the "after" period of the study was attempted on approximately 70 per cent of each of the two groups of children (339 test children and 362 control children), the remainder (147 test children and 148 control children) being excluded at the outset on the basis of three principles:

(a)   Public-school children in grade 1 (September, 1956) were excluded because they had no prior school records and there would be no way of estimating initial comparability of performance.

(b)   Public-school children in grades 10-12 were excluded because they would be scheduled to leave school before the end of the study and thus their "after" data would be incomplete.

(c)   Children in "special" schools (vocational, parochial, college or secretarial) were excluded because performance data in these schools would not be coordinate with the main body of information collected.

Table 1 gives the detailed numbers in each exclusion category.

Follow-up into the "after" period was successful with 293 test children (87 per cent of those attempted) and 287 control children (79 per cent of those attempted). These successful follow-ups will constitute the "school samples" which will be compared in the following pages. Inability to locate records in a complex school system accounted for a majority of the losses for children who were followed up. The tracing losses were somewhat heavier in schools attended by the control children presumably because more schools were involved and these were more widely scattered throughout the city.

Age, grade, and sex distribution

Age, grade, and sex distributions for the test and control children in the school samples are given in Table 2. In general, the test and control groups were fairly comparable in regard to all these variables.

The table shows that there were 5 per cent more boys in the control families than in test families. The age distribution reveals that approximately three-fifths of the children in both groups were below the age of 10, with a small excess of younger children among the test families. The school grade information reflects these facts; about two-thirds of the children in both groups were in grades 2-4, with a somewhat higher proportion of test than control children in these grades.

Tests Administered

Information from the school records was obtained on three kinds of tests: intelligence, arithmetic, and reading. For each pupil, data were collected about the tests that had been administered, and the grade the child attended at the time of testing. These matters will be dealt with in this section. The actual performance or scores will be dealt with in the next section. Only the tests most recently administered to the child are reported.

TABLE 2. Sex, age, and school grade of school samples.

	Test (293)	Control (287)
N:	Per cent	
Sex		
Male	48	53
Female	52	47
Age, as of June, 1956		
Age 7	22	18
8	21	17
9	19	19
10	13	12
11	4	10
12	6	9
13	6	6
14	5	5
15	3	2
16	1	1
17	—	1
School grade, as of September, 1956		
Grade 2	24	22
3	21	15
4	18	20
5	14	11
6	4	12
7	4	7
8	5	5
9	5	3
10	2	3
11	1	—
Special, ungraded	1	1
No information	1	1

Intelligence-test administration

The proportions of children given intelligence tests and the grade when tested are shown in Table 3. The Kuhlmann-Anderson test was used in the elementary grades, since it is not dependent on reading and writing skills. The Otis test was used in higher grades.

In the "before" period there is evidence of fair initial similarity of test exposure insofar as this is reflected in test administration. Of the test children, 66 per cent were tested as compared with 72 per cent of the control children. The two samples were roughly equivalent as to the specific test they took, but showed a detectable difference in the grade when tested. This difference appeared mainly in the proportion of children tested in grades 4, 5, and 6, which was higher among the control than the test children.

In the "after" period there was a difference in the type of test administered, the test children receiving relatively more Kuhlmann-Anderson tests. This appears to reflect differences in timing of intelligence testing. The Kuhlmann-Anderson test was used in the lower grades and the Otis in the higher grades.

TABLE 3. Tests administered: intelligence test, by type and by school grade.

	"Before" period (9/53–6/56)		"After" period (9/56–6/58)	
N:	Test (293)	Control (287)	Test (293)	Control (287)
	Per cent			
Type of intelligence test administered				
Kuhlmann-Anderson	54 ⎰ 66	62 ⎰ 72	61 ⎰ 75	51 ⎰ 74
Otis	12 ⎱	10 ⎱	14 ⎱	23 ⎱
Not administered	10	6	25	26
Not applicable[a]	24	22	—	—
Grade when tested				
2, 3	46 ⎱	44 ⎱	23 ⎱	19 ⎱
4, 5, 6	8 ⎰ 66	18 ⎰ 72	38 ⎰ 75	32 ⎰ 74
7 or higher	12 ⎰	10 ⎰	14 ⎰	23 ⎰

[a] Child in grade 1 as of 6/56.

Arithmetic-test administration

The Baltimore public schools used the Stanford and the Metropolitan arithmetic achievement tests sparingly in the "before" period, fewer than 15 per cent of the children receiving them (Table 4), with little difference noted between test and control children.

In the "after" period these tests were given to 86 and 79 per cent of the test and control children, respectively, with an excess of test children taking the tests in the earlier grades (2 through 6) and with more control children in the later grades (7th and higher).

Reading-test administration

In the early period the schools applied various reading tests (Metropolitan, Stanford, Iowa, etc.) to very few children. Test and control children were equally included in the tests that were given. In the "after" period, 88 per cent of the test children and 83 per cent of the control children received the Metropolitan or Stanford reading test. As with the intelligence and arithmetic tests, differences were observed in the school grade when the reading test was given, the test children being a little more likely to have been examined in an elementary grade.

TABLE 4. Tests administered: arithmetic test (Metropolitan or Stanford), by school grade.

		"Before" period (9/53–6/56)		"After" period (9/56–6/58)	
	N:	Test (293)	Control (287)	Test (293)	Control (287)
			Per cent		
Grade when tested					
2, 3		— ⎫	— ⎫	39 ⎫	32 ⎫
4, 5, 6		[a] ⎬ 14	[a] ⎬ 11	30 ⎬ 86	24 ⎬ 79
7 or higher		14 ⎪	11 ⎪	13 ⎪	20 ⎪
Ungraded special class		[a] ⎭	— ⎭	4 ⎭	3 ⎭
Not administered		62	67	14	21
Not applicable[b]		24	22	—	—

[a] Less than one-half of one per cent.
[b] Child in grade 1 as of 6/56.

Summary of test exposure

The evidence available reveals general similarity in the exposure to intelligence and achievement tests of the two groups of children, either before or after the rehousing. In the "after" period on all tests, however, there was a tendency for test children to be exposed in the lower grades and control children in the higher grades.

Comparison of the test administration data with the age and grade distributions suggests the reason for the test-control differences in grade when tested. At the outset of the "after" period, test children tended to be slightly younger and somewhat more likely to be in the lower grades. Since in the Baltimore school system the Kuhlmann-Anderson, arithmetic, and reading tests were administered uniformly prior to grade 7, more test than control children were exposed to these tests. Conversely, the Otis Intelligence Test is administered for the first time in the 7th grade; as a consequence, in the two-year "after" period more control than test children were exposed to this test.

TABLE 5. Tests administered: reading test, by type and by school grade.

	N:	"Before" period (9/53–6/56)		"After" period (9/56–6/58)	
		Test (293)	Control (287)	Test (293)	Control (287)
			Per cent		
Type of reading test administered					
Metropolitan or Stanford	8 } 12	5 } 11	88 } 88	83 } 83
Iowa or other	4	6	—	—
Not administered	64	67	12	17
Not applicable [a]	24	22	—	—
Grade when tested				
2, 3	1 } 12	2 } 11	40 } 88	31 } 83
4, 5, 6	3	4	30	25
7 or higher	8	5	14	24
Ungraded special class	[b]	—	4	3

[a] Child in grade 1 as of 6/56.
[b] Less than one-half of one per cent.

School Performance Measures

Performance on tests administered

The results of intelligence tests are generally thought to be fairly independent of educational and environmental influences, and so might be expected to remain fairly stable throughout the period of observation. Achievement tests, on the other hand, might be expected to be influenced by education, health, social adjustment, and other environmental factors. The mean test scores and standard deviation of the test and control children on the intelligence, arithmetic, and reading measurements are shown in Table 6.

Intelligence test scores. The intelligence test scores (I.Q.) ranged from 55 to 122, with both test and control children equally represented at both ends of the distribution. Mean scores were in general slightly higher than the medians because of the skewness.

Mean scores on intelligence tests showed great constancy in the "before" and "after" periods. In the "before" administration, mean

TABLE 6. School performance: intelligence, arithmetic, and reading test scores.

	"Before" period (9/53–6/56)		"After" period (9/56–6/58)	
	Test	Control	Test	Control
Intelligence test		I.Q. score		
Mean	93.3	92.9	92.8	91.7
Standard deviation	9.4	10.5	8.3	11.1[a]
Number tested	(194)	(208)	(221)	(211)
Arithmetic achievement test		Grade level		
Mean[b]	5.4	5.9	3.5	3.5
Standard deviation	1.1	1.4	1.3	1.5
Number tested	(42)	(33)	(253)	(226)
Reading achievement test		Grade level		
Mean[b]	4.7	4.9	3.4	3.4
Standard deviation	1.5	2.1	1.8	2.0
Number tested	(35)	(33)	(258)	(239)

[a] Test-control difference significant at level of .02 to .05.
[b] Grade adjusted.

score for test children was 93.3 and for control children 92.9 (Table 6). In the "after" period there was a slight but not statistically significant relative gain for test children, test and control mean scores being 92.8 and 91.7, respectively.

An unexpected finding was the difference between test and control children in their standard deviations in the "after" period. Although in the "before" period the test children appeared somewhat more uniform (smaller standard deviation) than the control children, in the "after" period this uniformity increased even further, while that of the control children decreased, making the difference statistically significant. Increased uniformity in the test children's intelligence scores after rehousing could be due to increased uniformity in such factors as health and social adjustment. Or, it could be due simply to their concentration in fewer schools, which might have reduced the variance contributed by the school and test situation, itself.

Arithmetic test scores. Arithmetic test scores, as shown in Table 6, are given in grade level of performance according to Stanford and Metropolitan norms. In the "before" period, test children averaged a

TABLE 7. School performance: number of semester promotions.

	N:	"Before" period (9/54–6/55)		"After" period (9/56–6/58)	
		Test (293)	Control (287)	Test (293)	Control (287)
		Per cent			
Number of promotions[a]					
0		2	3	—	[b]
1		2	4	1	—
2		<u>69</u>	<u>66</u>	5	15[c]
3		—	1	3	5
4		—	—	82	68[c]
5		—	—	—	1
Ungraded special class		2	2	7	7
Not applicable[d]		24	22	—	—
No record		1	2	2	4

[a] Normal number of promotions underscored.
[b] Less than one-half of one per cent.
[c] Test-control difference significant at level of .02 to .05.
[d] Child in grade 1 as of 6/56.

grade level of 5.4, control children one of 5.9, not significantly higher. In the "after" period, average grade-level score, adjusted for pupils' actual grade for both test and control children, was 3.5.

The reason for the grade adjustment is that the scoring was based on absolute rather than relative achievement (as is true of the intelligence quotient). To obtain a true comparison, it was necessary to take grade-when-tested (see Table 4) into account. The fact that mean grade performance level was lower for both groups in the "after" than in the "before" period is also explainable when grade-when-tested is considered. It will be recalled that only the most recently administered tests in any category were assessed. In the "before" period, there were arithmetic scores only on the children in the 7th grade (see Table 4). In the "after" period there were also arithmetic scores on children at several grade levels below grade 7.

Reading test scores. Reading scores follow very closely the pattern of arithmetic scores (Table 6). Given in grade-level terms, the "before" test mean score was slightly, but not significantly, lower (4.7) than the corresponding control mean score (4.9). In the "after" period, adjusted similarly for grade of administration of most recent reading test, the grade level of performance for both groups was 3.4.

Promotions

An additional kind of information systematically collected in an effort to illuminate the effects of differential housing was promotions from grade to grade. Normal progress through the school grades was examined as an index of general school performance. It was not, however, expected to be as reliable a measure of performance as test scores because of the greater possibility of being influenced by subjective factors such as variations in the grading systems among teachers.

Table 7 summarizes the promotions data for a two-semester period "before" and a four-semester period "after" the rehousing. A majority of the children in both periods and in both samples achieved the norm of the respective periods. In the "before" period, abnormal promotion (fewer than two) affected only 2 to 4 per cent of the children in each category, with test and control children similar in this respect.

In each of the "after" years, test children were more likely than controls to achieve normal promotions (two in each year). Table 7 shows the "after" data cumulated for the four normal promotion periods. Test children were more likely than control children to be promoted at a normal pace (82 per cent and 68 per cent, respectively).

Attendance

A final school-connected activity of interest is that of daily attendance. Attendance is, of course, not in itself a measure of school performance, but is generally suspected of being associated with it. Such information may also confirm conclusions regarding days of disability due to illness.

Table 8 gives the basic information for a single "before" year and for the two-year "after" period. In the "before" year in which there were 186 official days, mean number of days attended by test and by control children, respectively, was 168 and 166 days. In the two-year "after" period, out of 367 official days, mean attendance of test children was significantly greater (334 days) than that of control children (318 days). There was also considerably greater variability of attendance among control children.

Comparison of Children in Various Grade Levels

A comparison was made of the school performance of test and control children who at the start of the "after" period were in grades 2-3, 4-6, and 7 and higher. Special interest was in the children in the lower grades who would have had all or almost all of their school experience in the "after" period, compared with children in higher grades for whom the "after" period involved only a small proportion of their total school experience.

Analysis of test scores (intelligence, arithmetic, and reading) by grade groupings revealed general similarities to the over-all data given

TABLE 8. School performance: attendance days.

	"Before" period (9/54–6/55)		"After" period (9/56–6/58)	
	Test	Control	Test	Control
	Days of attendance			
Mean	168	166	334 (t =4.5)	318[a]
Standard deviation	17	19	35 (F =1.8)	47[a]
Number of complete records	(206)	(213)	(289)	(275)

[a] Test-control difference significant at level of .02 to .05.

in Table 6. Examination of promotion and attendance data by grade groupings showed test-control differences to appear approximately equally for children at all grade levels.

Summary

The findings regarding school performance of test and control children have been presented in this chapter. General expectations were that school performance would be affected by increased dwelling unit space in which to pursue school-related activities and by several psychological factors presumed to be the consequence of differences in housing. Based on these premises, it was hypothesized that school performance of test children would be superior to that of control children.

School information was obtained for a total of 293 test children and 287 control children (Table 1). Age and school-grade data showed the test and control children to be fairly comparable, but with a small excess of test children in ages 10 and under and in grades 5 and under (Table 2). Both groups of children were fairly equally exposed to administration of intelligence and achievement tests with small differences related to age and grade variation (Tables 3-5). School performance data were accordingly adjusted, when necessary, to take this difference into account.

The study hypotheses regarding housing and school performance were in general not borne out in connection with intelligence, arithmetic, and reading tests, mean scores being very similar for test and control children in both "before" and "after" periods (Table 6).

Only with respect to promotions was there indication of superior performance of test children, controls appearing less likely to have received regular promotions and more likely to have been held back one or more semesters in the two-year "after" period (Table 7).

Data on the regularity of attendance at school showed test children to be considerably more faithful in attendance than controls in the "after" period of the study (Table 8). While illness is, of course, not the only reason for school absence, it is a major one, and the attendance data may be taken as reflecting test-control differences of school-age children in regard to days of disability as described in Chapter VI.

PART **5**

REVIEW OF FINDINGS

CHAPTER XVIII

SUMMARY
AND CONCLUSIONS

This chapter provides the summary and conclusions for three principal components of a study of the effects of housing on physical and mental health. The study was carried out at The Johns Hopkins University in the years 1954-1960 and involved measurement of approximately 1000 families (5000 persons) over a three-year period of time (1955-1958).

The instigation to undertake the research arose from three principal considerations. First, is the scholarly general interest in the effects of man's physical environment on behavior, an environment which in our epoch is, of course, largely of man's own devising. Secondly, in a more pragmatic vein, is the belief and conviction among social planners and officials in public agencies that improved housing leads to an improvement in health and the amelioration of social ills. A third consideration to some extent bridges the first two. This is the need to gain experience in the conduct of the sort of systematic research on complex social variables that may lead to relatively unequivocal assessment of effects.

A review of forty representative researches (Chapter I) revealed some demonstration of the relationship between housing and health, the direction of the relationship in most cases being: the better the housing, the better the health, and the fewer the social maladjustments. However, in many instances, an equally plausible relationship could very likely be demonstrated between health and many correlates of housing quality, such as education, income, or general cultural level. In other words, because of the research design principally employed—

241

the cross-sectional study—it has been difficult to rule out the effects of non-housing factors.

In an effort to provide more conclusive findings, a nearly classical study design was adopted in the present research. It involved two samples, each surveyed 11 times during the study: a test group originally living in the slum but subsequently moving to a new public housing project; a control sample matched to the test families on many characteristics and slated to *remain* in the slum. The housing development to which the test families moved consisted architecturally of both high-rise and low-rise buildings.

Both groups were surveyed initially *before* the test sample moved to good housing. Subsequently, a total of 10 "after" surveys were conducted with each family in the home. Detailed assessment was made of housing quality, physical morbidity, and social-psychological adjustment. In addition, the performance of every child attending public school was assessed from school records.

Originally, the test group consisted of approximately 400 families (2000 persons); the control group of 600 families (3000 persons). Two problems arose which made necessary some adjustment of the two samples before the final analysis of the data began. The first problem was attrition in the samples over time. Such losses were not unexpected, and, in fact, unusually time-consuming measures were used to keep them to a minimum. In the course of the ten waves of morbidity and adjustment surveys in the "after" period of the study, the sample loss was approximately 1.3 per cent per wave, or about 13 per cent of the originally constituted matched groups.

The second problem was totally unexpected. It was found that control families were, in the passage of time, not only moving about in the city at the rate of approximately 10 per cent per wave, but also that much of the movement was to improved housing—both public and private. This development undoubtedly was due to the increasing availability of adequate housing in the period 1955-1958, while the study was being conducted.

In order to adhere to the experimental conditions required by the study design, the original samples were adjusted to take losses and moves into account. There resulted two reduced effective samples, well-matched on a number of demographic, initial health and initial adjustment characteristics: a test group of 300 families (1341 persons), all in good housing after the initial move, and 300 control families (1349 persons), who, despite some improvement in housing during the study, were in poorer housing on the average, than the test families. Both samples consisted of low-income Negro families. All subsequent findings were based on these adjusted samples.

Physical Health

At the outset of the study, consideration of the ways in which the housing quality of test and control groups would differ led to a number of hypotheses and expectations regarding the role of housing in disease. Among important housing items considered were density and crowding, hot water and facilities for cleanliness, toilet, sharing of facilities, screening, rodent infestation, food storage and refrigeration. It was anticipated, for example, that variation in the quality of these factors would affect introduction of infective organisms into the dwelling unit and their subsequent transmission among family members either by airborne or contact means.

Beginning with initial over-all comparability on morbidity matters, it was expected that, as a consequence of subsequent differences in housing quality, test rates of the incidence of illness would be lower than control rates. The prediction of lower test incidence included both serious and less severe episodes of illness. There was, in addition, the expectation that rates of disability would be lower in the test group than among controls. Finally, it was expected that certain categories of disease might be particularly affected by the housing differences: acute respiratory infections, the communicable diseases of childhoood, tuberculosis and syphilis, digestive complaints, and inflammatory and noninflammatory diseases of the skin. The incidence of accidents in and about the home was expected to be influenced by housing dimensions such as space, maintenance and repair. It was thought, also, that the generally "harder" living in the slum might contribute to a higher rate of exacerbation of chronic conditions in the control than in the test population.

Morbidity

The morbidity data as described in Chapters V through VIII provided findings which, in general, confirmed the hypotheses for persons under 35 years of age, and especially for children, but there was little confirmation of the hypotheses for persons of age 35-59.

Persons under 35 years of age: episodes of illness and disability. For persons under 35 years of age, general confirmation of the hypotheses was observed in the last two years of the study for serious episodes,[1] for less severe episodes, and for total days of disability. Several subgroups, distinguished by age and sex, varied in degree of confirmation of the general directional trend.

Males under 20 years of age as a group appeared to show the greatest effects, the magnitude of the test-control differences appearing larger for them than for girls, both in rates of episodes and days of disability. While all of the more refined age groups contributed to the general findings for persons under 20, the 5-9 year-old group, for both sexes, showed most consistently lower test than control rates of illness and of disability.

Among young adults ages 20-34, females showed far greater and more consistent effects than did males. Test rates among the females in this age group were lower than control rates in episodes of any severity as well as in days of disability.

Persons under 35 years of age: types of illness. Expectations regarding the categories of disease that would be most affected by housing quality were only partially borne out. Among *children* (under 20 years of age), the findings indicated that in the final two years of the study, test rates were regularly lower than control rates in three illness categories:[2] infective and parasitic conditions (mainly the communicable diseases of childhood), digestive conditions, and accidents. The findings with respect to accidents are especially important and clear. Accidents were one-third lower in the housing project as contrasted with the slum. The data showed general confirmation of this fact among all age and sex groups under 20. In at least one of the two years, test rates were also lower than control rates in respiratory conditions, and allergic and metabolic episodes.

Among *adults* (20-34 years of age), hypotheses regarding communicable diseases, such as respiratory and digestive conditions, were in general not borne out. However, slightly lower test than control rates of episodes were distributed over a wide range of conditions, including some that were predominantly chronic in nature, such as allergic,

---

[1] Serious episodes were those that involved either medical attention or had one or more days of attendant disability; less severe episodes were without either medical attention or disability.

[2] Disease classifications derived from the *Manual* of the *International Statistical Classification of Diseases, Injuries, and Causes of Death,* World Health Organization Geneva, 1949.

endocrine and metabolic diseases, mental disorders, and circulatory conditions.

Persons under 20 years of age: morbidity in the "interim" period. The data for children during the "interim" period, approximately five months following the resettlement of test families into their new quarters, was of considerable epidemiologic interest. The findings showed during this period that test rates of illness and disability were *higher* than control rates for almost every age-sex category in the group under 20 years of age. Further examination of "interim" period data by classification of disease revealed that the higher test rates were entirely accounted for by three categories of conditions: infective and parasitic, respiratory, and digestive, all of which have communicability as a principal feature. The most likely explanation was that the test children, newly assembled into the housing project, were strangers to one another in more than just a social sense, and lacked group immunity to common communicable diseases. A similar phenomenon has been observed in the rise of infectious disease in other newly assembled groups, for example, new recruits in the armed services.

Persons 35-59 years of age. In contrast to the morbidity data for persons under 35, the findings for persons 35-59 years of age showed general nonconfirmation of the study hypotheses in the "after" period. In the final two years, test rates were higher than control rates, among males, for serious episodes of illness and days of disability; among females, for both serious and less severe episodes and for days of disability. The test-control differences, while not statistically significant, were of considerable magnitude. Investigation of the reasons for this unexpected direction of differences revealed the existence of a small but disproportionate number—more among tests than controls— of persons with a relatively large number of episodes in the "interim" period, and with a history of chronic illness at Wave 1. Adjusting the data to take this inequality into account resulted, for males, in lower test than control disability rates in the final year of the study, and for females, resulted in lower test than control episode and disability rates in the last two years.

Mortality

It was found, unexpectedly, that 10 control deaths in contrast to 2 test deaths occurred in the "after" period of the study. The 2 test deaths were among children under 6 years of age. Of the control deaths, 5 were likewise very young children, and 5 were among persons 60 years of age and older.

Among the older persons, the finding of 5 control deaths compared to no test deaths was of interest in itself, although the numbers were too small to be anything but suggestive of the relationship of housing to mortality. One consequence of the control deaths among the older persons in the study was the necessity for removing the cohort of persons 60 years of age and older from the morbidity analysis. The 20 test and 20 control persons who originally constituted this age group had the highest rates of episodes of illness and disability of any of the age categories in the study. To analyze the morbidity of this cohort would therefore have involved estimating the illness rates of the controls who had died, and it was felt that this could not be done properly.

Freedom from illness

Wave-by-wave data as a per cent of all persons in the test and control samples showed only small differences between the two groups in the proportions of individuals who experienced *no* illness. At most, there was a modest directional trend in which tests were more likely than controls to be free of illness in nine out of the ten "after" waves. Test persons of all ages tended to be freer of illness than control persons, more so for males than for females.

Childbearing experience

The general childbearing experience of females in the study was described in terms of the outcomes of pregnancy and the morbidity of the mother. The data reported were for Waves 3-11, this time period being designated in order to insure that pregnancies of the test women began after the move into the project, and, therefore, that the prenatal experience took place under good housing circumstances.

The findings revealed little to suggest that differential housing affected, in any significant way, the outcomes of pregnancies. There was similarity between the test and control mothers as to the number of pregnancies that occurred and the ages of the women at outcome. There appeared to be a slight excess of perinatal mortality among the test outcomes, but there was evidence of somewhat greater incidence of prematurity among the control live births. Little difference occurred between the two groups in the incidence of either minor or more serious complaints during the pregnancies. A slightly smaller proportion of the test than of the control pregnancies were *free* of episodes of illness related to childbearing, the test-control difference being equally distributed among major and minor complaints.

Social Psychological Adjustment

Test-control differences in the quality of housing were expected to play a role not only in physical health but also in matters of social psychological adjustment. Of the specific elements that distinguished test from control housing, it was expected that a few factors, such as space in the dwelling unit, would influence both morbidity and social adjustment. However, several elements of housing quality that were thought to affect social attitudes and behavior differed from those believed to influence morbidity. Among these were aspects of the larger housing environment such as architecture and community facilities, as well as the esthetic qualities of the dwelling unit.

It was also apparent that there was a difference between social-psychological adjustment and physical health or illness, in connection with their dimensional aspects. Whereas morbidity may be considered as consisting primarily of a unitary dimension, measured by episodes of illness and days of disability, attitudes and behavior in social settings, on the other hand, were thought of as multidimensional, consisting of a number of relatively discrete components. Six major social psychological content areas were therefore delineated, and measures were devised for each area which were felt to be suitable for testing the relationship to housing quality.

For each major area, hypotheses were formulated regarding the differences that would be likely to emerge between the test and control groups over time, following the move of the test families to good housing. Various housing elements, individually or in combination, were singled out as likely to be related to the subject matter of the particular adjustment area. Since some of the content areas more clearly involved interchange with the physical environment while others were more deeply rooted in the self, the degree to which confirmation of the hypotheses was expected varied according to the area. Thus, the areas, in their anticipated order of confirmation of housing-connectedness, were: reactions to housing and space, relations with neighbors, personal and family relations, attitudes and behavior toward neighborhood and community, social self-concept and aspirations, and psychological state.

The basic social adjustment findings presented in Chapters X through XV indicated that a majority of the items in each area showed at least a directional trend confirming the expectations specified for the area. However, in most of the areas, by no means all of the test-control differences confirming the hypotheses reached statistically acceptable levels of confidence. The anticipated order in which the areas would confirm the hypotheses was in general borne out, the one major exception being personal and family relations. The status of each area is indicated in the following brief review of the original expectations and the subsequent findings.

Reactions to housing and space

It was expected that, due to the alteration in numerous physical aspects of their housing, test women would be more likely than controls to express "positive" reactions to specific aspects of the housing environment, and would in other ways indicate awareness of the improvement in their living circumstances.

The data showed marked confirmation of the expectations. A larger proportion of test than control women liked their apartments, commented favorably on the safety of their children's play places, felt they were getting their money's worth for the amount of the rental, indicated an increased likelihood for personal privacy, and reported less friction and dissension directly related to space.

Relations with neighbors

Closer and more amicable relations with neighbors were expected to occur among test than among control families as a consequence of differences in their physical environments. Some of the factors in the housing project that were considered conducive to the formation of these relationships by the test group were: a dwelling architecture providing many opportunities for daily contact, a dwelling unit possessing some esthetic qualities and sufficient room space, and the existence of facilities used in common and under non-competitive circumstances.

The hypotheses of this content area were in general confirmed.

Notably, the rehoused families, in contrast to the controls, underwent a marked increase in neighborly interaction of a mutually supportive variety, such as helping out with household activities, with children, and in time of illness. This heightened interaction was not viewed as infringing on privacy. The test women were more likely than controls to report both pleasant *and* unpleasant experiences with nearby women, but they were also more apt to have formed new, close friendships in the immediate neighborhood.

Personal and family relations

Housing-related factors, such as greater space, and general practical and esthetic improvement of the dwelling unit were expected to be conducive to better personal relations within the test families, as manifested by an increase in mutually shared activities (in connection with both routine tasks and leisure-time pursuits), greater feelings of warmth and compatibility, and lessened friction among family members.

The data for this area showed directional trends confirming the hypotheses only in connection with common family activities and the mothers' reactions to, and discipline of, children. Other aspects of intrafamilial activities, cooperation, and affect revealed findings that were mixed or counter to the hypotheses.

Attitudes and behavior toward neighborhood and community

The project and the slum neighborhoods were viewed as differing from one another with respect to general physical characteristics, availability and accessibility of community facilities, characteristics of the inhabitants, and quality of the individual dwelling unit. It was expected that these factors would give rise to differences between the test and control groups in feelings of allegiance to, and interest in, the neighborhood, extent of participation in community and neighborhood activities, and in other indicators of good citizenship.

The findings revealed that test-control differences in the expected direction emerged in a number of matters related to the immediate neighborhood. Test respondents showed more pride in their immediate neighborhoods than did control respondents, reported more activities devoted to keeping up the neighborhood, and gave far more favorable views regarding its adequacy as a place to live and to raise children. Other topics which pertained more to the "broader" neighborhood or community, such as satisfaction with proximity to various facilities, interest in "larger issues," and evaluation of Baltimore as a place to live, showed either no systematic test-control differences or only a slight advantage for the test group.

Social self-concept and aspirations

Although change in perceived social status is customarily associated with altered occupation and income, it was anticipated that an alteration in housing quality, alone, and without attendant increment in income, might give rise to upgrading of self-perceived class affiliation, particularly for members of a socially and economically deprived group like the test families. This in turn led to the supposition that having achieved as self-concept the image of persons "on the way up," the test families might also acquire heightened aspirations: for themselves, in connection with such matters as home ownership or better jobs; for their children, in connection with schooling, future jobs, and other benefits.

In general, the findings revealed partial confirmation of the hypotheses. Test respondents, more than controls, were likely to indicate felt improvement in their position in life, and to report themselves as rising in the world. However, the expectation that heightened aspirations would accompany this perceived betterment was, with a few exceptions, generally not borne out.

Psychological state

It was expected that the move from a generally depressed and deprived environment to good housing might result, for the test women, in some psychological alterations. These changes were viewed as probably involving intermediary processes rather than being directly relatable to the more tangible, physical elements of housing quality improvement.

Findings for the series of ten psychosocial scales consisting of variables pertaining to the *self*, revealed directional trends confirming expectations on all the scales. Those topics dealing with general morale (Optimism-Pessimism, Satisfaction with Personal State of Affairs, and Potency) were more likely than the scales involving stressful, inner feeling states (Mood, Control of Temper, and Nervousness) to show test-control differences confirming the hypotheses.

School Performance of Children

Consideration of several direct and indirect outcomes of differences in test-control housing quality suggested the possibility of differential scholastic achievement of the test and control children. The housing variable expected to be most directly related to school performance was that of dwelling unit density which, being lower for the test children, was expected to provide greater opportunity to study and to do homework unhampered by interruptions from other family members. In addition, there was the possible advantage accruing to test children related to some other expected effects of good housing: better morale, increased parental aspirations for the education of children, and activities related to these aspirations. Finally, it was anticipated that illness rates, expected to be lower among test than control children, might also play a role in school performance.

To test these hypotheses, a total of 486 test and 510 control school-age children were identified in September, 1956. Approximately 150 in each group were excluded in the interest of maintaining uniformity of school records and in view of the unavailability of data on initial comparability. After follow-up losses, the records of 293 test and 287 control children attending Baltimore city public schools were examined for evidence relevant to school performance. Age, sex, and grade distributions showed a generally fair degree of comparability between the two groups of children, with test children tending to be slightly in excess in age 10 and under, and grade 5 and under.

Three types of tests were administered to Baltimore public school children: intelligence (Kuhlmann-Anderson and Otis), arithmetic achievement (Metropolitan and Stanford), and reading achievement (Iowa, Metropolitan, and Stanford). The data showed that these tests were administered fairly equally to test and control children, slight differences in pattern of administration being related to the age and grade differences.

Mean scores of the test and control children on the intelligence and achievement measurements were similar in the "before" period, thus indicating close initial comparability of the groups. *In the "after" period, mean test scores (adjusted for grade level of children tested) were also closely similar. Thus, the hypotheses regarding housing and one measure of school performance were not borne out.*

Examination of records of promotions showed that, in a one-year "before" period, test and control children were comparable in the proportions experiencing normal promotions from grade to grade. *In a two-year "after" period, test children were considerably more likely to be promoted at a normal pace, control children being held back more often for one or more semesters. In connection with record of promotions, then, study hypotheses were confirmed.*

Efforts to reconcile the findings regarding test performance and promotions suggest several possibilities. One is that promotion standards varied systematically in schools attended by test children in comparison with those attended by control children. There is no evidence in the data to indicate such differential standards. In fact, many test and control children attended the same schools. Where they attended different schools, it is worth noting that "test" and "control" schools were under the same general school administration.

Another possible reason for the test-control promotion difference is suggested by the data on daily attendance at school. Corresponding to morbidity differences already described, mean daily attendance of test children was considerably higher than that of control children.

Improved housing quality may thus play an indirect role in school performance of children in a way not completely anticipated by the original hypotheses, by lessening illness and in turn making possible more regular attendance at school. School promotion, while undoubtedly affected by intelligence and intellectual achievement as in more general school samples, is evidently also related in a significant way to regularity of school attendance. The data suggest a modest but specific illustration of the interweaving of environmental, physical, and social variables.

APPENDICES

APPENDIX 1

Selected Bibliography

1. Barer, N. A Note on Tuberculosis among Residents of a Housing Project. *J. Housing, 2,* 133, 1945.

2. ———. Delinquency Before, After Admission to New Haven Housing Development. *J. Housing, 3,* 27, 1945.

3. Benjamin, B. Tuberculosis and Social Conditions in the Metropolitan Boroughs of London. *Brit. J. Tuberc. and Dis. of Chest, 47,* 4-17, 1953.

4. Benjamin, J. E., J. W. Ruegsegger, and F. A. Senior. The Influence of Overcrowding on the Incidence of Pneumonia. *Ohio State Med. J., 36,* 1275-1281, 1940.

5. Bernstein, S. H. Observations on the Effects of Housing on the Incidence and Spread of Common Respiratory Diseases among Air Force Recruits. *Am. J. Hyg., 65,* 162-171, 1957.

6. Brett, G. Z., and B. Benjamin. Housing and Tuberculosis in a Mass Radiography Survey. *Brit. J. Prev. and Soc. Med., 11,* 7-9, 1957.

7. Britten, R. H., J. E. Brown, and I. Altman. Certain Characteristics of Urban Housing and Their Relation to Illness and Accidents: Summary of Findings of the National Health Survey. *Milbank Mem. Fund Quart., 18,* 91-113, 1940.

8. Britten, R. H., and I. Altman. Illness and Accidents among persons Living under Different Housing Conditions: Data Based on National Health Survey. *Pub. Hlth. Rep., 56,* 609-640, 1941.

9. Britten, R. H. New Light on the Relation of Housing to Health. *Am. J. Pub. Hlth., 32,* 193-199, 1942.

10. Chapin, F. S. An Experiment on the Social Effects of Good Housing. *Am. Soc. Rev., 5,* 868-879, 1940.

11. Christensen, V. Child Morbidity in a Good and a Bad Residential Area. *Danish Med. Bull., 3,* 93-98, 1956.

12. Coulter, J. E. Rheumatic Fever and Streptococcal Illness in Two Communities in New York State. *Milbank Mem. Fund Quart., 30,* 341-358, 1952.

255

13. Dirksen, C. *Economic Factors of Delinquency.* Bruce Publishing Company, Milwaukee, Wis., 1948. 91 p.

14. Downes, J., and K. Simon. Characteristics of Psychoneurotic Patients and Their Families as Revealed in a General Morbidity Study. *Milbank Mem. Fund Quart., 32,* 42-64, 1954.

15. Glueck, S., and E. Glueck. *One Thousand Juvenile Delinquents.* Harvard University Press, Cambridge, Mass., 1934. 341 p., Tables, Appendices.

16. Harlan, H., and J. Wherry. Delinquency and Housing. *Social Forces, 27,* 58-61, 1948.

17. Henzell, L. I. Housing Conditions and Tuberculosis. *Med. Officer, 62,* 200-201, 1939.

18. Keller, M. Progress in School of Children in a Sample of Families in the Eastern Health District of Baltimore. *Milbank Mem. Fund Quart., 31,* 391-410, 1953.

19. Lander, B. *Towards an Understanding of Juvenile Delinquency.* Columbia University Press, New York, N. Y., 1954. 143 p., Tables, Maps.

20. Loring, W. C., Jr. Housing Characteristics and Social Disorganization. *Soc. Prob., 3,* 160-168, 1956.

21. Lowell, A. M. *Socio-Economic Conditions and Tuberculosis Prevalence, New York City.* New York Tuberculosis and Health Association, 1956. 42 p., Statistical Section, Appendices.

22. Martin, F. M., J. H. F. Brotherson, and S. P. W. Chave. Incidence of Neurosis in a New Housing Estate. *Brit. J. Prev. and Soc. Med., 11,* 196-202, 1957.

23. Mackintosh, J. M. Housing and Tuberculosis. *Brit. J. Tuberc., 28,* 67-70, 1934.

24. McMillan, J. S. Examination of the Association Between Housing Conditions and Pulmonary Tuberculosis in Glasgow. *Brit. J. Prev. and Soc. Med., 11,* 142-151, 1957.

25. M'Gonigle, G. C. M. Poverty, Nutrition and Public Health. *Proc. Royal Soc. Med., 26,* 677-687, 1933.

26. Mogey, J. M. Changes in Family Life Experienced by English Workers Moving from Slums to Housing Estates. *Marriage and Fam. Liv., 17,* 123-128, 1955.

27. Murray, A. M. T. The Growth and Nutrition of the Slum Child in Relation to Housing—One and Two-roomed House. *J. Hyg., 26,* 198-203, 1927.

28. Nelson, H. Housing and Health. *Brit. Med. J., 2,* 395-397, 1945.

29. Ogburn, W. F. Factors in the Variation of Crime among Cities. *J. Amer. Stat. Assoc., 30,* 12-34, 1935.

30. Riley, I. D. Housing Conditions and Children in Hospital. *Glasgow Med. J., 36,* 393-397, 1955.

31. Rumney, J., and S. Shuman. *A Study of the Social Effects of Public Housing in Newark, New Jersey.* Housing Authority of the City of Newark, Newark, N. J., 1946. 78 p.

32. Savage, W. G. Tuberculosis and Housing in Rural Districts. *Brit. J. Tuberc., 13,* 160-162, 1919.

33. Schmitt, R. C. Housing and Health on Oahu. *Am. J. Pub. Hlth., 45,* 1538-1540, 1955.

34. ———. Density, Delinquency and Crime in Honolulu. *Soc. and Soc. Rsrch., 41,* 274-276, 1957.

35. Schroeder, C. Mental Disorders in Cities. *Am. J. Soc., 48,* 40-47, 1942.

36. Shaw, C. R., and H. D. McKay. Social Factors in Juvenile Delinquency. In: *Report on the Causes of Crime, Vol. II.* U. S. Government Printing Office, Washington, D. C., 1931. 401 p., Maps, Tables.

37. Slawson, J. *The Delinquent Boy.* Gorham Press, Boston, Mass., 1926. 477 p., Tables, Diagrams.

38. Spence, J., W. S. Walton, F. J. W. Miller, and S. D. M. Court. *A Thousand Families in Newcastle-upon-Tyne.* Oxford University Press, London, Toronto, New York, 1954. 217 p., Tables, Appendices.

39. Stein, L. A study of Respiratory Tuberculosis in Relation to Housing Conditions in Edinburgh. *Brit. J. Soc. Med., 4,* 143-169, 1950.

40. ———. Glasgow Tuberculosis and Housing. *Tubercle, 35,* 195-203, 1954.

41. Wilner, D. M., R. P. Walkley, and M. Tayback. How Does the Quality of Housing Affect Health and Family Adjustment? *Am. J. Pub. Hlth., 46,* 736-744, 1956.

42. Wilner, D. M., and R. P. Walkley. The Housing Environment and Mental Health. In: *Epidemiology of Mental Disorder,* ed. by B. Pasamanick. American Association for the Advancement of Science, 143-174, 1959.

43. Wilner, D. M., and R. P. Walkley. (Abridgement of preceding title.) *Pub. Hlth. Rep., 72,* 589-592, 1957.

44. Wilner, D. M., R. P. Walkley, M. Glasser, and M. Tayback. The Effects of Housing Quality on Morbidity—Preliminary Findings. *Am. J. Pub. Hlth., 48,* 1607-1615, 1958.

45. Wilner, D. M., R. P. Walkley, J. Schram, T. Pinkerton, and M. Tayback. Housing as an Environmental Factor in Mental Health: The Johns Hopkins Longitudinal Study. *Am. J. Pub. Hlth., 50,* 55-63, 1960.

46. Wilner, D. M., R. P. Walkley, H. Williams, and M. Tayback. The Baltimore Study on the Effects of Housing on Health. *Baltimore Health News, 37,* 45-50, 1960.

47. Wilner, D. M., R. P. Walkley, T. Pinkerton, and M. Tayback. The Housing Environment and Family Life. Working paper prepared for Expert Committee on Public Health Aspects of Housing, World Health Organization, Geneva, 1961.

APPENDIX 2

Pretesting the survey instruments and examples of the survey forms

Pretesting the survey instruments

All survey instruments were pretested on substantial samples of non-study families, some of whom lived in slum dwellings and some in good housing. For the Wave 1 instruments, 50 well-housed (public housing) and 50 poorly housed families constituted the pretest sample. The purposes of the pretests were as follows:

(a)   To establish the optimal wording of the questions

(b)   To establish the most appropriate ordering of the items

(c)   To obtain information regarding distribution of responses

(d)   To make actual quasi "test"-"control" analysis

The end product of the pretests was final interview schedules, considerably tightened up from the original pretest versions, appropriate in language to the study population, with response distribution that had sufficient variance to permit the detection of "gains," and with items which, at least in a cross-sectional sense, distinguished between well-housed and poorly housed families.

Pretests for morbidity and adjustment instruments used in subsequent waves followed the pattern of the Wave 1 pretest.

Examples of the survey forms

The following pages provide an example of each of the three major kinds of survey forms used in the study: morbidity (the Wave 11 form), social adjustment (the Wave 7 form), and housing quality (Multiple-Wave form).

An Example of the Morbidity Survey Form
(Wave 11)

```
┌──────────────────────────────────────────────────────┬──────┐
│ ┌─────────────────────────────────┐                  │  11  │
│ │                                 │                  │      │
│ │  SERIAL NUMBER                  │                  │      │
│ └─────────────────────────────────┘                  │      │
```

BALTIMORE HEALTH QUESTIONNAIRE

Baltimore Study of Health and Adjustment	April, 1958
School of Hygiene and Public Health	Wave H–11
The Johns Hopkins University	

Interviewer's name _____ No. _____

Interview began _____ (a.m.) (p.m.) ended _____ (a.m.) (p.m.)

Date of Interview_____ Questionnaire _____ of _____ questionnaires

Date of last interview_____

Respondent's name _____ _____ _____

Address _____

WAVE

		LAST NAME ①	LAST NAME ②
1. (a) Will you please tell me if each of the following people is living here now? Your_____(Relationship and name) — is (he) living here now? How about your_____(Relationship and name)? (Etc. Get answer person by person. If "No", ascertain reason; enter reason and departure date in footnote.) (b) Have any new children or grownups been added to the household since we talked with you in_____ (Month of last interview)? Any new babies? (Do not enumerate anyone listed in the "Deletes" box.)		FIRST NAME & INITIAL	FIRST NAME & INITIAL
2. (Questions 2a, 2b, 2c, are to be asked only for new additions to household.) (a) How is_____ related to you?		RESPONDENT	RELATIONSHIP
3. Now I have some questions about your family's health. We are interested in any sickness whether serious or not, even though you might have told us about it before. (Were you) sick at any time during the past two months, that is since_____ (Date 2 calendar months previously)? (If "Yes"): (a) What was the matter? (If pre-recorded chronic condition, write "Yes" in "2 mos" column) (b) (Were you) sick with anything else during the past two months? How about_____ , (was_____ sick at any time during the past two months)?		☐ NO	

4. In the next questions please keep in mind each member of your household.	Check off		
(a) cold?	(a)		
During the past two months has ANYONE had (a)	(b) long-lasting skin rash or breaking out on any part of the body or head? (If "Yes"): What was the matter? — — Cause? — — Any other?	(b)		
	(c) severe stomach upset, with loose bowels, nausea, vomiting or constipation? (If "Yes"): What was the matter? — — Cause? — — Any other?	(c)		
	(d) frequent headaches? (If "Yes"): What caused the headaches?	(d)		
	(e) accidents, big or little, either around the house or away from home? (If "Yes"): What part of the body was hurt? Type injury? — — Any other?	(e)		
	(f) frequent aches or pains in any part of the body? (If "Yes"): What was the matter? — — Cause?	(f)		

	5, 6	2 MOS.	5,6
5. (If at least one pre-recorded entry in a column) (a) We (also) have listed . . . . as giving (you) trouble sometimes. (Were you) bothered by . . . . in the past two months, that is since_____ ? (Date 2 calendar months previously) (Enter "Yes" or "No" in Col: "2 mos")			
(b) During the past two months (were you) bothered by any OTHER chronic conditions or ailments? (If "Yes"): (1) What are they? (Enter "Yes" in Col: "2 mos.") (2) (Have you) been bothered by any OTHER chronic conditions or ailments?			
6. (If no pre-recorded entry in a column) During the past two months (were you) bothered by any CHRONIC conditions or ailments (that keep coming back — even if they don't bother (you) all the time)? (If "Yes"): (a) What are they? (Enter "Yes" in Col: "2 mos") (b) (Were you) bothered by any OTHER chronic conditions or ailments in the past two months? How about_____ , (was_____ bothered by any CHRONIC conditions during the past two months)?			

| 7. During the past two months did ANYONE in the household spend overnight or longer in a hospital or T.B. sanitarium? (If "Yes", ascertain WHO and FOR WHAT. If previously recorded enter Ⓗ after appropriate condition.) | ☐ YES
☐ NO | | |

2. (b) Sex: (If not clear from name, ask): **Is that a (boy or girl) (man or woman)?**	☐ MALE ☐ FEMALE	☐ MALE
(c) **How old (were you) on (your) last birthday?** (For children under 1 year of age, enter number of months old)	AGE	AGE
(d) **What (do you) do at present —** { work full or part time keep house go to school or something else? (If "something else", ask): **(Are you) not working because of a serious** physical condition, because (you are) unemployed, or for some other reason? (For children under 2 years of age, check "Other reason" without asking Q.)	☐ FULL TIME ☐ UNEMPLOYED ☐ PART TIME ☐ SCHOOL ☐ KEEP HOUSE ☐ SERIOUS PHYSICAL CONDITION ☐ OTHER REASON (E.G., RE- TIRED, UNDER SCHOOL AGE)	☐ FULL TIME ☐ U ☐ PART TIME ☐ S ☐ KEEP HOUSE ☐ SERIOUS PHYSI- CAL CONDITION ☐ OTHER REASON (RETIRED, UNDER SCHOOL AGE)
(e) (If child 12 years of age or older AND if "go to school"): **Does (he) also have a part-time job, a full-time job, or no job at all?**	☐ PART ☐ FULL ☐ NO	☐ PART ☐ FULL

						FOLLOW-UP OF

WAVE 11

9.	10.	11.	12.	13.	(DO NOT USE THIS SPACE)	14.	15.
(Enter person no.)	(Enter question no.)	(Enter Ⓗ for each condition for which person was hospitalized during past 2 mos.)	(If not Ⓗ): Was a doctor seen about . . . . in the past two months? (Enter "Yes" or "No") (If Ⓗ enter Ⓗ)	a. (If "No" to Q. 12 enter condition, or cause, if symptom. Then skip to Q. 15.) b. (If "Yes" to Q. 12 ask) c. (If Ⓗ to Q. 12, ask; then skip to Q. 15) What did the doctor say . . . . was? Did he use any (other) medical names? (If accident, enter part of body affected and type of injury; also ask for external cause and place of occurrence — i.e. dwelling unit, building, or other)		(a) Did (you) see the doctor as a clinic patient or as a private patient? (b) What is (the clinic's name) (the doctor's name and address)? (If outside of Baltimore, ascertain city or county and state)	(Were you) bothered by . . . . . yesterday or not?
					CLIN.		
					PR.	————————————	
					CLIN.		
					PR.	————————————	
					CLIN.		
					PR.	————————————	
					CLIN.		
					PR.	————————————	
					CLIN.		
					PR.	————————————	
					CLIN.		
					PR.	————————————	

CONDITIONS   **WAVE 11**   **DELETES**

16. (IF HOSPITALIZED — PAST 2 MONTHS)   **17. During the past 2 months:**

(a) What was the date (you) entered the hospital?	(b) How many days (were you) in the hospital because of..... not counting the day (you) left?	(c) What was the name of the hospital? (If outside of Baltimore, ascertain city or county and state)	(a,b) Did . . . . keep (you) from (your) usual activities or cause (you) to spend any days or parts of any days in bed (at home)? (If "Yes"): a. How many days in bed? b. How many (other) days were (you) kept from (your) usual activities?		(c) Were there any (other) days when (you) just didn't feel well because of. . . .? (If "Yes"): How many days?	(d) (Ask after last condition for each person.) Did any of these conditions bother (you) on the same days, that is (your) . . . . (or your) . . . .? Mention conditions for which days are enumerated, only). (If "Yes"): Which conditions?
			BED	**ACTIV.**		
			·			

FOOTNOTES

An Example of the Social Adjustment Survey Form
(Wave 7)

	Serial Number

Baltimore Study of Health and Adjustment   March, 1957

School of Hygiene and Public Health   Wave S-7

The Johns Hopkins University

Interviewer's name _____ No. _____

Interview began _____ (a.m.) (p.m.) ended _____ (a.m.) (p.m.)

Date of interview_____

Respondent's name _____

                Address _____

- 1 -

In order to really understand what makes people healthy, we need to know a little about them besides what sickness they may have had. It will help, for instance, to know something about how they live, what they do, how they feel about various general matters, and so on.

I would now like to ask you some questions about a few things like that. Please keep in mind that there are no right or wrong answers to the questions. I would just like to know what you do, or how you feel about these things.

4. In general, how do you feel about living in Baltimore: would you say it is --

    (1)_____Very good as a place to live,
    (2)_____Fairly good, or
    (3)_____Not very good as a place to live?

6. Which neighborhood do you think of as your real home -- that is, where you feel you really belong: would you say --

    (1)_____This neighborhood,
    (2)_____Some other neighborhood in Baltimore, or
    (3)_____Some neighborhood outside of Baltimore?
    (4)_____No special place
    (5)_____Don't know

8. In general, would you say this (project) (neighborhood) is --

    (1)_____Very good as a place to live,
    (2)_____Fairly good,
    (3)_____Not so good, or
    (4)_____Not good at all as a place to live?

9. (a). How well do you feel this (project) (neighborhood) is kept up, that is, in the way it looks: would you say it is --

        (1)_____Very well kept up,
        (2)_____Fairly well,
        (3)_____Rather poorly, or
        (4)_____Very poorly kept up?
        (5)_____Don't know

    (b). How interested are you in keeping up the (project) (neighborhood), that is, in the way it looks: would you say you are --

        (1)_____Very interested,
        (2)_____Fairly interested,
        (3)_____Not much interested, or
        (4)_____Not at all interested?

        (IF "VERY INTERESTED" OR "FAIRLY INTERESTED"): What have you done to keep it up?

        _____

        _____

        _____

    (1)_____Nothing

- 2 -

10. How good is this (project) (neighborhood) as a place to raise children: would you say --

(1)____Very good, (2)____Fairly good, (3)____Rather poor, or

(4)____Very poor?

⟹ Why do you say that?

_____

_____

_____

_____

14. In general, how do you like your apartment: would you say you like it --

(1)____A lot, (2)____Quite a bit, (3)____Only a little, or (4)____Not at all?

15. What do you like most about your apartment?

_____

_____

_____

_____

16. What don't you like about your apartment?

_____

_____

_____

_____

17. Do you feel that for what you are getting, the rent you pay for this apartment is high, about right or low?

(1)____High (2)____About right (3)____Low (4)____Don't know

- 3 -

23. How good do you think the chances are of your owning your own home some day:
would you say your chances are --

(1)_____Very good,
(2)_____Fairly good
(3)_____Not very good, or
(4)_____Not at all good?
(5)_____Don't know how good chances are
(6)___Don't want to own home, don't care, doesn't make any difference
(7)___Already owns or is buying home

25. About how many times during the month have you been going to church services,
including week days as well as Sundays?

(1)_____More than four times a month (more than once a week)
(2)_____Four times a month (once a week)
(3)_____Two or three times a month
(4)_____Once a month
(5)_____Less than once a month
(6)_____Never

26. (a). Do you belong to or take part in any clubs or groups such as social,
religious, civic, or any other groups?

_____Yes   (9)_____No

↳(IF "YES"): What are their names?
(ENTER NAME OF EACH GROUP ON A SEPARATE LINE.
IF TYPE OF GROUP IS NOT CLEAR FROM NAME, ASK:
"What kind of group is that?")

Name of club or group	Kind of Club or group

(b). (FOR NON-PROJECT RESIDENTS): (Does this group) (do any of these groups)
meet in this neighborhood?

(1)_____Yes (one or more meets in this neighborhood)
(2)_____No (none meets in this neighborhood)

(FOR PROJECT RESIDENTS): (Does this group) (do any of these groups)
meet in this project?

(1)_____Yes (one or more meets in this project)
(2)_____No (none meets in this project)

- 4 -

31. People have different opinions on how important certain ideas are. Please tell me how important the following idea is to you.

    How important is it to plan ahead step-by-step for the things you will be doing next year or the year after: would you say it is --

    (1)_____ Very important, (2)_____ Fairly important, or

    (3)_____ Not very important? (4)_____ Don't know

32. Compared to three years ago, do you feel you are --

    (1)_____ Better off in life now than you were then,
    (2)_____ About the same now as then, or
    (3)_____ Worse off in life now than you were then?

    ⟹ Why do you say that?

    _____

    _____

    _____

    _____

33. In general, how well do you like the people who live around here: would you say you like them --

    (1)_____ A lot, (2)_____ Quite a bit, or (3)_____ Only a little?

    (4)_____ Not at all (5)_____ Don't know

36. In general, how would you describe the people who live around here: would you say they --

(1)		(2)		(3)	
_____	Are loud and noisy	or _____	Quiet?	_____	Don't know
_____	Are unfriendly	or _____	Friendly?	_____	Don't know
_____	Don't help one another out	or _____	Do help one another out?	_____	Don't know
_____	Tend to stick their nose in other people's business	or _____	Mind their own business?	_____	Don't know
_____	Do quite a bit of drinking	or _____	Don't do much drinking?	_____	Don't know
_____	Have badly behaved children	or _____	Have well behaved children?	_____	Don't know
_____	Quarrel a lot	or _____	Don't quarrel much?	_____	Don't know
_____	Are clean	or _____	Dirty?	_____	Don't know

(1)	(2)	(3)

- 5 -

37. How many women around here do you know well enough to say "hello" to?

     ____None   ____1 to 4   ____5 to 9   ____10 to 14   ____15 to 19
      (1)   (2)   (3)   (4)   (5)
     ____More than 19   ____Can't decide
      (6)   (7)

44. How often do neighbors drop in when you'd rather they would not: would you say --

      (1)   Very often,
      (2)   Fairly often,
      (3)   Hardly ever, or
      (4)   Never?

             → (IF OTHER THAN "NEVER"): How much does their dropping in bother
                     you: would you say --

                       (1)____A lot, (2)____A little, or

                       (3)____Not at all?

46. About how often do people -- not counting relatives -- visit you for an evening, that is, about how many times a week?

      (1)   3 or more evenings a week
      (2)   1 or 2 evenings a week (or 4 times a month)
      (3)   Less than once a week (but at least 1, 2, or 3 times a month)
      (4)   Less than once a month
      (5)   Never

47. About how many times a week do you visit people -- not counting relatives -- for an evening?

      (1)   3 or more evenings a week
      (2)   1 or 2 evenings a week (or 4 times a month)
      (3)   Less than once a week (but at least 1, 2, or 3 times a month)
      (4)   Less than once a month
      (5)   Never

    → (IF OTHER THAN "NEVER" TO EITHER Q. 46 OR Q. 47, ASK Q. 48; OTHERWISE SKIP TO Q. 49)

- 6 -

48. In general, where do most of the people live whom you visit for an evening or who visit you: do they live --

    (CHECK AS MANY AS NECESSARY IN APPROPRIATE GROUP)

    (FOR NON-PROJECT RESIDENTS):

    (1) _____ In this building,
    (2) _____ Somewhere else in this block,
    (3) _____ Not in this block but within 4 to 5 blocks of here, or
    (4) _____ Farther away than that?

    (FOR PROJECT RESIDENTS WHERE THE ENTRANCE FROM OUTDOORS TO THIS APT. IS SHARED WITH ONE OR MORE OTHER APTS., INCL. TALL BUILDINGS IN L.C.):

    (1) _____ On this floor,
    (2) _____ In this building but not on this floor,
    (3) _____ In some other buildings in the project, or
    (4) _____ Outside the project?

    (FOR PROJECT RESIDENTS WHERE THE ENTRANCE FROM OUTDOORS TO THIS APT. IS PRIVATE i.e., NOT SHARED WITH ONE OR MORE OTHER APTS., INCL. SMALL BUILDINGS IN L.C.):

    (1) _____ In this building,
    (2) _____ In some other buildings in the project, or
    (3) _____ Outside the project?

49. Sometimes people don't invite their friends to their home as often as they would like, because they feel they don't have enough space to entertain them. Have you ever felt this way about your present apartment?

    (1) _____ Yes   (2) _____ No

50. Sometimes people don't invite other people into their home because they feel their home doesn't look quite nice enough. Have you ever felt this way about your present apartment?

    (1) _____ Yes   (2) _____ No

    =====> Why do you say that?

    _____

    _____

    _____

    _____

51. Did you vote in the election last November?

    (1) _____ Yes   (2) _____ No   (3) _____ Can't remember

- 7 -

> IF AT LEAST ONE CHILD 16 YEARS OF AGE OR YOUNGER,
> ASK FOLLOWING QUESTIONS; OTHERWISE SKIP TO Q. 76

63. Through what grade in school do you hope to be able to send (your child) (your children)?

    (1)_____Through grade school or less (any grade 1 to 6)
    (2)_____To junior high school (grade 7, 8 or 9)
    (3)_____Part way through high school (grade 10 or 11)
    (4)_____Through high school graduation (grade 12)
    (5)_____Part way through college
    (6)_____Through college graduation or more
    (7)_____Don't know

64. How good do you think the chances are of sending (your child) (your children) that far through school: would you say your chances are --

    (1)_____Very good, (2)_____Fairly good, (3)_____Not very good, or

    (4)_____Not at all good? (5)_____Don't know

> IF AT LEAST ONE CHILD BETWEEN 3 AND 16 YEARS OF AGE,
> ASK FOLLOWING QUESTIONS; OTHERWISE SKIP TO Q. 76

66. [Now please keep in mind only your ____, ____, ____, ... year old(s). (MENTION AGES OF ALL CHILDREN BETWEEN 3 AND 16)]

Where (does this child) (do these children) play most often?

    (CHECK AS MANY AS NECESSARY IN APPROPRIATE GROUP)

(FOR NON-PROJECT RESIDENTS):

    (1)_____Indoors
    (2)_____In the yard
    (3)_____On the street
    (4)_____On a playground
    (5)_____Somewhere else. Where? _____
    (6)_____Don't know

(FOR PROJECT RESIDENTS):

    (1)_____In this apartment or some other apartment(s)
    (2)_____In the outdoor corridor or play area ("tot lot") in one of the tall buildings
    (3)_____Just outside the building
    (4)_____On a playground in the project
    (5)_____On a playground outside the project
    (6)_____On the street in the project
    (7)_____On the street outside the project
    (8)_____In the community building
    (9)_____Somewhere else. Where? _____
    (0)_____Don't know

- 8 -

67. From your point of view, how satisfactory are the places where (this child plays) (these children play) most often: would you say the places are --

     (1)____ Very satisfactory,
     (2)____ Fairly satisfactory,
     (3)____ Not very satisfactory, or
     (4)____ Not at all satisfactory?

     ========> Why do you say that?

     _____

     _____

     _____

     _____

69. How often do you have to discipline or correct (this child) (these children): would you say --

     (1)____ Very often, (2)____ Fairly often, (3)____ Hardly ever, or (4)____ Never?

     ┌───┐
     │ IF AT LEAST ONE CHILD BETWEEN 6 AND 16 YEARS OF AGE,   │
     │ ASK FOLLOWING QUESTIONS; OTHERWISE SKIP TO Q. 76   │
     └───┘

74. [Now please keep in mind only your _____, _____, _____, ... year old(s).
     (MENTION AGES OF ALL CHILDREN BETWEEN 6 AND 16)]

     About how many times during the month (does this child) (do these children) go to Sunday School?

     (1)____ Four times a month (once a week)
     (2)____ Two or three times a month
     (3)____ Once a month
     (4)____ Less than once a month
     (5)____ Never

- 9 -

75. (a). (Does this child) (do any of these children) belong to or take part
         in any clubs or groups such as social, hobby, sports, school,
         religious, or any other groups?

                    ___Yes   (9)____No

                    └──→ (IF "YES"): What are the names of the clubs or groups?
                         (ENTER NAME OF EACH GROUP ON A SEPARATE LINE.
                         IF TYPE OF GROUP IS NOT CLEAR FROM NAME, ASK:
                         "What kind of group is that?")

Name of club or group	Kind of club or group

    (b). (FOR NON-PROJECT RESIDENTS): (Does this group) (do any of these
                                       groups) meet in this neighborhood?

                    (1)____Yes (one or more meets in this neighborhood)
                    (2)____No (none meets in this neighborhood)

        (FOR PROJECT RESIDENTS): (Does this group) (do any of these groups)
                                  meet in this project?

                    (1)____Yes (one or more meets in this project)
                    (2)____No (none meets in this project)

76. | REFER TO H QUESTIONNAIRE; CHECK ONE OF THE FOLLOWING CATEGORIES
     (WITHOUT ASKING QUESTION):

        (1)____R MARRIED NOW AND HUSBAND LIVING WITH FAMILY

        (2)____R MARRIED NOW BUT HUSBAND NOT LIVING WITH FAMILY, OR
               R NOT MARRIED NOW

- 10 -

> IF AT LEAST 2 ADULTS, OR IF 1 ADULT, AT LEAST 1
> CHILD 10 YEARS OF AGE OR OLDER, ASK FOLLOWING
> QUESTIONS; OTHERWISE SKIP TO Q. 86

77. We are interested in what things family members do together. How often do
ANY of the members of your family who live in this apartment do anything
together like --

	(1) Often	(2) Some- times, or	(3) Never?
Go shopping together: would you say....			
Sit and talk in the apartment?			
Go for walks together: would you say....			
Go to the movies together?			
Listen to the radio or watch TV together?			
	(1)	(2)	(3)

79. In general, how often do the members of the family who live in this apartment
do things to help one another out: would you say --

(1)_____Very often, (2)_____Fairly often, (3)_____Occasionally, or (4)_____Never?

85. In general, how much do the members of your family who live in this apartment
actually enjoy being together: would you say --

(1)_____A lot, (2)_____Quite a bit, (3)_____Only a little, or (4)_____Not at all?

=====> Why do you say that?

_____

_____

_____

_____

- 11 -

IF "R MARRIED NOW AND HUSBAND LIVING
WITH FAMILY", ASK FOLLOWING QUESTIONS;
OTHERWISE SKIP TO Q. 106

86. (a). How much does your husband help you out around the house: would you say --

(1)_____A lot, (2)_____Quite a bit, (3)_____Only a little, or

(4)_____Not at all?

(b). How much would you like to have him help you out around the house: would you say --

(1)_____A lot, (2)_____Quite a bit, (3)_____Only a little, or

(4)_____Not at all?

94. Did your husband vote in the election last November?

(1)_____Yes   (2)_____No   (3)_____Don't know

The personal feelings that people have about different things are of great importance in understanding what makes people healthy. I would now like to ask you a number of questions about yourself.

Following are some questions about yourself which are to be answered by a "Yes" or a "No". These questions are quite general and most people have no difficulty in answering them simply "Yes" or "No".

	(1) Yes	(2) No	(3) Don't Know
106. Is it often hard for you to control your temper?			
108. When you are angry, do you sometimes say things which you are sorry about later?			
109. Are you one of those persons who never gets nervous?			
111. Are you often so nervous or upset that you can't go on with what you are doing?			
	(1)	(2)	(3)

- 12 -

		(1)	(2)	(3)
		Yes	No	Don't Know
113.	Can you say that you hardly ever feel blue?			
114.	Do you generally take things calmly without getting upset?			
117.	Are you sometimes so blue that you feel there's no use going on?			
118.	Do you often feel that you are about to go to pieces?			
120.	Are you almost always able to control your temper completely?			
121.	Do little things often make you feel blue?			
123.	Are you the sort of person who almost never gets angry?			
125.	Can you usually control your temper pretty well, even when someone provokes you?			
129.	Are there times when you are so blue that you want to cry?			
130.	Are you a nervous person?			
		(1)	(2)	(3)

Now I would like to read you a number of statements that may or may not be true as far as you are concerned. If the statement is true for you or applies to you in your present situation, you can answer by saying "true". If it does not apply to you, you can answer by saying "not true".

For example, here is the first statement: "I'm really very happy about the way I've been getting along lately." Would you say that is "true" for you or "not true"?

- 13 -

		(1) True	(2) Not True	(3) Don't Know, Can't Decide
131.	I'm really very happy about the way I've been getting along lately.			
132.	When you come right down to it, there's nothing you can do to make things really better for yourself.			
133.	It's hardly fair to bring a child into the world the way things look for the future.			
134.	There's no reason to believe that things are going to be a great deal better in the future.			
135.	Everything seems to go wrong for me nowadays.			
136.	It's all right to try to improve yourself but things being the way they are, don't count on being able to accomplish too much.			
137.	Things will get better only if you actually get out and do something to make them better.			
138.	If things seem to be going well for a while, there's usually some trouble right around the corner.			
139.	I'm generally satisfied with the way things are going for me.			
140.	It's better not to look on the bright side of things because you will only be disappointed in the end.			
141.	No matter how hard you try, there's not much you can do to make a real change for the better.			
142.	Life is treating me pretty bad right now.			
143.	You can work and work and in the end you're back about where you started.			
		(1)	(2)	(3)

- 14 -

Would you say "true" or "not true" to the following statements?

	(1) True	(2) Not True	(3) Don't Know, Can't Decide
144. What young people need most of all is strict discipline.			
145. Any good leader should be strict with people under him in order to gain their respect.			
146. Most children get into trouble because their parents have not been strict enough with them.			
147. A good leader doesn't have to be strict.			
148. If you don't discipline a child from time to time, you will spoil him.			
	(1)	(2)	(3)

149. Do you have your own --

	(1) Yes	(2) No
TV set?		
Radio?		
Washing Machine?		
Car?		
Telephone?		
	(1)	(2)

CHECK COMPLETENESS OF QUESTIONNAIRE:
GO BACK TO THE BEGINNING -- Q. 4 -- AND INSPECT EACH QUESTION, INCLUDING
FREE-COMMENTS, FOR AN ENTRY IN EACH APPROPRIATE QUESTION. IF ANY QUESTION
HAS BEEN OMITTED THAT SHOULD HAVE BEEN ASKED, ASK IT BEFORE TERMINATING
INTERVIEW.

An Example of the Housing Quality Survey Form

Serial Number

Baltimore Study of Health and Adjustment   Mo. _____ Yr. _____

School of Hygiene and Public Health   Wave H- _____(Suppl.)

The Johns Hopkins University

Interviewer's name _____ No. _____

Interview began _____ (a.m.) (p.m.) ended _____ (a.m.) (p.m.)

Date of interview _____

Respondent's name _____

        Address _____

- 1 -

1.(a) How many separate rooms do the members of your household have in this apartment, not counting the bathroom? Please keep in mind that I would like you to count a room only if it is completely separated by walls or by floor-to-ceiling partitions from all other rooms in the apartment.

    _____ Number of rooms

        (COUNT AS A SEPARATE ROOM: A KITCHEN, KITCHENETTE, "HALF ROOM", ETC., WHICH IS PARTITIONED OFF FROM FLOOR TO CEILING.

        COUNT AS ONLY ONE ROOM: A COMBINED KITCHENETTE AND DINETTE, OR A COMBINED KITCHENETTE AND LIVING ROOM, OR A COMBINED LIVINGROOM AND BEDROOM, ETC., THAT ARE SEPARATED ONLY BY SHELVES, SCREENS OR CABINETS)

⟹ (IF ONLY 1 ROOM, SKIP TO Q. 3)

  (b) (IF 2 OR MORE ROOMS NOW RECORDED IN Q. 1(a)): In these _____ rooms (NUMBER MENTIONED IN Q. 1(a)), have you counted any halls or entrance-ways as a room? Any closets or places used entirely for storage? Have you counted as a room, a kitchen that is just set in the wall of another room?

        _____Yes (IF ANY "YES", CROSS OUT FIGURE ENTERED ON LINE: "NUMBER OF ROOMS" IN Q. 1(a), AND ENTER CORRECTED FIGURE)
        _____No (to all items)

2.(a) (IF 2 OR MORE ROOMS NOW RECORDED IN Q. 1(a)): How many of the _____ rooms (NUMBER MENTIONED IN Q. 1(a)) that you have in this apartment are used regularly as rooms to sleep in?

    _____ Number of rooms used regularly as sleeping rooms

⟹ (IF ONLY 1 SLEEPING ROOM, SKIP TO Q. 3)

  (b) (IF 2 OR MORE SLEEPING ROOMS): Who sleeps in the first sleeping room?

        (ENTER PERSON NUMBER(S) IN CHART BELOW. ASK ABOUT EACH SLEEPING ROOM RECORDED IN Q. 2(a))

	Person Number(s)	Is this room also used for anything other than sleeping?		(IF "YES"): What else is it used for? Anything else?
		No	Yes	
1st Sleeping Room			⟶	
2nd Sleeping Room			⟶	
3rd Sleeping Room			⟶	
4th Sleeping Room			⟶	
5th Sleeping Room			⟶	
6th Sleeping Room			⟶	

  (c) (FOR EACH PERSON NOT ACCOUNTED FOR IN Q. 2(b)): Where does _____ (NAME OF PERSON) sleep? (ASCERTAIN WHICH SLEEPING ROOM AND ENTER PERSON NUMBER ON APPROPRIATE LINE)

- 2 -

3. Now I would like to ask you about the kitchen facilities you have here. How do you keep food cold --

    _____ In a gas or electric refrigerator,
    _____ In an icebox which uses blocks of ice, or
    _____ In something else? What? _____

4. How good is the _____ (REFRIGERATION FACILITY MENTIONED IN Q.3) for keeping food from spoiling: would you say it is --

    _____Very good,   _____Fairly good,   _____Not very good, or   _____Not at all
                                                                                                                          good?

5. What kind of stove do you have for cooking: do you have --

    _____ A gas or electric stove,
    _____ An electric hot plate,
    _____ A coal, wood, or oil stove, or
    _____ Something else? What? _____

6. How good is the _____ (COOKING FACILITY MENTIONED IN Q.5) for doing the amount of cooking you have to do: would you say it is --

    _____Very good,   _____Fairly good,   _____Not very good, or   _____Not at all
                                                                                                                          good?

7. Does the kitchen have a sink with both running water and a drainpipe?

    _____Yes (sink with both running water and drainpipe)   _____No

8. Do you share the use of either the _____ (REFRIGERATION FACILITY MENTIONED IN Q.3), or the _____(COOKING FACILITY MENTIONED IN Q.5), (or the kitchen sink) with someone who is not a member of your household?

    _____Yes (share any or all facilities)

    _____No   (share no facility)

9. (Besides the kitchen sink) is there a wash basin with both running water and a drainpipe, in this apartment?

    _____Yes (wash basin with both running water and drainpipe)   _____No

10. Is there a washing machine or a regular laundry tub with both running water and a drainpipe someplace in the building that you can use?

    _____Yes (either or both)   _____No (neither)

- 3 -

11. Where is the toilet located?

     _____In the apartment (whether or not part of a regular bathroom)
     _____Someplace else in the building
     _____Outside the building

12. Is it the kind of toilet that is flushed with running water?

     _____Yes _____No

     → (IF "YES"): Is it --

               _____The glazed white kind with standing water in
               the bottom of the bowl, or
               _____The metal kind with no standing water in the
               bottom of the bowl?

13. Do you share the use of the toilet with someone who is not a member of your household?

     _____Yes _____No

14. How often is the toilet out of order: would you say --

     _____Often, _____Sometimes, _____Hardly ever, or _____Never?

15. Does your family have the use of --

	Yes	No
A bathtub?		
A shower?		

     → (IF "YES" TO EITHER OR BOTH, ASK
     FOLLOWING QUESTIONS; OTHERWISE SKIP
     TO Q.21)

16. Where is the bathtub located?

     _____In the apartment (whether or not part of a regular bathroom)
     _____Someplace else in the building
     _____Outside the building

17. Do you share the use of the bathtub with someone who is not a member of your household?

     _____Yes _____No

- 4 -

18. Is the bathtub in working order?

_____Yes   _____No

19. Does the bathtub have hot running water?

_____Yes   _____No

21. Do you have both hot and cold running water in this apartment?

_____Yes, have both hot and cold
_____No, have cold, only
_____No, have hot, only
_____No, have no running water in apartment

→(IF "NO, HAVE NO RUNNING WATER IN APARTMENT"): Can you get both hot and cold running water from someplace else in the building?

_____Yes, can get both hot and cold
_____No, can get cold, only
_____No, can get hot, only
_____No, can get no running water in building

22. Regarding the amount of hot water you have here, would you way you have as much as you need --

_____All of the time,   _____Most of the time,   _____Only some of the time, or

_____Almost never?

23. How is your apartment heated?

_____Central heating: single furnace in basement or elsewhere that supplies heat to all or some rooms (whether or not local room heaters are also used)

_____No central heating: only stove(s) or heater(s) in one or more rooms that are not connected to a central system; or no heating at all

- 5 -

24. Is there a radiator, stove or heater of some kind in <u>all</u> the rooms in your apartment?

    _____Yes   (all rooms have a radiator, stove or heater)
    _____No   (at least one room does <u>not</u> have a radiator, stove or heater)

      → (IF "NO"): Do <u>all</u> the rooms that lack a radiator, stove or heater get enough heat from other rooms to be comfortable?

              _____Yes (all rooms get enough heat)
              _____No (at least one room does <u>not</u> get enough heat)

25. Regarding the amount of heat you have here, would you say you <u>have as much as you need</u> --

_____All of the time,   _____Most of the time,   ___Only some of the time, or

_____Almost never?

26. Are there any "blind" rooms in your apartment -- that is, rooms that do not have windows opening to the outside?

    _____Yes   _____No (<u>all</u> rooms have outside windows)

      → (IF "YES"): (Is this "blind" room) (Are any of these "blind" rooms) used for sleeping?

              _____Yes   _____No (<u>no</u> "blind" rooms used for sleeping)

27. Are there any rooms in this apartment that do <u>not</u> have electric lighting?

    _____Yes   _____No (<u>all</u> rooms have electric lighting)

      → (IF "YES"): Is it because there is no electric fixture or outlet, <u>or</u> because the electric fixture or outlet is not in working order?

              _____No electric fixture or outlet
              _____Electric fixture or outlet is not in working order

              _____Something else. What? _____

28. Is the paint peeling or flaking on any of the window sills or walls anywhere in the apartment?

    _____Yes   _____No

- 6 -

29. Are there any leaks in the pipes or plumbing anywhere in this apartment?

_____Yes   _____No

30. Do you have anything in this apartment such as --

	Yes	No
Cockroaches?		
Flies?		
Mice?		
Rats?		
Bedbugs?		

31. Are there any garbage cans someplace <u>outside</u> the apartment that you can use?

_____Yes   _____No

→ (IF "YES"): Are there enough garbage cans <u>outside</u> the apartment so there is no overflow of garbage?

_____Yes   _____No

→ (IF "YES"): Do any of the garbage cans <u>outside</u> the apartment have loose-fitting lids or no lids at all?

_____Yes (at least one can has loose-fitting lid or no lid at all)

_____No (all cans have lids and none is loose-fitting)

> IF APARTMENT IS LOCATED ON 2ND FLOOR
> OR HIGHER, ASK FOLLOWING QUESTION

32. Is there a fire escape from this floor to the ground floor that you can use?

_____No   _____Yes

→ (IF "NO"): Are there two separate <u>stairways</u> from this floor to the ground floor that you can use?

_____Yes   _____No

→ (IF "YES"): Are there also two separate <u>doors</u> to the street that you can use on the ground floor?

_____Yes (two separate doors)
_____No   (only one door)

- 7 -

APARTMENT

D. Condition of interior of apartment (plaster or wood of floor, walls, ceiling, doorsills, doorframes)

	Yes	No	Unable to observe
Critical deficiencies			
*Substantial sagging of FLOOR or WALLS			
*Holes, open cracks, rotted, loose or missing materials over a considerable area of FLOOR, WALLS, or CEILING			
Minor deficiencies			
Holes, open cracks, rotted, loose or missing materials over a small area of FLOOR, WALLS, or CEILING			
Deep wear on DOORSILLS, DOORFRAMES, or FLOOR			

INTERIOR OF BUILDING

A. Condition of interior halls and stairs (plaster or wood of floors, walls, ceilings, stair steps, stair coverings, risers, balusters, railings, doorsills, doorframes)

_____ Not applicable (apartment entered directly from street)

	Yes	No	Unable to observe
Critical deficiencies			
*Substantial sagging of FLOORS or WALLS			
*Holes, open cracks, rotted, loose or missing material over a considerable area of FLOORS, WALLS, or CEILINGS			
Minor deficiencies			
Holes, open cracks, rotted, loose or missing materials over a small area of FLOORS, WALLS, or CEILINGS			
Broken, loose, or missing STAIR STEPS, RISERS, BALUSTERS, or RAILINGS			
Deep wear on DOORSILLS, DOORFRAMES, STAIR STEPS, STEP COVERINGS, or FLOORS			

- 8 -

EXTERIOR OF BUILDING

A. Condition of exterior of building (bricks, clapboards, wood, metal, glass,
    or stone of walls, porch, steps, railings, window panes, window frames,
    doorsills, doorframes)

		Yes	No	Unable to observe
Critical deficiencies				
*Substantial sagging of WALLS				
*Holes, open cracks, rotted, loose or missing materials over a considerable area of WALLS (including foundation)				
Minor deficiencies				
Holes, open cracks, rotted, loose or missing materials over a small area of WALLS (including foundation)				
Shaky or unsafe PORCH, STEPS, or RAILINGS				
Broken or missing WINDOW PANES				
Rotted or loose WINDOW FRAMES no longer rainproof or windproof				
Deep wear on DOORSILLS, DOORFRAMES, or STEPS				

OVERALL CONDITION OF DWELLING

(Take into account: categories checked "yes" in APARTMENT, item D; INTERIOR OF
BUILDING, item A; and, EXTERIOR OF BUILDING, item A)

_____ Dilapidated: one or more critical deficiencies, (*) or

                       combination of minor deficiencies, sufficient in number and
                       extent to indicate inadequate shelter or protection against
                       the elements or to constitute a hazard

_____ Not dilapidated: no critical or minor deficiencies, or

                           minor deficiencies not sufficient in number and extent
                           to classify as dilapidated

Comments worth noting on overall condition of dwelling:

_____

_____

_____

_____

- 9 -

LOCATION OF APARTMENT:

_____ Basement   _____ First floor   _____ Second floor   _____ Third floor

_____ Fourth floor or higher

MAIN ACCESS TO APARTMENT BUILDING:

_____ Street: principal entrance to apartment building is directly from the
street, or by a walk that leads directly from the street. A
street -- as distinct from an alley -- is wide enough to
accommodate at least two vehicles simultaneously.

_____ All other: principal entrance to apartment building is --

From an alley (only wide enough to accommodate one vehicle;
may or may not bear a street name)

From a rear yard or from a passageway between buildings
(so that apartment building is behind
buildings that are on a street or an alley)

Comments worth noting to amplify information already recorded in this questionnaire
regarding:

A. Physical layout of the apartment   (room arrangements)

_____

_____

_____

B. Sleeping arrangements

_____

_____

_____

C. Sharing of facilities

_____

_____

_____

APPENDIX 3

Data collection and processing

Two different types of data were collected during the field work phase of the study: *survey data* by means of personal interviews with the female head of each test and control household (morbidity, social-psychological adjustment, and, when required, housing quality) ; and *data from public agency records* (school performance of children).

Collection of survey data

The field office staff consisted of five permanent members: the field director, with responsibility for the entire field operation; the field supervisor and assistant supervisor; the assignment clerk and assistant assignment clerk. This group supervised the activities of the survey data collection staff, which consisted of ten regular interviewers and three or four alternates. In addition, there were three post-enumeration interviewers.

The survey cycle. Wave 1, the period when test-control samples were assembled and the initial "before" interview conducted, required almost an entire year to complete. However, in the "after" period, Waves 2-11, ten weeks were allowed for a single wave—the succeeding wave, with one exception, beginning on the eleventh week. The single exception followed Wave 7; field work was suspended for two months following this wave. The surveys for Waves 8-11 followed the earlier cycles exactly once field work was resumed.

For each "after" wave, interviewing generally began on "Zero Saturday." Saturday was an important interviewing day among the study population because of the substantial proportion of working women. In four weeks, approximately 65 per cent of the test and control samples had been successfully contacted. By the end of six weeks, 85 per cent had been interviewed. By eight weeks, 95 per cent or more of the active sample had been seen; the interviewing for the wave was generally terminated at the end of the eighth week.

During the "after waves," all interviewers worked full time for about the first four weeks. Since an effort was made to keep each interviewer supplied with a packet of approximately sixteen assignments at all times, by the fifth week, with only a third of the interviews still to be accomplished, a furlough system would be put into effect. Each week from then on, one or two interviewers would be furloughed until the end of the eighth week, when interviewing was usually completed. At the beginning of the tenth week of the wave, all interviewers were back for general refresher training and instruction in the use of the instruments for the next wave. The furlough system, in addition to being an economy in what was at best an expensive operation, also served two other functions. First, since intensive interviewing is an exacting job, the period of furlough permitted the interviewers to rest. Second, it was convenient for interviewers to be able to schedule other activities during the period of the furlough.

Interview assignment procedures. During Wave 1, assignment procedures followed the comparatively irregular receipt of lists of prospective Lafayette Courts residents from the Housing Authority. The objective was to distribute test and control interviews (when the control matches were selected) equally among all interviewers, and to shift interviewers from neighborhood to neighborhood in the city.

During Waves 2-11, four major principles of interviewing assignment were employed in the interest of insuring proper implementation of the study design:

(a)   Each interviewer was assigned—and was to interview—the same proportion of test and control families; this insured balance of any interviewer variability that might arise.

(b)   Test and control interviewing was paced simultaneously so that at any point in the wave, the ratio of test to control interviews completed was approximately 2:3. This provision cut down the possibility of bias due to within-wave seasonal differences, a matter of considerable importance in the morbidity phase of the study.

(c)   While interviewing control families, interviewers were systematically rotated through all sections of the city. This device reduced the possible bias stemming from the interaction of interviewers and localities.

(d)   A tickler system was employed in which assignments were not "ready" for interview until the two-month date had elapsed since the interview with the family on the preceding wave. This insured sensible morbidity interviewing since, it will be recalled, the morbidity survey canvassed "illness in the last two months."

Recruitment and training of interviewers. The interviewing staff consisted of Negro women. This hiring policy was based on the premise that Negro interviewers might establish better rapport and in general be more successful with Negro respondents than would white interviewers. Almost all the interviewers were without prior interviewing experience; most of them had college or university training, although a number were high school graduates. A certain amount of recruiting, hiring, and training of new interviewers was necessary before the start of almost every wave. This was partly to insure that there would always be three or four alternates available, and partly to replace regular interviewers who left the staff.

The initial contact with a prospective interviewer included a test for interviewer adeptness and a mock interview in which the applicant was given a chance to show her native abilities in regard to establishing a good interview relationship, intelligence in probing, etc. After hiring, every interviewer, without exception, was given a two-week training course conducted by the field director and the two field supervisors.

For new interviewers, instruction was offered in general interviewing techniques and methods of coping with characteristic problems of the household survey. For both old and new interviewers alike, intensive training was given in the conduct of interviews with the instruments to be used in the next wave. This phase utilized training manuals prepared by members of the study staff. Group methods of instruction were used predominantly. Entire interviews and excerpts illustrating special problems were tape-recorded and played for the group. Interviewers participated in round-robin questioning and in mock interviews, with every person present playing the role at various times of interviewer and respondent. The training sessions were climaxed by field trials in which interviewers were observed in practice household interviews. At no time were the interviewers informed of the hypotheses of the study.

Quality control. The control of the quality of interviewing is a crucial matter in the conduct of a long-term test-control study. Any household survey, whatever the topic under study, must pay careful attention to problems of management and organization when relatively large groups of persons are involved in the data collection process. The keys to controlling the quality of interviewing lie in training, retraining, and supervision.

During initial training, during retraining, and during the actual interviewing on a given wave, interviewers were reminded of the scientific purpose of the study and the need for data of the highest quality and integrity. Corner cutting was taboo and the stern consequences of slipshod work or deliberate negligence were brought to the interviewer's attention at various times. In addition to exhortation, five methods were employed to insure that interviewers were doing their jobs appropriately.

(a)   *Reviewing and editing.* Interviewers customarily spent at most two days in the field without an office contact. On the third day, at the latest, each interviewer brought her work into the assignment office. Completed questionnaires were set aside for reviewing and editing on the same day, if possible, or the next day at the latest. A number of characteristic recording errors were detected in this way. Omissions and inadequate probing on open-ended questions suggested careless interviewing. At the earliest possible time, the nature of the errors and ways to avoid them in the future were communicated to the interviewer by one of the supervisors.

(b)   *Staff meetings.* Interviewer staff meetings were held once each week for at least the first five or six weeks of a wave. These meetings were generally held on Wednesday mornings, a midweek meeting being indicated as desirable, since it broke up an arduous week of interviewing. A good deal of *esprit* developed as a result of the Wednesday meeting and it apparently yielded results in unifying a group working under very difficult survey conditions.

At the staff meeting, attended by the field director, the field supervisors, and from time to time by the study directors, matters relevant to the study were discussed. An important feature of the staff meeting was open discussion of the general problems emerging from the particular forms being used. Pervasive types of errors that had been found during reviewing and editing of the previous week's work were summarized by the supervisors and discussed by the group. The staff meeting was a powerful device for unifying individual approaches of interviewers.

(c)   *On-site interviewer observations.* Throughout every wave, each interviewer was observed at least once a week in an actual interview in the home by one of the field supervisory staff. These observations were balanced in the course of a wave among test and control families in proper proportion. The purpose was to gain assurance that manner, approach, and actual interviewing technique were uniform and satisfactory. The supervisor who acted as observer recorded along with the interviewer on a duplicate interview schedule. Outside the apartment at a convenient rendezvous, supervisor and interviewer would compare their respective recordings, and the supervisor would suggest improvements, if needed. In addition, the supervisor sometimes commented on other aspects of the interviewer's performance. Occasionally these comments were discussed in the staff meetings.

(d)   *Interviewer variability tabulations.* When interviewers are assigned dwelling units in fairly random fashion, responses for various questions asked should, when tabulated for each interviewer separately, bear similarity to one another within the bounds of random sampling error. An interviewer whose responses are notably out of line with those of other interviewers is suspected of idiosyncratic or careless interviewing.

Interviewer variability tabulations were instituted as a regular procedure early in Wave 1. During this particular period, when interviewer variability comparisons were being used as the main device to check the reliability of the field work, the method was useful in detecting three interviewers whose work was suspect. To be on the safe side, the respondents in question (fifty in number) were reinterviewed and some of the original interviews were augmented.

Throughout the period of data collection, careful scrutiny was given by the supervisory staff to the results of the interviewer variability tabulations. Special attention was paid to any interviewer whose distribution of responses to the items tabulated was markedly and consistently different from that of the other interviewers. Questionnaires completed by such an interviewer were reviewed even more carefully, and the rate of on-site observations was increased in such cases.

(e)   *Post-enumeration.* The principal safeguard against faulty interviewing practice was systematic post-enumeration. From late spring of 1955 through Wave 11, one quarter of all interviews conducted in a ten-week period were post-enumerated with abbreviated morbidity forms (every wave) and abbreviated adjustment instruments (Waves 1, 5, 7, 10, and 11).

Post-enumeration was done as soon as possible after the initial interview, often within two days, for optimal interpretation of comparisons between original and post-enumeration interviews. The pairs of interviews were compared not only for similarity of responses but also for similar administrative characteristics of the interviews (time of day, length of interview, etc.).

The pace of one-in-four interviews for post-enumeration was

adopted in order to keep to a minimum the double visiting of respondents in any one wave. With a one-in-four schedule and good post-enumeration record-keeping, only once a year was a particular respondent subject to both a regular interview and a post-enumeration interview in a single wave.

Post-enumeration interviews were conducted by special post-enumerators: two women, who made daytime calls, and a man, who did the evening interviewing.

Keeping the samples intact. A problem in long-term studies of equal importance to control of the quality of interviewing, is that of forestalling undue attrition in the population under study. A loss of 10 to 15 per cent usually acceptable in a cross-sectional survey could not be tolerated on a per-wave basis in the present study. Substantial wave-by-wave losses in the test and control groups would have forced an early termination of data collection due to too few cases remaining for analysis. Furthermore, had differential test-control losses occurred, the situation would have been even more serious, resulting in far more complex analysis problems and increased difficulties in drawing appropriate inferences from the data. To insure against these eventualities, three major safeguards aimed at keeping the test-control samples intact were instituted after the two groups were established, and maintained regularly through Wave 11. One safeguard consisted of repeated call-backs to obtain interviews with respondents who were not at home; another pertained to the recovery of respondents who showed disinclination to continue in the study; the third involved a systematic tracing of families who moved.

(a)   *Call-backs.* A majority of the interviews on each wave were obtained on the first or second call. Of the remainder, some required five or six calls, and, in addition, there was always a small group of respondents who consistently were not at home an even greater number of times. Occasionally, as many as ten or twelve calls were necessary before an interviewer was able to contact one of these respondents. The field supervisory staff made a special effort to prevent such an accumulation at the end of a wave. Once an assignment was made, it was never allowed to lie dormant. Rather, those that were returned with a not-at-home report were immediately reassigned, and the interviewers were instructed always to try these assignments first before proceeding to new ones.

(b)   *Refusals.* Each wave throughout the study, between fifteen and twenty-five respondents indicated in some way that they were unwilling to continue participation. This set in motion a procedure whereby the field director and the supervisor of interviewing called on the respondent to urge her to continue in the study; if they were not successful, the study directors then saw the respondent and made an additional attempt to persuade her to continue. A variety of appeals were used in these situations: the respondent was reminded of such matters as the importance of each family, once chosen, continuing in the study; the opportunity that participation in the study provided for contributing to scientific knowledge of "what keeps people healthy and what leads to sickness"; the value of such studies in public planning for the health and social needs of the city; the future benefits that could thereby accrue, especially to the children of the present generation; the absolute confidentiality of all information revealed to the interviewer. The outcome of these tactics was that all but about four or five of the potential per-wave refusals would be recouped. Even these hold-outs would not be abandoned immediately; rather, they would be contacted again the next wave, which usually resulted in the salvaging of another two or three. Only after two consecutive waves of hard and fast refusing was a respondent declared a permanent loss.

(c) *Move tracing.* As indicated in Chapter III, moves occurred among both test and control families, and especially among controls. As a consequence, several procedures were established to trace families who had moved from addresses where they were interviewed the previous wave:

(1) Interviewers were instructed to bring back the results of routine inquiries from neighbors (and neighborhood storekeepers).

(2) The post-enumerators also acted as move tracers in the field.

(3) Since the school of attendance was known for each child of school age in the sample, inquiry was made of the appropriate school office concerning current addresses.

(4) Use was made of the criss-cross telephone directory which, since it lists addresses rather than names, provided easy telephone contacts with people in the neighborhood from which the family had moved.

(5) Relatives and former employers whose names appeared in the original applications on file at the Housing Authority were contacted.

These procedures, followed systematically on every wave, helped materially in preventing loss of sample: only a very small proportion of the total study losses were due to untraced moves.

Collection of data from public school records

The source of data pertaining to school performance of test and control children was the pupils' individual cumulative records in public elementary, junior high, and high schools.

The data collection was done in five major steps: first, a sample of records was reviewed to determine the kinds of information they provided, their completeness, their format, etc.; second, detailed forms were devised which specified the exact items of information contained in the records that were considered relevant to the study; third, the study forms were pretested on a sample of school records and revised where necessary; fourth, transferal of information from the records to the study forms was done according to predesignated procedures; fifth, all of the completed study forms were verified.

Data processing

All data collected during the study were coded and punched on IBM cards. In almost all instances, coding was preceded by thorough editing of the instruments or forms. The actual coding was verified either on a total or random sample basis depending upon its complexity. Coding of responses to open-ended or free-comment questions was accompanied by reliability checks. Pairs of coders independently coded a sample of responses, the codes they assigned were compared, and the reliability coefficient was calculated. If reliability was below the 85 per cent level, the code was reviewed and revised, if necessary; the coders were reinstructed in its use, and the reliability check was repeated on a new sample of responses. All IBM card punching was completely verified, and the cards were systematically "cleaned" for impossible punches, consistency between codes, etc.

Editing, coding, card punching, and tabulating began a few months after the start of data collection, with a special effort toward diminishing the length of time that elapsed between the collection and tabulation. This procedure enabled preliminary analysis and formulation of early findings while data collection was still going on.

APPENDIX 4

Description and analysis of Baltimore Housing Authority files

Description of Housing Authority files

In 1954-1955, the Baltimore Housing Authority maintained a general pool of all applicants. As the time approached for occupancy of Lafayette Courts, the new housing project, a special pool was also set up consisting of up-to-date applications of persons who had indicated they desired to live in East Baltimore or who were understood to have no objection to living in the next project opened anywhere in the city. By May, 1955, when fewer than fifty families had moved into Lafayette Courts, the special pool numbered 1884 applications in varying stages of readiness; the remaining general pool contained an almost identical number of applications. It was realized that of the two pools, the Lafayette Courts special pool might be the better source for controls from the standpoint of possibly providing a greater potential for good matches for the test samples. But use of this pool was not deemed feasible, since at the time when matching of controls to tests had to begin, occupancy of Lafayette Courts was far from complete and there was too great a risk that a control, once chosen, might soon move into the new project. The general pool, therefore, appeared to be the most likely source of control families. Before the final decision was made, however, certain preliminary data were assembled and analyzed in order to illuminate the crucial question of whether or not good control matches could be found in this pool.

Analysis of Housing Authority files

It was already known that families in the general pool differed from those in the Lafayette Courts pool in at least one respect, namely, that the general pool consisted of up-to-date applications of families who did not indicate a desire for an apartment in eastern Baltimore. The question was, to what other characteristics was this difference in preference related, that might make it difficult to obtain suitable test-control matches? Several possibilities came to mind. The first was that geographical preference was related to differences in culture and so to style of life; such differences obviously would affect the comparability of the two groups of families on matters related to health and social adjustment. Related to this was the observation of students of residential mobility that Negro newcomers to Baltimore (often from the deep South) tended to settle in west-central Baltimore. Presumably these persons would not express preferences for apartments in eastern Baltimore and so would be found in heaviest proportion in the general pool. If this were the case and if control families were to be chosen from this pool, it would mean an imbalance between the test and control groups on the point of recency of arrival in the city. It might also mean an imbalance in certain other factors such as status of health: recent arrivals from the deep South, for example, might be expected to have somewhat poorer health than would the test group with presumably longer residence in Baltimore.

In order to facilitate understanding of characteristics of both pools and for later matching purposes as well, selected data were taken from every application in all Housing Authority files, and the information punched onto specially prepared McBee Keysort Cards. A list of the items that appeared on the McBee Card is shown in Appendix 5.

A series of tabulations was made from the McBee Cards of samples of families in the Lafayette Courts pool and in the general pool. The tabulation of addresses, using postal zone as the most convenient summary measure, revealed that while there was considerable overlap, there was, as suspected, a distinct tendency for families in the Lafayette Courts pool to have present addresses in eastern Baltimore, and for families in the general pool to have present addresses in western Baltimore. Following is a summary of the findings from tabulations of additional demographic characteristics of families from the two pools:

(a)   *Husband present:* very similar distributions in both pools; in lower income families in both pools, about three-fourths were without husbands, and in higher income families about one-third were without husbands.

(b)   *Date of birth, female head of household:* very similar; in both pools, related to number of children.

(c)   *Occupational status of female head of household:* very similar; in both pools, the greater the number of children, the less likely was the female head of household to be employed.

(d)   *Number of children 20 years of age or younger:* similar; in both pools related to size of apartment to be awarded.

(e)   *Length of residence in Baltimore:* similar; in both pools, four-fifths had been living in Baltimore ten years or more.

(f)   *Overcrowding:* similar; in both pools, two-thirds were living in overcrowded conditions.

(g)   *Water:* similar; in both pools, almost half did not have both hot and cold running water in their dwelling units.

(h)   *Toilet facilities:* similar; in both pools, about half shared the toilet with one or more families.

Tabulations of two final items, date of initial application and of last renewal, showed that families in the Lafayette Courts pool tended to be more recent applicants or to have renewed their applications more recently. Since the entire effective range of initial application dates was five years, and since many of the more recent renewals in the Lafayette Courts pool were instigated by the Housing Authority at the time of setting up this pool, the main reason for the differences between the two pools in these respects was apparently the pragmatic one of ease of locating the family rather than one of intrinsic difference in families related to the health and adjustment variables which the study intended to measure.

The final outcome of the analysis of the constitution of the Lafayette Courts and the general pools was the conclusion that the general pool would be an adequate source for finding suitable matched controls for the test families. This conclusion was based on the fact that, although families in the two pools tended to be presently located in different parts of the city, this difference did not appear to be associated with other important demographic characteristics.

APPENDIX 5

Information extracted from Housing Authority files and entered on McBee Keysort Cards for each potential test and control family

Last
Name   --

1. a. Fir. and Mid. Name,
       M. Head (Husb.) --
                ----------Listed   ----------Not listed
       Fir. and Mid. Name,
       F. Head (Resp.) --
Address   --
Zone----------------------H. A. No.--

1. b.   Assigned rent: ....

2.   Original Application Date: .....1949 or earlier .....1950 to 1952
.....1953   .....1954, 1955

3.   Unit Size: .....3½   .....4½   .....5½ 6½

4.   Priority Category: .....1, 2 or 3 4   .....5 or 6   .....7 Vet.
.....8 Non-Vet.   .....7 Ser.   .....No. ind.

5.   Date of Birth of Female Head:
.....1930 or later   ..... 1920 to 1929   ..... 1910 to 1919
.....1900 to 1909   .....1899 or earlier   .....No ind.

6.   Occupational Status of Female Head:
.....Unemployed, housewife or house mother   .....Employed,
part or full-time   .....No ind.

7.   No. of Persons Born 1935 or Later: 1 2 3 4
..... 5   .....6 or more   .....None

8.   Date of Birth of Oldest, OR, of Only
Person, Born 1935 or later:
.....1951 or later .....1947 to 1950 .....1944 to 1946 .....1941 to 1943
.....1938 to 1940 .....1937 or earlier   .....No ind.   .....None

9.   No. of Adults Born 1934 or Earlier: 1 2 3 4
.....5 or more

10.   Income Estimate Coming Year, TOTAL NET INCOME:
.....Less than $1,000   .....$1,000 to 1,499   .....$1,500 to 1,999
..... $2,000 to 2,499   .....$2,500 to 2,999   .....$3,000 to 3,499
.....$3,500 to 3,999   .....$4,000 and over

11.   Public Assistance: .....Yes   .....No ind.

12.   Length of (Family Head's) Residence in Baltimore, Up-to-Date:
(Refer to Table in "Instructions")
.....2 years or less   .....3 or 4 years   .....5 to 9 years
.....10 to 14 years   .....15 or more years, or "life"   .....No ind.

13.   Overcrowded (Appl. Int.) :   .....Yes .....No   ..... No ind.

14.   Doubled Up (Appl. Int.) :   .....Yes .....No   .....No ind.

15.   Insurance (any kind) :   .....Yes .....No ind.

16. Home Visit Report:
    _____Yes (and same address as Appl. Int.)
    _____No (or different address from Appl. Int.)
       (IF "NO" SKIP TO ITEM 24)

Neighborhood (Home Visit Report)

17. Nearby Buildings Appear: _____Good   _____Fair   _____Dilapidated
    _____No ind.

18. (Type) :   _____Commercial   _____Residential   _____Industrial
    _____Mixed   _____No ind.

Dwelling Facilities (Home Visit Report)

19. Water: _____In dwell., hot and cold or hot, only   _____In dwell.,
    cold, only   _____In struc., hot and cold or hot, only   _____In struct.,
    cold, only   _____None in dwell. or struct.   _____No ind.

20. Toilet: _____In dwell., private   _____In dwell., shared
    _____In struc., private   _____In struct., shared   _____Outside structure
    _____No ind.

21. Bathtub or Shower: _____In dwell., private   _____In dwell., shared
    _____In struct., private   _____In struct., shared   _____None
    _____No ind.

Housing Quality Score (Home Visit Report)

22. Basic TOTAL: _____3 or less   _____4   _____5   _____6   _____7   _____8
    _____9 or more   _____No ind.

23. Secondary TOTAL: _____5 or less   _____6   _____7   _____8
    _____9 or more   _____No ind.

Housing Costs: _____Home Visit Report, or
                  _____Application Interview

24. Monthly Rent: _____$19.99 or less   _____$20.00 to 29.99   _____$30.00
    to 39.99   _____$40.00 to 49.99   _____$50.00 to 59.99   _____$60.00 to
    69.99   _____$70.00 or more   _____No ind.

25. Heating Fuel: _____Included in rent   _____Not included in rent
    _____No ind.

26. Most Recent Renewal Date: _____1951 or earlier   _____1952
    _____1953   _____1954   _____1955

APPENDIX 6

Work sheet for matching test and control families

The items are listed in the order of importance; parenthetical phrases indicate the specifications for matching. The status of the match was indicated on the lines to the extreme right of each item: either "OK" if the match met the specification, or the actual category codes if the match did not meet the specification.

Test family: Name _____

Control family: Name _____

Order No.		McBee Item No.
1	Unit size (category for category)	3: _____
2	Assigned rent (category for category)	1b: _____
3	Housing Authority priority category	4: _____
4	Husband listed or not (category for category)	1a: _____
5	Date of birth, female head (adjacent category)	5: _____
6	Date of birth of oldest or only person born 1935 or later (adjacent category)	8: _____
7	No. of persons born 1935 or later (adjacent category)	7: _____
8	Occupational status of female head of household (category for category)	6: _____
9	Public assistance (category for category) If no match Item 11, match Item 10: Income (category for category) _____	11: _____

10	Water ("In dwell, hot & cold" to "In dwell, hot & cold"; permit any match among remaining categories)	[H.Q.: 19: _____]
	Toilet ⎫ ("In dwell, private" to	[20: _____]
	Bathtub or ⎬ "In dwell, private";	
	shower ⎭ permit any match among remaining categories)	[21: _____]
	H.Q.: 2 out of 3: _____	

11   Length of residence in Balto. (adjacent category)   12: ....

12   Most recent application renewal date
      [only (4) or (5), Control]   26: ....

13   Original application date [(1,2) to (1,2) or
      (3,4) to (3,4)]   2: ....

APPENDIX 7

Items in the housing survey, the deficiency weights (penalty score) for each item, and maximum score for each index

Exact items appear in Appendix 2, "An Example of the Housing Quality Survey Form."

INDEX I: Structure

Item	Penalty score
1. Main access to apartment	
Entrance from street	0
All other	3
No answer	1
2. Location of apartment	
1st or 2nd floor; house	0
Basement; 3rd floor or higher; no answer	2
3. Dual egress	
Fire escape or 2 separate stairways with 2 separate street doors; house; basement and/or 1st floor	0
Two separate stairways with 1 street door; no answers	2
No fire escape; not 2 separate stairways or no answer	6
Maximum:	11

INDEX II: Unit Facilities

Item	Penalty score
1. Kitchen facilities	
a. Refrigeration	
Gas or electric	0
Icebox; no answer	3
Other, none	5
b. Cooking	
Gas or electric stove	0
Coal, wood, or oil stove; no answer	1
Electric hot plate, other, none	2
c. Sink	
With running water and drain	0
Without running water and drain, or no sink	3
No answer	1
d. Sharing	
No	0
Yes	3
No answer	1
2. Toilet facilities	
a. Location	
In apartment	0
Someplace else in building; no answer	5
Outside building	8
b. Type	
Flush, standing water; no answer	0
Flush, not standing water; not flush	7
No answer	1
c. Sharing	
No	0
Yes	5
No answer	1
3. Bathing facilities	
a. Availability	
Bathtub and/or shower available	0
Bathtub and/or shower not available	10
No answer	1

INDEX II: Unit Facilities (Cont.)

b. Location

In apartment; not available	0
Someplace else in building; no answer	1
Outside building	4

c. Type

Hot water; bathtub or shower not available	0
Cold water, only	2
No answer	1

d. Sharing

No; bathtub or shower not available	0
Yes	3
No answer	1

4. Water supply and other washing facilities

a. Water supply: kind and location

Inside, hot	0
Inside, cold only; no answer	4
Elsewhere in building, hot; no answer	5
Elsewhere in building, cold only	6
Outside building	7

b. Washing facilities

(1) Wash basin in apartment

Yes	0
No	3
No answer	1

(2) Laundry tub in building

Yes; no answer	0
No	1

5. Other

a. Electric lighting available

All rooms have electric lighting, may or may not be in working order	0
No electric lighting—no fixture	8
Something else; no answer	2

b. Central heating available

Yes	0
No	2
No answer	1

INDEX II: Unit Facilities (Cont.)

c. Rooms lacking heating unit

All rooms have heating unit	0
Not all rooms have heating unit, but enough heat; no answer	4
Not all rooms have heating unit and not enough heat	10

d. Rooms lacking window

All rooms have windows	0
Not all rooms have windows, but none used for sleeping; no answer	8
Not all rooms have windows, and 1 or more used for sleeping	15
Maximum:	89

INDEX III: Maintenance

Item	Penalty score
1. Structure deterioration	
a. Interior of apartment—**critical** deficiencies	
No critical deficiencies; mixed	0
1 critical deficiency	3
2 critical deficiencies	6
Unable to observe; no answer	1
b. Interior of apartment—**non-critical** deficiencies	
No non-critical deficiencies; mixed; unable to observe; no answer	0
1 non-critical deficiency	1
2 non-critical deficiencies	2
c. Interior of building—**critical** deficiencies	
No critical deficiencies; apartment entered directly from street; mixed	0
1 critical deficiency	3
2 critical deficiencies	5
Unable to observe; no answer	1
d. Interior of building—**non-critical** deficiencies	
No non-critical deficiencies; apartment entered directly from street; mixed; unable to observe; no answer	0
1 non-critical deficiency	1
2 or 3 non-critical deficiencies	2

INDEX III: Maintenance (Cont.)

e. Exterior of building—**critical** deficiencies

No critical deficiencies; mixed	0
1 critical deficiency	3
2 critical deficiencies	5
Unable to observe; no answer	1

f. Exterior of building—**non-critical** deficiencies

No non-critical deficiencies; mixed; unable to observe; no answer	0
1 non-critical deficiency	1
2 or more non-critical deficiencies	2

2. Kitchen, bathroom facilities

a. Refrigeration (how good)

Very good, fairly good; no answer	0
Not very good, not at all good	1

b. Cooking facilities (how good)

Very good, fairly good; no answer	0
Not very good, not at all good	1

c. Toilet (out of order)

Often	2
Sometimes; no answer	1
Hardly ever, never	0

d. Bathtub or shower (in working order)

Yes; bathtub or shower not available	0
No; no answer	1

e. Water supply (amount of hot water)

All of the time, most of the time	0
Only some of the time, almost never; no answer	1

3. Other

a. Electric lighting (in working order)

Electric fixtures in working order; no electric lighting—no fixture; something else; no answer	0
Electric fixtures not in working order	2

b. Heating (amount of heat)

All of the time, most of the time	0
Only some of the time, almost never; don't know; no answer	1

INDEX III: Maintenance (Cont.)

c. Paint peeling or flaking (any)

No	0
Yes; no answer	1

d. Pipe or plumbing leakage (any)

No; no answer	0
Yes	2

e. Refuse containers (any; lids)

Enough garbage containers with lids; no answer	0
Not enough garbage containers or not all with lids; no answer	1
No garbage containers	3

4. Infestation

None	0
Rats, only	3
Other, only; no answer, only; other plus no answer	1
Rats, plus other	4

Maximum: 40

INDEX IV: Occupancy

Item	Penalty score
1. Persons per sleeping room	
2 persons or fewer	0
2.1–2.4 persons; no answer	3
2.5–2.9 persons	6
3.0–3.9 persons	9
4.0 persons and more	12
2. Persons per room	
1 person or fewer	0
1.1–1.5 persons; no answer	3
1.6–1.9 persons	6
2.0–2.9 persons	9
3.0–3.9 persons	12
4.0 persons and more	15

Maximum: 27

Combined Index: Total Housing Quality—Maximum 167

APPENDIX 8

Data on the initial comparability of intact and reduced effective samples

As indicated in Chapter III in the section on the initial comparability of the intact and reduced effective samples, an analysis of Wave I "before" survey data was made in order to determine whether or not any significant bias would arise from the use of the "reduced effective test and control samples." These samples resulted when, within the originally constituted intact test and control groups, two kinds of exclusions were made: families (or individual family members) who missed specified survey waves, and families who changed their basic independent variable status, i.e., tests who moved from public to private housing and controls who moved from private to public housing.

The feasibility of the reduction procedure was assessed in two ways: first, the test group before reduction was compared to the test group after reduction, a similar kind of comparison also being applied to the controls; second, the reduced test and reduced control groups were compared. It was felt that, if Wave 1, "before" data showed similarity in these kinds of comparisons, use of the reduced effective samples in the "after" analysis would be justified. The data for this assessment are shown in Tables 1 through 7. All tables show the intact samples at the start of the study; that is, the test and control groups as originally constituted. *Throughout, the data for the intact control groups are weighted in order to take into account the fact that some test and control families were matched 1:1, while others were matched in the ratio of 1:2.* All tables also show data for the test and control reduced effective samples.

Age and sex composition

Because of its importance in the calculation of age-specific morbidity rates, age-sex composition of test and control groups is presented in some detail in Table 1. The age indicated is the "median age"; that is, age as of April, 1957, at the mid-point of the study.

Comparability of intact and reduced tests; intact and reduced controls. There was very close comparability by age groups within the sexes. Among males, 70 per cent of the intact tests, compared to 72

TABLE 1.   Age and sex composition of test and control families.

		Intact samples at start of study		Reduced effective samples	
		Test	Control[a]	Test	Control
		Per cent			
Males					
Age:	Under 5	19	19	20	19
	5–9	33	32	35	34
	10–14	11 } 70	15 } 72	12 } 72	15 } 73
	15–19	7	6	5	5
	20–24	5	4	3	3
	25–34	15	14	14	13
	35–44	6 } 30	6 } 28	7 } 28	7 } 27
	45 and over	4	4	4	4
	Number	(818)	(1341)	(579)	(618)
Females					
Age:	Under 5	18	19	18	18
	5–9	23	24	25	24
	10–14	11 } 57	12 } 60	11 } 58	12 } 57
	15–19	5	5	4	3
	20–24	8	8	7	8
	25–34	23	19	22	22
	35–44	7 } 43	8 } 40	7 } 42	7 } 43
	45 and over	5	5	6	5
	Number	(1101)	(1602)	(762)	(731)

a Control per cents weighted.

per cent of the reduced tests, were under 20 years of age. Among females, 57 per cent and 58 per cent, respectively, were under 20 years of age. Comparison of the intact and reduced controls shows similar comparability of age-sex groups.

Comparability of test and control reduced effective samples.
Test and control reduced effective samples were comparable in age-sex distributions. Test differed from control by only 1 per cent among males under 20 years of age. A correspondingly small difference occurred between the two groups in the proportion of females under 20.

Initial personal and family background

It will be recalled that at the outset of the study, test and control families were matched family by family on a number of personal and family background characteristics. Table 2 shows how the test and control families were distributed on a number of important background items. For easier presentation, some of the items are shown

TABLE 2.   Initial personal and family characteristics of test and control.

		Intact samples at start of study		Reduced effective samples	
		Test (396)	Con-trol[a] (633)	Test (300)	Con-trol (300)
	N:				
		Per cent			
1. Usual activity of:					
a. All persons	Works full or part time	19	19	18	18
	Keeps house	16	14	17	16
	School	33	32	33	33
	All other (pre-school, etc.)	32	35	32	33
b. Female head of household	Works full or part time	31	32	31	28
c. Husband[b]	Works full time	84	83	82	82
2. Occupation of:					
a. Employed female head of household[c]	Service	67	71	73	71
b. Husband[b]	Unskilled	34	38	34	40
3. Annual income	Under $1500	12	14	14	14
	$1500–1999	26	25	27	23
	$2000–2499	26	21	24	21
	$2500–3499	29	31	28	32
	$3500 and over	7	9	7	10
4. Receiving welfare assistance	Yes	22	23	24	25
5. Monthly rent	Under $40	36	32	37	34
	$40–49	24	26	22	27
	$50–59	18	16	19	16
	$60 and over	21	24	20	21
	Unclassified	1	2	2	2

TABLE 2 (contd.). Initial personal and family characteristics of test and control.

		Intact samples at start of study		Reduced effective samples	
		Test (396)	Con-trol[a] (633)	Test (300)	Con-trol (300)
N:					
		Per cent			
6. Marital status	Married now and living with husband	61	61	59	59
	Separated	22	21	22	22
	Divorced, widowed, single, etc.	17	18	19	19
7. Veteran status	Veteran family	29	31	30	33
8. Number of children	None	6	8	7	8
	1 or 2	34	33	33	31
	3 or 4	41	38	42	40
	5 or more	19	21	18	21
9. Age of oldest child	Under 5 years	24	23	23	21
	5–9 years	36	33	36	35
	10–14 years	21	24	21	25
	15 years or older	13	12	13	11
	(No children)	6	8	7	8
10. Education of:					
a. Female head of household	Less than 10th grade	58	62	59	65
	Grade 10 or 11	24	24	26	21
	High school graduate	14	12	12	12
	Any college	4	1	3	1
	Other	d	1	—	1
b. Husband[b]	Less than 10th grade	54	56	57	60
	Grade 10 or 11	19	20	17	19
	High school graduate	13	9	10	8
	Any college	1	2	1	3
	Other, don't know	13	13	15	10
11. State of origin	Maryland	69	76	68	75

TABLE 2 (contd.). Initial personal and family characteristics of test and control.

			Intact samples at start of study		Reduced effective samples	
			Test (396)	Con-trol[a] (633)	Test (300)	Con-trol (300)
		N:		Per cent		
12. Length of residence in Baltimore	Ten years or more		76	85	74	87
13. Length of residence at "initial" address	Three years or more		41	40	42	45
14. Original date of Housing Authority application	1952 or earlier		37	32	39	32

[a] Control per cents weighted.
[b] Among families in which respondent is married.
[c] Among respondents who reported full or part-time employment.
[d] Less than one-half of one per cent.

in abbreviated form, only a single line being given from the full distribution. However, the "sense" of the distribution is communicated by the line presented.

Comparability of intact and reduced tests; intact and reduced controls. There was general close comparability on the numerous items shown in Table 2, whether intact and reduced tests or intact and reduced controls were compared. At most there was a 6 per cent difference; this occurred in item 2a of Table 2 in which 67 per cent of the intact test sample, compared to 73 per cent of the reduced tests, reported a service-type occupation for the employed female head of the household. Intact and reduced controls differed on the items of initial personal and family background by, at most, 5 per cent on a single item; this occurred in item 13 of Table 2 in which 40 per cent of the intact and 45 per cent of the reduced controls indicated three or more years of residence at their "initial" addresses.

Comparability of test and control reduced effective samples. The largest difference between reduced test and control groups occurred in connection with item 12, Table 2, length of residence in Baltimore: 74 per cent of the tests and 87 per cent of the controls reported ten or more years of residence, a difference of 13 per cent. Among the remaining items, the largest differences (in five instances) amounted to 6 per cent or 7 per cent: husband's occupation reported as unskilled, annual income exceeding $2500, education of the female head of the household specified as less than tenth grade, Maryland indicated as the state of origin, and original application for a project apartment made in 1952 or earlier to the Housing Authority. The dozen remaining items shown in Table 2 indicated even less difference between the two reduced groups. In general, close comparability was maintained between test and control in the reduced effective samples.

Initial housing quality

The assessment of the quality of dwelling units was made at Wave 1 for both groups, for test families prior to moving to Lafayette Courts, and for control families prior to the occurrence of any moves. Table 3 shows a number of individual items of initial housing quality, as well as the weighted total index. The index, similar to the presentation in Chapter III, Table 6, uses three descriptive categories from the deficiency summary scores.

Comparability of intact and reduced tests; intact and reduced controls. Whether intact and reduced tests or intact and reduced controls were compared, 2 per cent was the largest difference observable in any of the measurements shown in Table 3. Thus, on initial housing quality assessment, reduced and intact groups yielded nearly identical results.

Comparability of test and control reduced effective samples. Of the various housing quality measurements presented in Table 3, the weighted total index (item 12) was the one which showed the largest difference between the test and control reduced effective samples. Ten per cent more of the tests than of the controls were in initially "bad" housing; 61 per cent and 51 per cent, respectively. Inspection of Table 3 shows small test-control differences on the individual items, half the items showing differences of 4 per cent to 7 per cent. There was, however, marked consistency of direction. On most of the items, tests were slightly worse off than controls.

Initial morbidity

During the Wave 1 and Wave 2 surveys, information was obtained regarding the initial comparability of test and control families on various items of medical history. Table 4 gives data for previous

TABLE 3.   Initial housing quality of test and control families.

		Intact samples at start of study		Reduced effective samples	
	N:	Test (396)	Con-trol[a] (633)	Test (300)	Con-trol (300)
		Per cent			
1. Type and availability of water supply	Hot and cold, in the apartment	72	76	72	76
2. Location of toilet	In the apartment	81	83	80	83
3. Type and availability of bathing facilities	Bathtub, in the apartment	71	71	70	72
4. Sharing	One or more facilities	51	45	49	47
	All facilities (toilet, bath, and kitchen)	32	28	31	30
5. Type of heating	Central	53	51	51	49
6. Adequacy of heat	At least one room not getting enough	33	29	33	29
7. Crowding	More than three persons per sleeping room	33	27	33	27
8. Condition of pipes or plumbing	Leaks	25	21	25	21
9. Type of infestation in the apartment	Rats	27	21	29	22
10. Critical deficiencies in the apartment	One or more	24	18	23	18
11. Overall condition of dwelling	Dilapidated	37	32	37	30
12. Weighted total index of housing quality[b]	"Good"	9	14	9	13
	"Moderately bad"	31	35	30	36
	"Bad"	60	51	61	51

[a] Control per cents weighted.
[b] Derived from APHA Appraisal Method.

TABLE 4. Initial history of surgery, serious accidents, and hospitalization for TB or mental illness.

		Intact samples at start of study[a]		Reduced effective samples[a]	
		Test	Con-trol[b]	Test	Con-trol
		Per cent of persons			
1. Previous surgery	Males	10	11	10	13
	Females	18	19	18	20
2. Previous serious accident	Males	12	16	11	16
	Females	7	10	7	9
3. Previous hospitalization for tuber-culosis or mental illness	Males	1	1	2	1
	Females	1	1	1	2

a N's on which per cents are based are identical to total N's shown in Table 1.
b Control per cents weighted.

surgery, serious accidents, and hospitalization for tuberculosis or mental illness. Table 5a shows the findings regarding previous history of communicable diseases of childhood for the population under 20 years of age. Finally, Table 6 reports rates per 1000 persons for various chronic conditions present in the two years prior to the Wave 2 survey.

Comparability of intact and reduced tests; intact and reduced controls. Comparison of intact and reduced *tests* showed virtually no difference on initial history of surgery, serious accidents, and hospitalization for tuberculosis or mental illness (Table 4), and at most a 4 per cent difference between any age-sex group reporting a specific prior childhood communicable disease (Table 5a). Comparability between the two test samples was also close on reports of chronic conditions present two years prior to Wave 2 (Table 6). Intact tests and reduced tests mentioned chronic conditions at the rate of 499 and 532 per 1000 persons, respectively, a difference of 33 per 1000. The largest difference in any single chronic disease category was 10 per 1000 and pertained to diseases of the circulatory system.

Intact and reduced *controls* also showed generally close comparability, especially on prior history of surgery, accidents, and hospitalization for tuberculosis or mental illness (Table 4), and on incidence of chronic disease (Table 6). Initial history of childhood communicable diseases (Table 5a) showed inequalities ranging as high as 8 per cent for females, ages 5 to 9 and 10 to 19.

Comparability of test and control reduced effective samples.   Reduced tests and controls were very similar on initial history of surgery, accidents, and hospitalization for tuberculosis or mental illness. The

TABLE 5a.   Initial history of communicable diseases of childhood.

			Intact samples at start of study[a]		Reduced effective samples[a]	
			Test	Con-trol[b]	Test	Con-trol
	Sex	Age	Per cent of persons			
1. Scarlet fever	Males	Under 5	1	1	2	—
		5–9	c	—	c	—
		10–19	1	1	2	—
	Females	Under 5	1	—	1	—
		5–9	c	1	1	3
		10–19	2	2	3	6
2. Mumps	Males	Under 5	3	5	3	4
		5–9	25	23	26	18
		10–19	40	48	40	43
	Females	Under 5	3	3	4	2
		5–9	21	24	23	20
		10–19	48	43	51	45
3. Measles	Males	Under 5	12	15	11	12
		5–9	62	63	63	63
		10–19	83	79	80	77
	Females	Under 5	10	16	9	10
		5–9	61	65	62	59
		10–19	92	83	90	82
4. Whooping cough	Males	Under 5	3	4	2	4
		5–9	13	14	9	14
		10–19	43	38	44	37
	Females	Under 5	3	2	3	—
		5–9	13	16	13	16
		10–19	52	48	52	55

TABLE 5a (contd.).   Initial history of communicable diseases of childhood.

			Intact samples at start of study[a]		Reduced effective samples[a]	
			Test	Con-trol[b]	Test	Con-trol
	Sex	Age	Per cent of persons			
5. Chicken pox	Males	Under 5	11	9	12	9
		5–9	35	37	37	38
		10–19	60	52	61	50
	Females	Under 5	9	13	10	13
		5–9	41	36	39	39
		10–19	59	60	63	68
6. Diphtheria	Males	Under 5	—	—	—	—
		5–9	—	—	—	—
		10–19	1	1	1	—
	Females	Under 5	—	—	—	—
		5–9	—	—	—	—
		10–19	1	—	1	—

[a] For N's on which per cents are based, see Table 5b.
[b] Control per cents weighted.
[e] Less than one-half of one per cent.

TABLE 5b.   Number of persons involved in initial history of communicable diseases of childhood.

		Intact samples at start of study		Reduced effective samples	
		Test	Control	Test	Control
Sex	Age	Number of persons			
Males	Under 5	161	241	113	113
	5–9	270	416	201	212
	10–19	145	302	98	124
Females	Under 5	179	289	138	134
	5–9	239	376	193	181
	10–19	161	283	113	109

TABLE 6. Chronic conditions present in the two years preceding Wave 2.

	Intact samples at start of study		Reduced effective samples	
	Test	Control[a]	Test	Control
N:	(1819)	(2943)	(1341)	(1349)
Chronic condition	Rate per 1000 persons			
Tuberculosis	8	5	9	4
Venereal disease	4	5	4	6
Neoplasms	9	10	12	10
Hay fever	15	13	15	16
Asthma	17	19	13	18
Diabetes mellitus	5	3	7	2
Diseases of the blood	24	17	27	19
Mental, psychoneurotic and personality disorders	46	55	48	53
Circulatory system	97	108	107	104
Rheumatic fever	9	6	10	4
Hypertension	26	32	25	32
Other heart disease	8	7	10	7
Varicose veins	11	12	11	9
Hemorrhoids	17	18	20	19
Other circulatory	21	25	25	26
Hypertensive heart and general arteriosclerosis	5	8	6	7
Ulcer of stomach	7	5	7	5
Hernia	22	17	25	12
Liver and gall bladder	3	3	3	3
Skin and cellular tissue	28	28	30	24
Bones and organs of movement	41	35	47	37
Impairments	173	194	178	202
Total	499	517	532	515

[a] Control rates weighted.

largest inequality occurred in previous serious accidents which were
reported, among males, by 11 per cent of the tests and 16 per cent of

TABLE 7. Selected initial adjustment measures.

		Intact samples at start of study		Reduced effective samples	
N:		Test (396)	Control[a] (633)	Test (300)	Control (300)
		Per cent			
Reactions to housing					
How do you like your apartment?	"A lot"	14	22	14	25
Personal and family relations					
Family members do things together?[b]	Three or more activities "often"[c]	44	51	45	50
Style of life					
Interviewers' ratings of cleanliness of furnishings	"Clean"	57	56	54	57
Relations with neighbors					
Number of women visit back and forth with?	"None"	57	57	57	58
Social self-concept and aspirations					
Compared to 5 years ago, how do you feel?	"Better off" (now)	56	58	55	60
Attitudes and behavior toward neighborhood and community					
How is this neighborhood as a place to live?	"Very good"	27	25	27	27
Psychological state					
Mood	Positive	37	37	37	37
Satisfaction with personal state of affairs (status quo)	Positive	36	37	37	40

[a] Control per cents weighted.

[b] Among families of appropriate family composition: at least two adults, or if one adult, at least one child 10 years of age or older.

[c] Data consist of a five-item index of the following activities: go shopping, sit and talk, go for walks, go to movies, listen to radio or watch TV. Data shown are responses of "often" to any 3, any 4, or all 5 items.

the controls, a difference of 5 per cent. History of childhood communicable diseases showed somewhat larger differences, especially for 10-19 year-olds; four out of twelve comparisons showed differences between reduced test and control groups ranging from 6 per cent to 11 per cent. Total chronic conditions present in the two years before Wave 2 were reported at a rate of 532 and 515 per 1000 persons by the reduced test and control groups, respectively. The reduced tests were somewhat less likely than controls to report impairments, by a difference of 24 per 1000 persons, but more likely to report hernias, diseases of the bones and organs of movement, and diseases of the blood, by differences of 13, 10, and 8 per 1000, respectively. Any remaining test-control variations in reports of chronic conditions were of lesser magnitude.

Initial social adjustment

It will be recalled that the several social psychological content areas singled out for investigation were enumerated in Chapter II in a discussion of the hypotheses of the study. Initial "before" measures were obtained on numerous social adjustment items in each of these areas. All of the initial measures together with the "after" data are presented in Chapters X-XVI. For present purposes, in order to complete the assessment of initial comparability, only one or two representative "before" items from each area will be discussed. The data are shown in Table 7.

Comparability of intact and reduced tests; intact and reduced controls. In general, close comparability was apparent between intact and reduced tests, and intact and reduced controls, on the selected initial measures of social adjustment shown in Table 7; the largest intact-reduced difference on any item was 3 per cent.

Comparability of test and control reduced effective samples. The most marked difference between test and control reduced effective samples was in connection with the item, "How do you like your apartment?" Fourteen per cent of the tests and 25 per cent of the controls said "a lot," a difference of 11 per cent. This difference was consistent with that reported earlier in Table 3, which showed a larger proportion of tests than of controls living in initially "bad" housing. Of the remaining "before" social adjustment measures shown in Table 7, the largest difference was of the order of 5 per cent.

APPENDIX 9

Number of persons in standard age-sex groups of reduced effective samples of 300 test and 300 control families

| | Males | | Females | |
| | Test | Control | Test | Control |
Age		Number of persons		
Under 5	113	113	138	134
5–9	201	212	193	181
10–19	98	124	113	109
20–34	100	101	223	212
35–59	58	60	84	88
60 and over[a]	9	8	11	7
35 and over	67	68	95	95
All, under 60	570	610	751	724
Under 20	412	449	444	424
20–59	158	161	307	300

[a] Does not include a total of 5 controls, ages 60 and over, who died during the study period.

APPENDIX 10

Significance of differences corrected for family clustering

Test and control families generally consisted of two or more persons, and in most cases there were several children in a single family. It seemed likely that the within-family correlation would be positive for any morbidity variable under consideration. Critical ratios of differences computed without taking this into account might as a consequence be spuriously inflated. This would very likely be true even in refined age-sex classes. For example, for males, ages 5 to 9, there could be families having two or more boys in that class.

In order to take the within-family correlation into account when testing differences, the variance of the mean *per person* was found by a formula derived[a] for computing[b] convenience:

$$\text{Var } (\bar{y}) =$$

$$\frac{(\sum^N M_i)^2 (\sum^N Y_i^2) - 2(\sum^N M_i)(\sum^N Y_i)(\sum^N M_i Y_i) + (\sum^N Y_i)^2(\sum^N M_i^2)}{(\sum^N M_i)^4},$$

where M_i is the cluster size, the number of persons of a selected class in the ith family, e.g., the number of males ages 5 to 9 in the ith family;

$\sum^N M_i$ is the total number of persons in the selected class, e.g., males ages 5 to 9, summed over all N families;

Y_i is the total of the variable (episodes, days) in the ith family cluster;

$\sum^N Y_i$ is the grand sum of the variable for all family clusters, summed over all N families;

$\sum^N M_i Y_i$ is the sum of the family cluster totals Y_i, each weighted by its cluster size M_i; and

$\bar{y}$ is the grand mean of the variable per person, i.e., $\sum^N Y_i / \sum^N M_i$, for the selected class.

The standard error of the difference of the test and control means is $[\text{Var } (\bar{y}_T) + \text{Var } (\bar{y}_C)]^{\frac{1}{2}}$, where both variances are computed as above.

The within-family correlations were in fact found to be positive, and so the refined variance estimate was applied to all differences close to significance at the $P < 0.05$ level by the uncorrected test.

---

[a] From Sukhatme, P. V., *Sampling Theory of Surveys with Applications,* Ames, Iowa: The Iowa State College Press, 1954, p. 267.
[b] Acknowledgment is made of use of the IBM 7090 computer at the Western Data Processing Center, University of California, Los Angeles.

APPENDIX 11

Statistical significance of the difference in mortality

Mortality data for the test and control samples in the "after" period of the study were:

	Test	Control
	Number of persons	
Alive at beginning of period	1343	1359
Survived through period	1341	1349
Died in period	2	10
Death rate (per person)	0.00149	0.00736
Survival rate (per person)	0.99851	0.00264

The small advantage in survival rate among the test persons is statistically significant at the $P < 0.05$ level. Assessment of this difference in survival would be based on a conceptual model similar to that used for a clinical trial of an improved drug or treatment.[a] The "treatment" (in this case the rehousing) is expected to improve the survival chances only of those who would die without it, since it could not possibly "improve the chances" of those who survive the period without it. The effectiveness of the housing in improving chances of survival may be estimated as

$$1 - \frac{\text{Test death rate}}{\text{Control death rate}} = 1 - \frac{0.00149}{0.00736} = 0.7976.$$

In other words, it might be said that the test persons experienced about 80 per cent effective protection, or that the rehousing shifted 80 per cent of the potential deaths into the survival column.

Because of the small sample, the statistic is extremely imprecise. Gart[b] has shown that the 95 per cent confidence limits on this estimate extend from very nearly zero per cent effectiveness to very close to 100 per cent. Much larger samples or possibly a much more extended

[a] Sheps, Mindel C., "An Examination of Some Methods of Comparing Several Rates or Proportions," *Biometrics, 15*:87-97, 1959.
[b] Gart, J. J., "A Simplified Method for Finding Confidence Limits on the Relative Risk in 2 × 2 Tables" (abstract), *Ann. Math. Stat., 31*:234-235, 1960.

period of observation would be required for a confident assessment of this difference.

No correction was made for within-family correlation since there was no case of more than one death in a family.

APPENDIX 12

Numbers of serious episodes of illness (males, females)

	Interim period Waves 2–3		"Early after" period Waves 4–7		"Late after" period Waves 8–11	
	Test	Control	Test	Control	Test	Control
			Number of serious episodes			
Males: Age						
Under 60	450	410	587	704	652	849
Under 20	351	321	427	570	476	689
20–59	99	89	160	134	176	160
Females: Age						
Under 60	891	806	1364	1380	1487	1456
Under 20	372	312	460	477	580	579
20–59	519	494	904	903	907	877

APPENDIX 13

Number of cases included (of total 300 tests and 300 controls) on the basis of applicability of particular items

	Before		Early After		Late After	
	Test	Control	Test	Control	Test	Control
			Number			
Among families who had at least one child:						
Between 3 and 16 years of age	241	237	260	255		
Between 6 and 16 years of age	182	184	223	209	223	220
Between 6 and 19 years of age					232	225
Six years of age or older attending school					225	226
Between 10 and 19 years of age					142	138
Sixteen years of age or younger	271	269			269	262
Sixteen years of age or younger: a boy[a]					129	137
Sixteen years of age or younger: a girl[a]					136	124
Among families consisting of at least two adults, or if one adult, at least one child 10 years of age or older	245	251	262	258	267	258
. . . and who reported any quarrels, arguments or hard feelings	207	215			221	229
Among families with husband present	176	180	187	179	182	180
. . . and who had at least one child 16 years of age or younger					166	161
. . . and who reported any quarrels, arguments or hard feelings between respondent and husband					109	120
. . . and who was employed					157	159
Among respondents who reported: Any unwanted dropping-in by neighbors					232	212
Any evening visiting	269	263	263	264		

	Before		Early After		Late After	
	Test	Control	Test	Control	Test	Control
Having made any new friends in past three years					205	160
Being "better off in life" by "early-after" period than they were "three years ago"			230	181		
Belonging to group of "people who are going up in the world"					213	191
Hoping to send children through twelfth grade	133	150			147	151
Hoping to send children through college	120	99			114	97
Wanting to own their own home	263	282				
Belonging to one or more clubs or groups	148	148			175	171
Being "very interested" or "fairly interested" in keeping up (project) (neighborhood)			299	281		
. . . and who indicated some action to keep it up			269	219		

[a] A few respondents did not answer the questions applying specifically to boys and girls. Therefore, the sum of families with boys of age 16 and younger and with girls of age 16 and younger did not equal total families with children of both sexes in this age group in the "late after" period as shown immediately above.

APPENDIX 14

Activities for children and adults offered at the Lafayette Courts Community Center

The Lafayette Courts Community Center, located in a non-residential building which also housed the project office, consisted of a large room of auditorium size for general functions, and a series of smaller rooms for more specialized activities. The auditorium had a small stage and provisions for erecting seats and tables as circumstances required. Activities in the center were conducted by representatives of the Bureau of Recreation, Department of Recreation and Parks, with the assistance of project administrative personnel.

Project records of enrollment in the center by various age categories revealed that 35 per cent of all the project children under 10 years of age were enrolled, and more than 95 per cent of those between 10 and 20 years of age participated, as did 38 per cent of all adults. Facilities were considerably more extensive for children than for adults.

Activities for children

Sports and games. Equipment and space for a variety of sports activities were available under general supervision every day and included basketball, softball, volleyball, wall tennis, dodge ball, etc. Special instruction in wrestling and tumbling was provided twice a week for groups of 30 to 35 boys. There were also facilities for quiet games such as checkers.

Dancing, dramatics, music, and movies. These activities were held for teen-agers of both sexes as well as for younger children. The number and ages of children attending such activities were:

Activity	Number participating	Age	Frequency
Social dancing	120	6-10, 10-13	1 two-hour session a week
" "	195	14-18	1 night a week
Tap dancing instruction	55 (girls)	10-14	1 lesson weekly
Modern dancing instruction	25 (girls)	10-14	1 lesson weekly
Dramatics	Varying	10-12	Once a week; gave plays on holidays
Young children's choir	40	6-8	Twice a week
Young children's orchestra (toy instruments)	30	6-8	Twice a week
Movies	Many	All ages	Once a week

Special interest groups.   For varying age-sex groups, several specialized activities were provided, among them:

(a)   A teen-age council, consisting of four boys and four girls, which planned special functions such as dances and shows.

(b)   A nature club for boys and girls, which studied birds, foliage, the solar system, etc.

(c)   A "boy adventurers" club for very young boys, that made field trips and learned new games.

(d)   A group of 5- to 9-year-old girls who put on programs for parents.

(e)   A drill and marching group of 75 children of both sexes.

Activities for adults

"Adult night."   Held once a week, "adult night" customarily began early in the evening with card playing, ping pong, and general "socializing," with about 100 persons participating. Later in the evening, social dancing would begin, with dance instruction available at specific times. Between 200 and 300 persons attended the project dance each week.

Sports and special interest groups.   There was a football team for men, and softball teams for women; a women's service or hostess group, and a men's service group, both of which assisted at large gatherings and in special events such as Christmas activities for children. For persons 65 years of age or older, there was a "Golden Age" club.

APPENDIX 15

Individual items in each psychological state scale; for each item, positive and negative categories indicated

Originally, eight or ten items were constructed for each psychological state scale. The entire battery of items was tested for scalability, using a standard Guttman Scalogram Board. Non-scale items were eliminated in the process, and the resulting unidimensional scales, consisting of four or five items each, had coefficients of reproducibility of about 90 per cent. Thereafter, the scales were administered during the course of a regular interview: the items were *read to the respondent* and her answers were recorded.

Presented below are the individual items constituting each of the psychological state scales. A plus sign (+) in a column shows the response that indicates probable "better psychological state."

Scale 1. *Mood*

		Yes	No[a]
a.	Can you say that you hardly ever feel blue?	+	
b.	Are you sometimes so blue that you feel there's no use going on?		+
c.	Do little things often make you feel blue?		+
d.	Are there times when you are so blue that you want to cry?		+

[a] A "don't know" or "can't decide" alternative was also provided for each item in all scales.

Scale 2. *Control of temper*

		Yes	No
a.	Is it often hard for you to control your temper?		+
b.	When you are angry, do you sometimes say things which you are sorry about later?		+
c.	Are you almost always able to control your temper completely?	+	
d.	Are you the sort of person who almost never gets angry?	+	
e.	Can you usually control your temper pretty well even when someone provokes you?	+	

Scale 3. *Nervousness*

		Yes	No
a.	Are you one of those persons who never gets nervous?	+	
b.	Are you often so nervous or upset that you can't go on with what you are doing?		+
c.	Do you generally take things calmly without getting upset?	+	
d.	Do you often feel that you are about to go to pieces?		+
e.	Are you a nervous person?		+

Scale 4. *Potency (efficacy of self-help)*

		True	Not True
a.	When you come right down to it, there's nothing you can do to make things really better for yourself.		+
b.	It's all right to try to improve yourself but things being the way they are, don't count on being able to accomplish too much.		+
c.	Things will get better only if you actually get out and do something to make them better.	+	
d.	No matter how hard you try, there's not much you can do to make a real change for the better.		+
e.	You can work and work and in the end you're back about where you started.		+

Scale 5. *Optimism-pessimism*

		True	*Not True*
a.	It's hardly fair to bring a child into the world, the way things look for the future.		+
b.	There's no reason to believe that things are going to be a great deal better in the future.		+
c.	If things seem to be going well for a while, there's usually some trouble right around the corner.		+
d.	It's better not to look on the bright side of things because you will only be disappointed in the end.		+

Scale 6. *Satisfaction with personal state of affairs (status quo)*

		True	*Not True*
a.	I'm really very happy about the way I've been getting along lately.	+	
b.	Everything seems to go wrong for me nowadays.		+
c.	I'm generally satisfied with the way things are going for me.	+	
d.	Life is treating me pretty bad right now.		+

Scale 7. *Authoritarianism*

		True	Not True
a.	What young people need most of all is strict discipline.		+
b.	Any good leader should be strict with people under him in order to gain their respect.		+
c.	Most children get into trouble because their parents have not been strict enough with them.		+
d.	A good leader doesn't have to be strict.	+	

Scale 8. *Aggression toward authority figures*

	"Heavy punishment"	*"Some punishment"*	*"No punishment at all"*	*More information needed to decide*
a. A policeman who shoots a teen-ager should get:			+	+
b. An employer who fires a good employee should get:			+	+
c. A doctor whose patient dies should get:			+	+
d. A welfare official who cuts the welfare allowance of a family should get:			+	+
			+	+
e. A judge who sends an innocent man to prison should get:			+	+

Scale 9. *Self-esteem*

		True	Not True
a.	Sometimes I feel that my life is being wasted on things that don't matter much to others.		+
b.	Quite often I feel that no matter what I do or how hard I try, I just can't seem to please others.		+
c.	Sometimes I feel that if I were gone, no one would miss me.		+
d.	In general I feel that others have a low opinion of me.		+
e.	Sometimes I feel that others go out of their way to avoid me.		+

Scale 10. *General anxiety*

		True	Not True
a.	Sometimes I feel uneasy and sort of afraid without knowing exactly why I feel this way.		+
b.	Some of the things that worry or frighten me are things I really can't explain— even to myself.		+
c.	Even when things are going along just fine, I still feel uneasy and sort of afraid about what's going to happen next.		+
d.	I often dream about things that I don't like to tell other people.		+
e.	Being home alone makes me nervous— even in the daytime.		+

INDEX

Accidents: 6; rates, children, 101; adults, 112

Acknowledgments, ix

Adults, types of illness among, 111

Adjustment. *See* Social adjustment.

Age: median age concept, 63; distribution in school samples, 229; distribution in test and control samples, 322

Aged persons: exclusion from morbidity analysis, 64; mortality, 74, 75; numbers, 76

Aggression toward authority figures, 209; scale, 333

American Public Health Association (APHA): xix; Housing Quality Appraisal Method, 45, 59

Anxiety, 210; scale, 334

Apartment: access, location and means of egress, 303; characteristics in slum and in Lafayette Courts, 24; attitude toward, 139; space, 142; privacy, 143

Arithmetic achievement tests, 231, 234

Aspirations, 177

Attitudes: and behavior toward neighborhood and community, 30, 184; scaling, 202, 329. *See also* Psychological state.

Attrition of samples: 41, 46; keeping the samples intact, 294; call-backs, 294; refusals, 294; move tracing, 295

Authoritarianism: 209; scale, 333

Baltimore: 9, 10, 23, 35; City Health Department, xix, 129n

Baltimore Housing Authority: xix, 25n, 26n, 35, 38; analysis of files, 297; Keysort cards for matching, 298

Barer, N., 17

Benjamin, B., 6, 16

Benjamin, J. E., 6, 9

Bias, possibilities of, 51

Bibliography, 255

Births, 129

Brett, G. Z., 9

Britten, R., 6, 14, 15

Causation in epidemiologic studies, 21

Chapin, F. S., 14, 15, 18

Childbearing experience: 126; summary, 246. *See also* Pregnancies.

Children, types of illness among, 100, 105n, 109

Christensen, V., 6, 14

Chronic illness, 57, 120

Church attendance, 190; Sunday school, 192

Clustering, family, correction for intraclass correlation, 322

Community, attitudes toward, 197

Community center, Lafayette Courts, 191, 193, 327

Condition of area, buildings and interiors, 24, 194

Consumer goods ownership, 220

Control sample. *See* Design of study. *See also* Sample.

Cross-sectional study method, 20, 34

Crowding: 6, 10, 16; index, 59, 308; initial, 315

Data collection: the survey cycle, 289; quality control, 291; public school records, 296; data processing, 296

Deaths. *See* Mortality.

Death rates and housing, 8, 324

Demographic characteristics of samples, 54, 310

Density of occupancy, 10, 66. *See also* Crowding.

Dependent variables: in review of literature, 13; in present study, 26. *See also* Morbidity, Social adjustment, School performance of children.

Design of study: xix, 23; independent variables, 23; dependent variables, 26

Dirksen, C., 7

Disability: 69, 90; rates, 91 days in bed or kept from usual activities, 94

335